FOR GOD,
FOR COUNTRY...
FOR LOVE.

The true story of one man's journey.

R. J. SLAUGHTER

Published by R. J. Slaughter

Published by
R. J. Slaughter 2012
60, Lineholt Cl, B98 7YU. U.K.

slaughterrj60@yahoo.com

To order please go to -
www.freewebstore.org/mybookstore

ISBN 978-0-9573685-1-4

Second reprint by ScandinavianBook 2016.

Cover illustration by R. J. Slaughter © 6th June 2012

To those

whose stories

will never be told

The Preface

The stories told over meals and at family gatherings eventually touched my consciousness as my years matured. On realising that they were actually very interesting and historically valuable, I became compelled to record them before they were lost. I did so not with the intention of writing a book, but as I organised my written notes onto computer so a book gradually evolved. It was a long time before I started talking about 'my book' but as my confidence grew so did the chapters.

It became clear to me after several false starts that the information had to be presented in the form of a biographical novel. In that way I felt it would be read by more than avid family members keen to learn of their roots. Now, on this third print run, I can safely say that many family members have indeed read it. It has also been read by thousands of others, in several countries around the world – a wonderful bonus.

Some aspects and the portrayal of some individuals may not sit comfortably with everyone, but I hasten to add that this story merely represents my perception of people and events, both first hand and from the information portrayed to me by those I thank in the acknowledgements and sources.

I visited every place of any significance mentioned in the book - from Tidworth to Weymouth, from walking the streets of London and Martinsburg, visiting Omaha Beach and its cliffs, the fields of Normandy and Virginia. I communicated at length with B Company veterans (116th Regiment, 29th Infantry Division, US Army) as well as people local to the places and time about which I have written. I was helped by many: historians, researchers and by those who claim no title but who provided invaluable insights, priceless information of days gone by.

I spent many interesting hours poring over B Company's morning reports, detailed maps of France and veterans' memories to piece together the battle trail of Dalton and B Company. I have followed that trail and looked out upon the same landscapes, attempting to understand what it must have been like and probably did not even come close. I accepted and tried to take account of the fact that not all memories are sound after 60 years and can change due to experiences in the intervening years. Only by cross-checking could I be sure that I was getting near the truth and yet some people may still feel I am far from it. Well, that's life.

Writing this book was truly a journey for me of many years; a journey driven partly by weight of events and partly by my desire to do justice to them. It grew from being something I did in my spare time to absorb me with a passion. It's a war story, a love story, a social and military history – but most importantly, it's my parents' personal story.

Please note;

I have called Hetty's sister by the name of Edith instead of her real name Ethel to save confusion with their mother, also Ethel.

Dalton's brother Edward was always referred to as Kenny, but I have kept to his given name Edward.

I have changed the names of two or three soldiers to protect reputations and used pseudonyms for characters whose true identities have been lost in the years. Dalton and other B Company veterans only gave me the bare bones of characters and I hope my elaborations sit comfortably with the reader.

According to B Company records, Leonard Appleby died 18th July 1944. B Company veteran John Andryka told me otherwise and it is his version I have kept to.

I found no written record of replacement men joining B Company when they first went into reserve on the 9th June. This information was provided to me by veterans.

Nicholas McNeal was an old school friend of mine who died in his prime; he was therefore not an Air Raid Warden. I just felt it would be nice to remember him this way. (Had he been a Warden, he would definitely have been a fastidious one.)

Some events have been merged and their chronological order changed where I felt it helped readability.

The 'Accident on the Bridge' occurred after 1950 and not as described in the book.

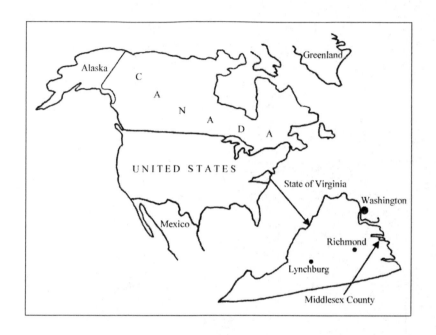

Virginia

Area 40,000 sq miles
(Area of England, U.K. 50,000 sq miles)

Capital – Richmond.
Population of Richmond in
1930 – 183,000

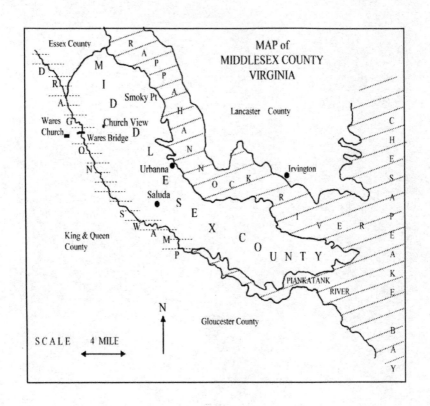

Middlesex County

Area – 130 sq miles

County seat - Saluda

Chapter 1

Moonless Night

Church View, Middlesex County, Virginia.
Early autumn, 1929.

Dalton stood by the wall of the home place with Robbie and Evelyn whilst their daddy paced the yard. The children had quickly sensed the atmosphere; he was angry, mighty angry. And when Kelly Granville Slaughter got that ways, he became agitated, like a man possessed, until he'd 'put the wrong to rights'.

He glared at Evelyn as she drew in her two younger brothers. "Where's ya momma?" he demanded. But he knew darn well where Fleda was, busying herself in the depths of the vegetable garden, her silence portraying disapproval of his intentions. Women, God damn them, Kelly thought, say they want discipline but can't take the upset it causes. "A good reputation is worth more than money," he spat out in staccato form as he retraced his steps, so dumbfounded was he by family events.

At ten years of age, Dalton wasn't sure what 'reputation' was, but just knew it must be real precious, like gold or silver. His daddy said a lot of things he wasn't sure about, just like the Preacher. They sounded like each other sometimes; maybe Daddy should be a preacher he thought.

Kelly's tall, strong frame arched uncomfortably over the farm gate as he again looked down the dirt road toward Route 17. Neither sight nor sound of anything, even the crows seemed to have gone quiet as if they too were waiting for Edward and Bertha to arrive back in the farm truck. The Wares Bridge Road was little more than a narrow track that ran from King and Queen County across the Dragon Run into Middlesex County and past the Slaughter home place. Its tree lined route broken only intermittently by farm houses and a few cultivated fields as it continued toward the Dragon Run Storehouse. The truck would come that way from Remlik Wharf, Urbanna via Route 17.

On happier days their momma traded eggs, butter and other farm products at the store for the things they couldn't produce themselves, like coffee beans and shotgun shells. Sometimes Momma gave the children an egg to spend and it would be 'wasted on candy' so Kelly would say.

Neighbors were few and far between and Church View no more than several farms with one or two 'colored' families, the older generation of whom had been born as slaves. In such a sparsely populated area, everyone knew everyone else and could spot a stranger instantly, and it wasn't easy to conceal a family matter for long; people knew the business of others right quick.

Kelly walked back to the corn shucking barn, flinging the door open, before again striding toward the fence which separated his 73 acres from the road. He had inherited the land from his father, Sylvester Carey Slaughter, who'd bought it at a public auction for $100 in 1887. Kelly had built the barns, like the house, with his bare hands using Virginian pine, cut from the woods out back. Wood was in plentiful supply, pine, oak, poplar and gum being the most common. It was used to build everything from homes to fences, provided the fuel to cook with and the warmth to carry the family through the cold winters.

Ten children had been born to Kelly and Fleda at the home place and nine raised; for Annie Ruth had died in infancy. And of his children, Kelly felt that his six boys were half as difficult to handle as the girls, despite there being twice as many of them and Bertha the worst of the bunch.

The three children could hear their daddy muttering as he stood waiting at the gate. Dalton had upset his father before, not intentionally, for only a fool would do so. Yet fools there were amongst the offspring, rebels as they preferred to be called. Annie Ruth might have been a rebel, for every alternate child seemed to be, but she wasn't blessed with a long enough life. Doctor said her illness would have to run its course and despite some real hard praying, she lived for just five months and was buried at

Wares Church in an unmarked grave.

Fleda Mae finished picking in the garden and returned to the kitchen. The three youngsters were still beside the farm house watching their father, as still as logs fixed with rusty nails to the side of the house.

"Go into the woods and play," she told the boys and to Evelyn, "I need some help with the preparation."

"Ok Momma," they replied almost in unison and made to move but once she entered the kitchen, they remained where they stood. With just thirteen months between them, Dalton and Robbie were as close in age as they were in friendship, the woods and Dragon Run their playground, but not today.

The Dragon Run was deceptively only twenty yards wide at Wares Bridge and the narrow wooden structure provided for a good vantage point to view the beautiful and remote landscape which bordered it. Trees growing alongside its smooth, gently flowing waters created the characteristic earthy brown sheen from the tannic acid in their bark. It was good for swimming and cooling off in summer: for fishing, bending birches and for wildlife. They caught frogs, chased wild turkeys along its edge and spotted turtles, water snakes, beavers, mink and otter. And the days of idle play didn't cost a penny. The Dragon flowed into the Piankatank and together the two rivers formed Middlesex County's southern boundary all the way to the Chesapeake Bay. At times of high rainfall, the Dragon spread from its banks to cause false turns and a swampy vastness with few notable land marks where hunters easily became lost. The first crossing point of the Dragon was a ferry, Turks Ferry, at the site of an Indian crossing and it was only at such spots, hours apart, that a canoeist might identify his whereabouts. Middlesex County was like a long finger of land, a peninsula almost, eight miles at its widest and some twenty-four miles long with the Rappahannock River forming the northern boundary. Compared to the Dragon and even the Piankatank Rivers, the Rappahannock was huge with three miles of water separating the south and north banks. Within Middlesex County's 130 square miles lay the swamps and woods and intermittent farms from which together with fishing, the inhabitants made their life. Kelly both farmed and fished and with Edward, his second born, produced enough to keep the family fed.

Kelly trusted Edward and it was Edward he'd sent to collect Bertha from the ferry. If you didn't like the way Kelly ran things at the home place then it was simple, you either shut up or got out. Preston the eldest son and Myrtle the eldest daughter had both married at sixteen; and at twenty-three, Preston now had four children of his own. Bertha had gone to live with Myrtle in Irvington when she turned sixteen. Wilson said she left for the same reason he would be leaving, 'leaving on my sixteenth birthday, yes sir!' he'd said in a voice as much like Kelly's as Dalton had heard from anyone.

Dalton thought Wilson second only to Bertha when it came to being a rebel and their punishments always that much harsher. But then Daddy had to keep on at them about the same 'darn things', cutting corners with their chores and not responding at the first asking. But guilty as Dalton felt, he couldn't help admiring Bertha's bravery. For one thing, she sure liked her bed, particularly in winter when the frozen ground provided even less incentive to walk the two miles to school. Everyone would be up long before Bertha and Kelly would call up to her without getting an answer. A few minutes later he would call again and she might utter something causing Kelly's face to darken like thunder approaching from the Carolinas. He would then shout from the bottom of the stairs and in response, Bertha would thump on the floor to pretend she was getting up. After several more minutes with no appearance and with anxiety welling in Dalton's stomach, Kelly would storm upstairs and beat her. A few days later when Bertha had forgotten the pain, the whole cycle started over again.

With Evelyn at thirteen years old and the tallest, standing between her two little brothers, the three skinny children blended with the gray unpainted bare wooden wall of the farm house. Small and vulnerable they appeared in the brewing storm. When in trouble they were beaten with a switch torn from the nearest tree and whacked across the back side, hard and as many times as Kelly felt it took to make his offspring truly sorry.

Dalton and Robbie usually ended up getting into trouble together, even though it was often Robbie who instigated it. Like pulling fruit from Momma's garden before it got ripe or creeping out late at night to fish on the Dragon. When summoned, Robbie might run and hide under the house, but with Dalton standing obediently to take his father's punishment, Robbie would reluctantly conform to save Dalton getting his share of the beating, as Kelly promised if Robbie didn't appear 'right quick'.

Kelly had the knack of knowing when they were putting it on and when the tears were for real. Pretending only made it worse because he punished them more for the dishonesty. As Dalton watched his father pacing the yard with anger rising by the minute, Dalton just knew that Bertha's punishment today would be harsh and the use of a switch a blessing compared to Kelly's fists.

'Accept the wrong and face the punishment' Kelly would say. And to Fleda Mae he would add 'spare the rod and spoil the child'. Fleda would nod in agreement but Kelly always sensed disapproval. Perhaps that's why he felt obliged to say it to her, the one hundredth time of saying, forever the optimist, hoping that his wife would give him the support he wanted. Maybe if she had, the punishment would have been less harsh. Optimism - one of a few characteristics he passed onto Dalton.

Kelly had been brought up with a strong sense of how a poor family survived the hardships of country life. Of how to ensure there was enough food in stomachs and clothes on backs. He knew the difference between need and want, and that you 'reap what you sow' and he constantly reminded his children of such virtues.

Kelly was born into a world where a man's word was his bond and the father's word the last on the matter. And so it was for his children or else. 'Bertha had been warned' he was overheard to say one night, overheard because 'little pitchers have big ears', so their momma said.

Dalton worried as to why his daddy had left the barn door open; he always told them to close it and a chill ran down his back as he watched the tension mounting, his daddy's fists clenched, listening for the truck. The warmth of late summer was slipping from the Virginian countryside and the overnight rain had not yet fully dried. Dalton took comfort from the dampness and the dirt clinging to his feet, for it reminded him of happier days, of hot humid summer days just passed. Of the mud in the Briery and Dragon Swamps squelching up between his toes, engulfing his whole foot like a smooth, cold, wet shoe being changed at every footfall. At night in bed, bits crumpled off when he rubbed his feet together and before the job was finished he was usually asleep.

Kelly kept striding back to the barn, looking in then back to the gate, now oblivious that the three children were still watching him. Why was the barn so important, Dalton wondered? Maybe Bertha had done something real, real bad this time.

After the church service last Sunday, Kelly and Fleda had left early and that was unusual. Normally Fleda would be keen to catch the latest gossip and if the truth be known, that was normally Kelly's real intention also. Though the men would first discuss real important issues such as the growth of the corn crop, the blight on the wheat or the cost of the new farming aids, well beyond reach of the Slaughters. But it wouldn't be long before the men's conversation moved onto more interesting topics such as baseball or the yield of Kelly's whiskey distillery. Kelly had a distillery in the woods at the back of his land. One advantage of the swampland that constituted the upper part of the Briery Stream was its inaccessibility to prying visitors and with Virginia a dry state, such a location was essential. After alcohol they would move onto local gossip and so finally the men caught up with the women.

Sunday was the one day Dalton and the other children would have to wear shoes and try to look smart. Dalton feared God as the Baptist Preacher said he should and always did his best to listen for 'fear of damnation'.

Part way through the sermon, the Preacher would stop shouting and look in silence at the faces of the congregation, before continuing his scolding of the unworthy people there gathered. Dalton believed that during these silences, the Preacher was making a mental note of those who had sinned the very sin he had just described. When one Sunday the Preacher had talked something about 'coveting your neighbor's wife', Dalton felt sure he had seen Mr. Preedy shift very uneasily in his pew. Why Dalton himself should feel so guilty at the age of ten about some of the more adult sounding sins he didn't know, maybe it was because he wanted to know what some of these sins were. Dalton thought that whatever it was, 'coveting' sure sounded bad. The Preacher sometimes waved his arms so much that Dalton felt that God might be controlling them and that perhaps they would suddenly stop and point to the person who had committed the sin, the very sin that God had told the Preacher about, presumably committed that week. But on the theme of stealing, Dalton had good reason to feel guilty. He had dropped his head as the Preacher moved his penetrating gaze from Robbie to him. After leaving a safe pause, Dalton glanced sheepishly across at John Fletcher. The Preacher was always reminding his congregation that God spoke to them and that they should listen and not shut him out. Would Mr. Fletcher be listening now or shutting God out, Dalton wondered? For if he was listening then he would soon know that Dalton had stolen two eggs from him that week. John Fletcher was his momma's brother who raised chickens for a living. Wilson had started working for him two years earlier at the age of thirteen and was now, not surprisingly, spending as much time as he could on his uncle's farm. Dalton had decided to visit Wilson there and had regretted the visit because Wilson had dared him to 'do something bad for a change.' Wilson had a stubborn, mean streak in him, always the dare-devil and found it easy to wind up his siblings. He would pick on the younger three, although Dalton was normally the exception because for some reason, Wilson didn't get as much satisfaction from picking on him. But on that day he was in a real mood and had to take it out on someone. The eggs were burning holes in Dalton's pockets as he walked over the field with Wilson watching him leave, a big grin spreading across his face.

Leaving church was always a relief for Dalton and particularly so on the day the preaching was against stealing. It seemed to Dalton that you had to go to church to appreciate the freedoms of the countryside. He always felt uplifted like the Preacher said he would feel after attending, but he wasn't sure he felt uplifted for the right reasons.

Kelly walked again to the barn and stepped inside with the growing darkness partly concealing him. The shadow of the poplar tree, cast by the setting sun added to the gloom that had befallen the yard, a place which normally witnessed happier events. Kelly threw the corn shucking stalls and some sacks to one side and stood back. He walked out, again leaving the barn door open.

After praying at Wares Church, in fine weather the Slaughters would spend much of the rest of their Sunday sitting or playing in the yard. 'God's rest day' as Kelly referred to it and even Momma got a little rest except for family needs. 'Momma bring me a drink of water', Kelly would call from his chair. And Fleda would winch fresh cool water up from the well, pour it into a glass and take it to him.

Six years earlier there were eight children playing in the yard and with Preston married it was left to Edward to referee the younger siblings as they played baseball, rook cards, dominoes, checkers or perhaps horseshoes. Preston and his wife lived on land that initially belonged to the Harts and later belonged to the Marshalls. It lay just on the other side of the road to the Slaughter home place and on Sundays they would eat dinner with the rest of the Slaughters, but made a point of leaving before the games started; for Bertha or Wilson usually caused a fight.

At the age of thirteen, Bertha had been the secretary for the Sunbeams group at the church and despite her attitude at home, had been real good with the younger ones. Dalton hadn't wanted Bertha to leave home, he hadn't wanted any of his brothers or sisters to leave; but just as those happy Sunday afternoons slipped away too quickly, so did the years. Bertha had walked out with a flick of her hair and a defiant glance toward Kelly, yet now she was coming home and Dalton couldn't understand why. She'd be back any minute now. Kelly stayed by the gate and each time a vehicle approached so the three children stiffened, but Kelly could identify each one. The Fletcher truck or the Ashley logging truck with its deep throbbing noise as it climbed the shallow incline from the Dragon and then rumbled across the Briery Swamp Bridge. It left deep tracks in the rain softened road and was driven by Steve, one of the Ashley boys from Dragonville. They knew him from church and despite being ten years Evelyn's senior, she considered him very handsome and 'so strong'. Wilson would tease Evelyn about her attraction and thought her even more stupid than normal when Steve was 'within spitting distance'.

As the watery sun finally dropped behind the trees, a crow alighted from them as if disturbed by the growing shadow. But then a groan in the distance was instantly recognized, Kelly quickly opened the gate and within seconds, from around the bend came Edward in the farm truck with Bertha.

Kelly watched as they approached, slowed down and cautiously entered the yard through the opened gate. Edward brought the truck to a stop half way between the gate and the house and Bertha bided her time getting out. Her face was pale and drawn not glowing with pride as it might have been. And as she stepped out, the younger three could see that she had put on weight, a healthy weight as their momma might have said in different circumstances. She walked to Kelly, his fists clenched, breathing hard and staring with a face so stern it frightened even Edward, who remained in the truck. Bertha stepped tentatively closer and as she reached out to her daddy she made as if to speak but Kelly instantly grabbed her arm and dragged her past the children toward the barn. Bertha's face crumpled up as she started to plead, "Daddy, no Daddy, please no!"

But Kelly kept dragging her, pulling her into the barn. Throwing her onto the floor he slammed the door shut. Bertha's screams became louder as the blows rained down and Kelly released his anger. The screaming continued for what seemed like an eternity, to eventually be replaced by sobbing when Kelly walked out leaving Bertha to her misery. He passed the three young children and went into the kitchen, the scraping of a chair telling them that their daddy was ready to eat now and trying to make himself comfortable at the table.

Bertha stayed on the floor of the barn for some time, sobbing and holding her stomach. It was almost dark before she slid into the house, the food almost eaten as all tried to consume what Momma had worked so hard to fix. The oil lanterns were snuffed out early that night. The children talked little as they got into bed and the home place was quiet well before the dark outside settled to a moonless night.

The Children of Kelly Granville and Fleda Mae Slaughter

GRANVILLE PRESTON
4th Sept.1906 Ch. View

EDWARD KELLY
20th Jan. 1908 Ch. View

MYRTLE MAE
21st Dec.1909 Ch. View

BERTHA LEE
2nd June1911 Ch. View

AMOS BENNETT
10th Nov.1912 Ch. View

KELLY GRANVILLE SLAUGHTER
14th Sept. 1877 Church View
Married 28th May 1905 in King & Queen.
Fleda Mae (Fletcher)
16th October 1885 Gloucester Co.

WOODROW WILSON
28th Aug. 1914 Ch. View

EVELYN SALOME
3rd Mar. 1916 Ch. View

ANNIE RUTH
Feb 1918 Church View
July 1918 Wares
DALTON ROY
30th June 1919 Ch. View

WILLIAM ROBBIE
31st July 1920 Ch. View

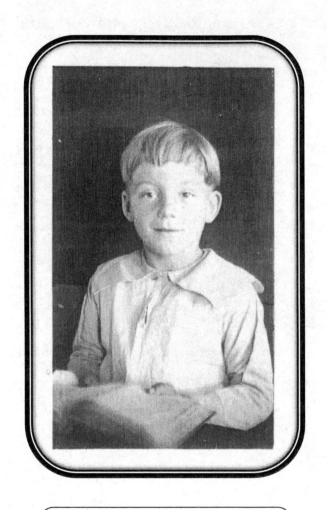

Dalton Roy Slaughter

Circa 1928 - about 9 years old

Evelyn with Dalton and Robbie.
Circa 1928.

Chapter 2

Breaking the Ice

Church View, Virginia, February 1932.

Dalton lay in his bed watching snowflakes flutter down from the rafters to settle on the sleeping children below, feeling security in the company of his siblings and the growing peacefulness outside. The persistent glow from the oil lamp that had once been Bertha's just reached into the depths of the roof and as the wind picked up, more flakes lost their way and came in from the cold. The one upstairs room had no ceiling, just the wood roof capped with cypress shingles separated the family from the stifling humidity of summer and the cold of winter. Bare wood, the fruit of Virginian soil with its pattern of knots, grain and shades crafted by God's own hand.

Dalton came to the conclusion that you got a good night's sleep if you first listened to things natural like the rain, wind and snow. He could hear a rhythm in the rain, a rhythm which depended on how big the drops were and from which direction they came. When the wind blew in through the gaps it too made different sounds, the pitch reflecting its mood, the stronger it got the noisier it became. The wind and rain were 'God's gifts' the Preacher reminded them, to feed the plants and spread the seeds.

The Preacher also told them to appreciate other things like family but that wasn't always easy. Dalton tried real hard to appreciate Wilson's grunting or Evelyn and Robbie fidgeting endlessly to get comfortable at night, but he rarely succeeded. He just couldn't understand how anyone was uncomfortable in bed. With the covers pulled up to his chin, the way his momma used to place them when he was young, Dalton would listen to the weather or the country night sounds and fall asleep in their making. The bull and peeper frogs in spring, the hoot and screech owls in winter, the whip-poor-will and the mocking bird. The hoot owl seemed to say 'who, who are you' and Dalton would whisper 'Dalton Roy Slaughter' and chuckle to himself as he gradually entered a night of dreams. Without fail, Dalton tried to remember to say his prayers as his momma reminded him, but listening just caught him unawares and before he knew it, morning had arrived. With the rising light he would forget that he had forgotten and his day of play and chores passed without conscience.

Rain was good but snow was best because then Dalton had to listen hard, for everything was muffled, dampened by the softness. Snow at night kept him awake longest for he would keep getting up to see how deep it was, so excited he would become at the prospect of the next day's play.

This February night was very special. Bertha's baby, Virginia Mae, had come to live with them. Wilson was home for a few days and to crown it all the rain turned to snow early, the first real snow of the winter. Gradually the tell-tale signs of a falling temperature filtered through the house. The patter of rain on the roof became softer, like someone turning down the volume on Mr. Fletcher's wireless. Chilling air sank from the rafters to creep across the blankets and suck out the warmth. The windows became smudged as if being purposefully thickened by a layer of gray white. And so the mood drifted as did the snow and Dalton watched intently, absorbing the transformation.

When the snow was a few inches thick, he heard Momma get up and talk sweetly to Virginia Mae. It was late and the child had been whimpering. Judging by the movements and sweet talk, Dalton knew that Momma had taken Mae into bed with her. By the time the snow was twelve inches deep, so judged by Dalton, he had got up more times than he could remember and enough times to make him so cold that he would not look again until morning. Shivering, he returned to tracing the snowflakes driven in by the wind; driven through cracks and gaps in the timber into a warmer world to melt as his wakefulness gradually melted into sleep.

Dalton woke not wanting to venture downstairs until

Momma or Edward, Daddy's 'right hand man', had lit the kitchen stove. The younger children had learned to regard Edward as another parent. Dalton once made the mistake of being cheeky to him whilst keeping his company farming rented land. Edward warned Dalton to shut his mouth but devilment took hold and Edward ended up whacking him down the back with a horse whip. Dalton jumped off the wagon and ran home, only to meet his daddy, be beaten again and sent back. Dalton wasn't cheeky to his brother again.

Edward was also highly regarded by local folks for getting so involved with church, particularly Sunday school work. But he wasn't confident when it came to women. Wilson, who could talk his way into any girl's heart, predicted that Edward would still be working for their daddy when old and gray.

After hearing Edward removing wood from the kitchen box and stoking the fire, the tell tale sounds of a breakfast in preparation sang out to the hungry stomachs. Momma going to the tall kitchen cupboard to extract her pastry bowl. The familiar squeaking of the hinges as the doors concealed her from anyone standing in the hallway. Predictable sounds, each in their sequence and usual intensity. The bowl being placed on the small kitchen table, a table without chairs, which Momma used as a work surface. The lid coming off the tin of lard; wholesome hog fat scraped from the animal and boiled until changing from white to yellow. The quiet period as his momma measured out two quarts of flour to make the first 24 biscuits, adding a pinch of salt and a teaspoon of baking powder. After the tap, tap of the wooden spoon on the edge of the bowl which accompanied the mixing of the ingredients, Dalton heard the clabber pot being pulled from under the table. The sour milk, turned really sour, was then poured onto the flour, just enough to moisten. Kneading it until it held together in a bundle, she then rolled it flat with her rolling pin until it was about a quarter of an inch thick. Again the cupboard doors were opened and extracting a glass jar kept specifically for the purpose, Momma finally cut out discs of dough and placed them with a quiet slap onto the biscuit pan. Momma always wiped extra lard across the pan beforehand to stop the dough from sticking and to brown the base of the biscuits. And the biggest incentive for getting up first was to pick the brownest. Dalton knew that it would be about fifteen minutes after he heard the pan go into the oven before his biscuits would be ready and stayed in his warm bed until the last moment.

Calling out that breakfast was almost ready, it never failed to surprise Momma that the boys could get dressed so quick in winter and take so long in the spring time. Reaching the kitchen within seconds of pulling back his blankets, Dalton sat at the long dining table with Robbie arriving just before him, taking his favorite place, closest to the stove.

"You'll die in that seat," Wilson predicted as he too arrived, and his prediction was to be proven correct in the course of time.

Like all the rest of the furniture in the house, the bench table had been made by Kelly. Learning from Grandpa Sylvester who had been a house carpenter, Kelly's chairs, tables and cupboards with their grooves and rings looked good enough to be in a furniture store. Like Momma said to her boys, if you can build a house then why not the furniture as well and told them that they might be lucky enough to do the same one day.

The youngest boys always ate more than their fair share of the hot biscuits and Momma had to prepare more dough before bringing over the coffee. Strong, hot coffee to warm them through before the boys braved the snow and went 'exploring'.

The snow was now twice as thick as Dalton could remember from his night time observations. Evelyn and Wilson joined him and Robbie as they left the house, each trying to push past the other to make the first footprints in the front yard. Momma told them to "Stop the pushing," but they paid no attention. At five years older than Dalton, Wilson's big feet were the first, but the others ran in their own directions to let it be known that they too could be first.

With Wilson against the other three in a snow ball fight, Evelyn lasted only until she was hit on the side of the face. With a look that might have killed, her laughter ceased and she retreated to the house, placing Virginia Mae on her knee to watch from the safety of the kitchen. And as Daddy took his first bite from the latest batch of hot biscuits to come out of the oven, Momma got on with her other chores. Being Sunday, she would prepare dinner before going to church. Daddy hated Momma 'banging around the kitchen' but as Momma said, 'if Jesus could go hungry for forty days and nights' then he could put up with a little noise so that they might get to church and still feed their bellies afterward.

The children later reflected on how Momma always drew Daddy round to her way of thinking. The fuss Daddy had made about Bertha getting pregnant, yet within eighteen months her baby was living with them. It was as if Daddy had to get real mad before he was confident of getting his way. And time seemed to prove that right cause Kelly couldn't stay mad forever, and 'God darn it' as Wilson said so often, 'sweet Momma gets her way in the end'.

After abandoning Bertha at an institution for unwed mothers, Kelly had travelled off to Irvington and made contact with Broaddus Tate, Virginia Mae's father. Bertha had been living in Irvington with Myrtle and her husband for two years until she got pregnant and returned home aged eighteen. Kelly met Broaddus at least twice and money was offered, maybe even a slice of Slaughter land, but Broaddus wouldn't take the bait, nor would he take his share of the responsibility. Afterward the children heard Daddy say that if he saw Tate walking in the woods he would shoot him and throw him in the swamp.

'Can still shoot straight' he'd told them pointing to his one good eye, having lost the other when a steel splinter flew into it working at a shipyard on the Rappahannock - times had gotten harder and the family had needed more money than the land could provide.

Kelly felt that he had done all he could and more than Bertha deserved and he left her at the institution for three months before she gave birth at Spring Grove Hospital. When Bertha came out, Kelly didn't want to know her and so she lived with Preston and his wife Melva on Mr. Marshall's land opposite the home place. With four children, they barely scraped enough money together for their own needs, but what else could Preston do? He was the eldest and Momma helped, taking over a little extra food when Kelly wasn't around. Fortunately for Preston, ten months later, Bertha married William Henry Emme, a man forty-one years her senior and moved away with him. Dorothy Lee Emme was born July 1931 and to every cloud there's a silver lining, for Dalton had gained another niece and almost a sister in Virginia Mae.

Having proved his snow balling skills, Wilson became bored with his younger brothers and called a truce, a truce which Dalton and Robbie immediately broke. Wilson slammed them one last time before turning and looking directly at Dalton saying, "Be careful now if you go near the Dragon, saw a deer fall through the ice just the other day," in a tone as serious as he could project and made his way to the house. Then, as he opened the screen door he turned toward the boys and with a grin added, "and mind you don't run into Ben Ashley."

Wilson knew that Dalton was scared of Ben Ashley. Ben had led a group of ten boys, some carrying broom handles against Wilson and Amos at School. When the Slaughter boys drew knives the gang backed off and Amos and Wilson ran out of school to get away. Ben didn't live nearby but just the faint possibility of meeting up with him in the woods worried Dalton.

Without Wilson as a target, Robbie and Dalton agreed to leave each other alone and made their way toward the edge of the fields and enter the entanglement of trees. Wandering aimlessly they threw snowballs at hollows and challenged each other to see who could shake the most snow from saplings. Dropping toward the Briery Swamp, they used gravity's advantage to leap and stride in a competition to see who could leave the largest gap between footprints. Beyond the Briery they passed the gum tree which acted as a marker and stepped out of Slaughter land.

How Grandpa Sylvester had raised the $100 to buy the 73 acres no one really knew. The only knowledge being that George B and Sarah Elizabeth Anne were Sylvester's parents. Kelly said that Sarah had borne many children, for he had uncles and aunts all over. But Dalton knew none of them, even though Kelly said that he was likely related to all the Slaughters as far as you could travel in a week from Church View. Maybe George Slaughter helped his son raise the purchase price, but rumor had it that the family of Sylvester's wife, Martha, previously a Revere, was the main source of finance.

Struggling up a slippery incline to push through snow-laden holly they arrived at the divide between the Briery and the Dragon. With the land sloping down again, the boys became distracted by animal tracks - rabbit, squirrel and deer. The play drifted, one minute following the tracks of dangerous animals, the next being intrepid explorers discovering Virginia for the first time. And as the play drifted so did the boys, getting closer and closer to the Dragon. Getting colder they eventually fell almost as quiet as the woodland, simply scuffing the snow to make monster steps as they descended toward the river.

As a boy, Grandpa Sylvester had played in these same woods with his brothers, likely playing soldiers as Robbie and Dalton often did. Grandpa was about the same age as Dalton when the American Civil War reached its final throws and the Confederate Army was in retreat. Kelly told them that Grandpa's oldest brother, Americus, joined the Confederate Army at the age of fifteen; fought at Manassas, Petersburg and even at Appomattox Court House under General E. Lee. The Confederate States of America were outnumbered, out-gunned and out-financed and the war should have been over quickly. But the rustic southerners were driven by a different passion for they were fighting for their livelihood as well as their way of life. Lore would thus have it that when the two youngest Slaughter boys played soldiers, Robbie was always the 'Gray Coat' winning every battle like General Stonewall Jackson at the First Battle of Manassas.

The teacher at Middlesex County School still seemed proud of the southern heritage and American history was forcefully taught. There seemed to be glory in defeat and she always insisted that General Jackson's famous victory was the First Battle of Manassas, not the first Battle of Bull Run as it was called by the northern states.

The problems had started when the industrial and commercially orientated North began to dominate the agriculturally dependent southern states. The dominance spread to congress and in 1861 Abraham Lincoln was elected president on a platform that opposed slavery, the South's largest single agricultural investment. Virginia thus joined ten other states to form the Confederacy and with an army of 900,000 men, fought a costly four year war.

It had been passed down that the war was not so much about slavery but about self determination and not wanting to be controlled by godless, city folk who didn't understand country ways. 'And now we will always be dominated by the North,' the teacher had said indignantly, 'at least for as long as we produce food for people's stomachs and not automobiles and tractors to rush around in and get lazy.'

Grandpa Sylvester had never talked badly of 'coloreds' and there seemed to be no lingering resentment in the Slaughter home. The children had to call older colored friends Uncle or Aunt as a mark of respect, like Uncle Dick Tucker. And Momma gave spare food to those families who were down on their luck, whether white or colored. When the Yankee forces under Grant and Sherman burned down local court houses they destroyed everyone's heritage; records of births, marriages, deaths, wills and deeds of land, indiscriminately turned to ashes.

As the boys got closer to the Dragon the woods thinned to a hushed expanse of white, a white interrupted only by streaks of brown that had been missed seemingly purposefully by nature's hand. Passing under burdened tree limbs, over fallen logs now concealed and around oaks stretching out their branches in search of warmer days, the two boys arrived at the edge of the river with just the crunching compression of snow beneath their feet.

After Dalton nudged his brother to stop fidgeting and keep his feet still, a silence, a complete and utter silence enveloped the boys. A silence impossible to achieve in a city, one which allowed thoughts to stray and a person to escape the world.

"What would happen to a man if he fell through the ice?" Robbie asked his older brother as they stood and absorbed the tranquility.

"Freeze and die, I guess, unless he could find the hole he fell through," Dalton replied with a shiver.

"The water will still be flowing underneath won't it?" Robbie said quietly as the thought of being carried by the current under a sheet of ice stirred in his imagination.

"Guess it would be," Dalton said staring at the place where in the summer they would swim and mess. How different it all looked now to those hot, humid days. A time when the boys fished and enjoyed climbing trees, usually birches near the bank, thin ones so that they would start to bend when they had climbed ten to fifteen feet up. Then by throwing their weight away from the tree, the trunk would curve into almost a U shape before dropping them into the river with a submissive splash. They would bend trees like this in other parts of the wood too, but it was more fun on the river bank.

The creek had a plentiful supply of bass, pike, perch and catfish and they seemed to jump onto the boys' lines as soon as the bait was in the water. Momma was always pleased with the catch for it provided variety at the dinner table. Sometimes the boys would cook out and miss dinner, lighting a fire by the Dragon and eating their quarry as moonlight settled upon grubby, but contented faces. Dalton could almost smell the smoke on himself and the lingering odor of fish as he recalled their last foray. The Dragon provided such a respite from the sweltering temperatures in summer that it was frightening to think of the water now, so cold and uninviting.

The two boys walked up onto Wares Bridge and stood looking at the ribbon of white threading its way into the woods as it stretched out in both directions from the wooden structure. Snow covered ash, beech and maple with branches bending from the weight, joined ranks with the pine and oak - trees waiting to be brightened up with the spring flowering redbud and dogwood.

It had been intended to clear the Dragon to make it navigable to the bridge upon which the boys now stood, to transport logs to the mill at New Dragon Bridge. But it was too easy to carry the lumber the few miles north to the wide Rappahannock. The same river upon which the steam boats plied, carrying animals and other farm produce from the county to Baltimore. The eggs collected by Wilson on Uncle Fletcher's farm travelled that way as did poor Bertha when she was summoned back from Irvington.

Here, close to the bridge, the Dragon was more like a creek, but further away it spread many hundreds of yards on either side becoming a swamp in the true sense of its title. Anyone falling into it would likely never find their way out.

A few yards downstream from the bridge stood Mr. Lumpkin's cypress trees. Seldom found this far north, they were almost unrecognizable in the winter landscape. Last summer Mr. Lumpkin had allowed the Slaughters to cut the cypress trees they needed for roofing tiles. The felled trees were pushed to the bank by the younger boys to then be hauled out by those who had become men. With a two-man saw the men cut the trunks into lengths just over eighteen inches long. They then removed the bark with an axe and squared the sections, before splitting the block into thin slices six inches wide using a frow. The 'cypress shingles' were then physically carried back through the woods to retile the house and barn, making them watertight.

Mr. Lumpkin never charged, it was a favor, for money rarely passed hands in the country. Kelly told the boys that tradition ran deep and 'ways are for reasons good'. It was rumored that Grandma Slaughter, previously a Revere, was a distant relative of Paul Revere, famous for his bravery during the war of independence, so maybe their daddy was right about tradition running deep.

Dalton looked at his brother now leaning over the bridge preparing to drop a log onto its surface and wondered what they would both look like when they were Daddy's age. 'Just like Daddy' so Momma always told them. Robbie was getting very cold, his lips were blue and he had one hand shoved inside the waist of his pants. Dalton smiled at his brother's vulnerability for Robbie always picked fights with him, perhaps knowing that Dalton wouldn't hurt his favorite brother. Impulsively Dalton decided to grab Robbie and show him his growing strength. Pretending to shove Robbie over the rail, he then dumped him on his back perilously close to the edge with one leg dangling over the river. Running off and leaving him, Dalton slid down the bank on the other side of the bridge and without hesitation ran over the snow covered ice in the direction of home. Once he had reached half way across the river, Dalton stopped and looked back for Robbie. Having chased after Dalton, Robbie now stood on the river bank, not daring to step even upon the first few inches of ice.

"What's wrong little brother ... scared?" Dalton asked tauntingly.

Robbie was speechless, his face disbelieving at his brother's devilment, so uncharacteristic. But then Dalton was changing, even hitting back when things got rough at school. Any moment Robbie expected to see Dalton disappear through the ice. If a deer fell through as Wilson said, then surely Dalton would break the ice too. Dalton turned away from Robbie and continued across, moving more carefully now, accentuating his movements, each step thoughtfully placed, crunching and squeaking into the snow cover.

A few yards before the bank Dalton turned to see Robbie's still horrified face, "Now you try," Dalton said with a big grin.

Robbie wasn't going to be outdone; he swallowed hard and stepped lightly onto the edge. After a brief pause whilst he listened for the ominous sound of cracking, he stepped forward again and then again until he was well into what would have been the fastest flowing part. He hadn't thought to cross in a different place in case Dalton had weakened the ice. Nor had he gone the same way thinking that if Dalton hadn't broken it then nor would he. Robbie just stepped onto the ice because he had been challenged to do so.

For some reason Robbie stopped in the center of the river, probably out of sheer anxiety than to take in the beauty of the spot. Looking up and down at the long expanse of white, his skinny frame was visibly shaking, a combination of fear and the cold reaching his core. The normal quiet and peacefulness of the woods, which had been brought to near silence by the blanket of snow, seemed to enhance his sense of impending doom. Then as Robbie turned to continue across, a cracking noise broke through the silence and what color there was in Robbie's face instantly drained away. Robbie's heart stopped as he flung out his arms before the plunge into the icy flowing waters. Staring in horror, Robbie's eyes fixed on the surface close to his feet ... and there they stayed for as long as it took for the hysterical laughter to penetrate his terrified state of mind. But laughter it was and as he slowly raised his eyes from his feet, he saw Dalton rolling round on the snow holding his stomach, crippled with laughter. Just to Dalton's right was a branch freshly snapped in two and similar in size to the one Wilson had used just a few days earlier to play the same trick on Dalton.

The Dragon

Taken from Wares Bridge

Chapter 3

'Once too many Times'

Church View, Virginia, June 1940.

With the temperature in the high eighties and humidity heading toward the uncomfortable, Dalton hoed out the weeds from the corn field. Close to the woods it had been cooler with a slight breeze from the shadows, but now he was working further into the rows of young corn with the sun on his back. Shirt wet and sweat dripping from his forehead, Dalton stopped, laid both hands on the top of the handle and surveyed the freshly exposed earth. Satisfied, he shifted forward and started again. It would take several days to cover the fifteen acres.

Dalton would turn twenty-one on the thirtieth and for seven years he had worked the land with his father and brothers. Having reached elementary level at Middlesex County School, Church View, there would be no sophisticated college education for him. His education was in farming and the Bible. Dalton knew what it meant to work hand in hand with nature, following its cycles, coping with its tantrums and he no longer had to be told that 'you reap what you sow'. It gave Dalton a secure feeling that if need be, he now had the knowledge to keep a large family fed all year round, something which required a sensitivity of the way things just had to be. His most precious attribute however was that he slept easy in his bed knowing that there would be a greater power than he guiding the next day. As the Preacher at Wares often said, 'God can ask no more of you than to do your best with the tools he provides'. Dalton also knew that when the sun cut across to make a narrow shadow of his sweltering frame, it would be time for dinner and a welcome respite from the long hours of toil. No watch for him but he planned to buy one, just as soon as he had enough money.

How many times had he and Robbie walked the length of

the fifteen acre corn field? Corn was the most sustaining crop and it had to be done right. Its grain provided food for the family as well as their animals and its foliage was used for all manner of things. Work had begun back in March when Kelly said the soil was good to plow; using the handles, Dalton had pushed the plow point into the earth and the horses had started pulling almost without being told. He liked to break the first furrow, to watch the dark damp soil lap over the unbroken ground. It was like cutting the earth free of winter and releasing it into the arms of spring. Dalton would guide the team toward a point he had fixed in the woods on the other side of the field. Maintaining a straight line was paramount and he might pick out a young sapling or a broken tree trunk to ensure his line was true, often selecting the same markers as the previous year. It took skill and strength to plow a straight furrow, strength in the lower body as well as the upper. Over time Dalton had developed the physique to cope with the adult task and his muscles bulged with the exertion. Dalton was proud of his ability to work all day in the Virginian humidity and if the truth be known, Kelly was proud of his boy.

Some families could afford casual workers at hectic times, but not the Slaughters. They might call in favors during the wheat harvest but otherwise the boys did everything. When they complained about helping others, Kelly told them it would cost nothing, yet the returns would be plentiful. Robbie thought his father old-fashioned and when Kelly reminded them that favors were the currency of poor country folk, Robbie would raise one eyebrow at Dalton as if to say 'here we go again'.

Robbie had a way of getting under Kelly's skin. Robbie was the least compliant and as Kelly considered, the least reliable. Whilst he trusted Dalton almost as much as Edward, Kelly knew that Robbie would dodge work if he could. Worse, Robbie was starting to drink and 'too much at that'. Nothing wrong with a small shot once you hit twenty-one, as Kelly's Briery Swamp distillery testified, but Robbie was starting to drink in excess and 'long before time' so Daddy said. Yet in Dalton's eye, Robbie could do little wrong for they were still as close as they had ever been and even dated sisters, the Carlton girls. But Dalton worried when Robbie drove the Model A Ford they jointly owned; too often he would be high on booze and speed along at over 40mph.

Hoeing, unlike plowing, allowed Dalton's thoughts to wander; of the farm he hoped to own one day and the family he might raise, perhaps with Lucy Carlton. After all they had been dating a good while. How long was it now? Had to be over two years! And as the scraping of the soil and ting of stones hit by the blade accompanied his dreams so he wondered how he might scrape together the money to make his dreams come true. 'A real romantic' so Lucy said of him. He didn't tell Lucy, but he would have to leave home for sure, to earn money in the city as Wilson was doing. Left on his sixteenth birthday as threatened.

Unlike Wilson, Dalton knew that he would miss Church View. He still missed Bertha and standing again with his hands upon the hoe handle he smiled to himself. For the thought crossed him that perhaps caring for Bertha and Virginia Mae had upset Preston's pattern of having a baby every two years. It wasn't until 1932 with the birth of Lewis that the pattern resumed. How many nieces and nephews did Dalton have now he pondered as he shifted forward again to work the next section of earth. He had done the math many times, but did it again all the same. Preston had eight now and Bertha two, Myrtle one, Amos one and Evelyn three. Why there were fifteen already and Edward, Wilson and Robbie hadn't even got started! Whilst everyone predicted that Edward would never marry, it seemed obvious that Wilson would soon do so. He always noticed women and found it easy to strike up a conversation with them. Dalton had watched him closely and had learned much.

Whilst Robbie stood at the edge of the field waving at him to come in, Dalton moved forward again, determined to reach the end of the row before he did so. It was too early to go to dinner, but Robbie would just tell Kelly that when he was drafted he wouldn't be getting any work from him, so what did a few minutes matter now. Robbie was convinced the US would be dragged into Europe's war. Maybe his drinking friends talked of such matters but Dalton rarely heard anyone else speak of it. Robbie told Dalton that the young brothers would be drafted first and that Edward at thirty-two would likely remain to manage the farm. Robbie was sharp, always calculating and probably right. Dalton wondered how Robbie kept to one task for so long; he was just as fidgety with his chores as he was in his sleep. Robbie had been cutting oak, producing four foot lengths and then using steel wedges to split the wood into smaller pieces; dangerous work for someone who couldn't keep their mind on the task. Stacking the lengths in a square pattern, they would be left in the woods to dry through summer and brought back to the barn before fall. The surplus would be left outside the barn, stacked in such a way as to keep the water out and allow air to penetrate.

Dalton knew that Robbie would have left his tools lying in the dirt when he went back for dinner and as he inched his way close to the end of the row, could predict the exact exchange now progressing between father and son.

The plowing and the hoeing were only part of the story of the corn crop. After the plowing came the disking where sharp metal disks were pulled on a frame behind the horses to slice through the clods. To further break up the soil into a loose grainy texture the field then had to be harrowed. Metal prongs pointing earthward from a frame were dragged across the field time and again until the soil was right. Finally, before the seeds could be set, the field had to be marked off. Here two hoe blades three feet apart were pulled by a single horse to open up two shallow trenches. Coming back across at right angles, trenches crossed trenches to form a square pattern and the seeds were finally planted at the intersections, the corners of the squares.

The Slaughters used seed kept from the previous year and coated them in tar to prevent rodents and crows eating away at all their hard work. Tar was far better than any other preventative method. Scarecrows just didn't work and no matter how many crows the boys shot, they always came back with reinforcements once the coast was clear. Tar on the corn seed still allowed it to grow but rendered it undesirable to the wildlife and assured the Slaughters of a good crop, God willing, with gentle winds and the right rain. So just the hoeing was left to be done and this would be the last. Soon the corn would be high enough to suppress opposition from those plants that so loved to spread from the woods. Years before, Bertha had told Dalton at Sunday school that seeds spread by clinging to animals and by birds and of course by the wind. No ways of stopping all the animals and birds Dalton thought so the hoeing just had to be done.

Corn planting didn't occur until early May. The boys would take a bucket of seed in one hand and walk across the field dropping three or four seeds into each intersection. Then with their boot they would shove the loose dirt over the seed and lightly press down on the pile before moving on to the next. It was hard work and carried out in a rhythmical stop, bend and sweep manner hour upon hour in the heat and dust.

With his shadow indicating that it was time for dinner, Dalton walked back with his hoe to Momma, who fussed him like a setting hen. A quick wash of hands, arms and face and the men sat down to a wholesome hot meal of cabbage, corn bread, chicken and baked apples; the smell of which almost overpowered the smell of sweat. Everything Momma served was produced from scratch, even the bread made from the flour ground at the mill from last year's harvest. Nothing was wasted least of all from the hogs, killed generally in late fall, 'except the squeal' so Momma remarked.

After their heavy meal, the men left Momma to the dishes and wandered out into the yard to take air and sit a while under the poplar tree. Whilst the men took their favored positions in the shade and sat quietly in the country stillness, on the other side of the Atlantic, British troops were evacuating mainland Europe via Dunkirk and the first English phrase books were coming off the printing presses to be given to German troops in preparation for the invasion of Britain.

Fleda was glad the men were out of the way. Supper would have to be prepared as soon as the dishes were done. Heat was building in the kitchen and by the time the sun came around to the side windows it would get unbearable at the wood stove. Fleda knew just how to place her pans to get the speed of cooking she needed and the type of fire for the food in question. After years of cooking for twelve or more, Fleda considered things were getting a whole lot easier with just eight. In addition to her boys and Virginia Mae, Fleda was looking after another grand-daughter, Lucille. Lucille was one of Preston's eight children and had come to visit the previous summer. Still there in September, Fleda had sent her to Middlesex County School. Arriving a week late to pick her up, Preston agreed she could stay the year. Lucille was fussed by the boys just as much as Virginia Mae and Edward even drove them to school when it was raining. Fortunate, Fleda reflected, that at thirty-five she had been wise enough not to have any more of her own. At a little under five feet tall, Fleda's lack of height was more than compensated by her character; her sturdy build and hardy complexion concealing to those unacquainted, the kind hearted, generous woman she was.

With eight instead of twelve mouths to feed there was still a lot of planning to be done for the winter months. But the cold helped because food prepared one day might last for several more. In summer butter, cream, milk and even eggs went off quickly, despite being placed in the well or in trays of water in one of the barns. Few families had an ice house, a wooden building which shaded a deep pit with steps to the bottom. The pit would be filled with ice during the winter, cut from the swamps and ponds once it was near three inches thick. Lined and covered with straw and saw dust, the ice might last till the end of summer. Great for cooling drinks, making iced tea and ice cream. The Waldens and Eubanks had an ice house but for other families like the Slaughters, ice was a real treat. It could be bought in Urbanna, however timing for need was paramount.

Sitting in the shade of the poplar tree for all of five minutes, Dalton was edgy to get back to the corn field. The poplar tree stood to the left of the house, with the well separating it from the kitchen door. Not far enough from the house for Dalton's liking, for the sound of clattering dishes flowed across to the shade, disturbing his peace, which for him was like having a sore foot on a long walk. As Kelly started to fall asleep, Fleda came out to haul water from the well and Robbie gave her a sweet smile as if butter wouldn't melt in his mouth. There was plenty of shade up behind the barns, but the poplar tree was the chosen spot for an after dinner rest. The corn crib, where the boys ground corn to feed the chickens, was small by comparison to the large barn behind it. The barn was used for the horses and cows and had a hay loft, making it a tall structure and three times the size of the house. Dalton and Robbie preferred to lie between it and the smaller barn behind it, where the old horse drawn buggy had been abandoned. The shade between the two buildings seemed cooler and they could talk about women as long as Momma wasn't around. Momma's vegetable garden lay behind the small barn and the path to it from the kitchen was well worn.

With her strong thick arms, Fleda hauled the bucket of water from the well, poured it into a large tin kettle and set about the dishes, the white crockery flashing in the sunlight. Dalton watched his momma busying herself, hurrying to finish in case Daddy woke to ask something of her. The chicken coops, hog pens and smoke house were her back drop and Dalton wondered if his momma still had any dreams, or had they all come true. A heat haze was starting to rise from the fields beyond and he knew that the afternoon would prove a whole lot harder than the morning. Once the hoeing was over, the crop was in God's hands and the harvest work would begin in earnest toward the end of August. Firstly to pull the green blades to be dried in the barn for winter fodder and finally by late October the harvesting of the corn ears themselves. A good harvest meant a nutritious and full diet for the family and their animals through winter. They fed their horses, hogs and even their milk cows on corn. Corn flour, ground at the mill was used for the animals as well as for making batter bread with eggs and buttermilk.

As Dalton watched his momma finish off her chore, Kelly's snoring started to overwhelm even the dishes. Edward had also fallen asleep - getting old just like Daddy! Edward's birth-mark which covered one side of his face was now pressed up against the bark of the poplar and the youngest brothers couldn't understand how someone could sleep like that. Robbie was wide awake like Dalton and with mischief written all over his face. As Daddy's head fell back onto the tree trunk for the umpteenth time, the mischief on Robbie's face rippled into a smile. With Momma's back turned, Robbie winked at Dalton as he fiddled with a spent match, positioning it as if to flick it at someone. Looking at Daddy's graying hair, swept across his aging brow, Robbie aimed for the bark just above the whitening strands and released the match. But instead of the bark, the charcoaled end of the match hit Daddy squarely on the forehead leaving a small black dot which Robbie found hilarious. Dalton couldn't help but break into a smile which quickly disappeared as Kelly jumped up and strode toward his son.

Robbie stood up, staring as Kelly approached. At first Dalton thought Robbie was going to confront his father, but at the last second he span round as if to get away. Kelly jumped on his back, Robbie tripped and went down and then Kelly started punching. Each punch represented a release of frustration, frustration with the wayward son who showed so little respect.

"Stop it Daddy, I don't wanna hurt you," Robbie shouted covering his face and getting up despite the blows. The words struck a nerve, Kelly pulled up, mentally bruised, then slapped Robbie across the mouth. A pointless gesture, as pointless as it had been when Robbie was small. Kelly stood motionless, breathing hard as Robbie looked at him with hateful eyes. But Kelly's vulnerable stance, his chest heaving and his face drained of blood seemed to quell Robbie's anger. As Kelly reached up to hold his chest, Robbie walked over to the Model A and sped off toward

Wares Bridge, the single track bridge over the Dragon.

As the car's engine noise petered out, an awkward silence befell the shade of the poplar tree. Robbie had asked for trouble and got it, but it didn't stop Dalton from hurting for his brother as much as he hurt for his daddy.

Everyone just had to get on with their work after the fray and Dalton picked up his hoe to make his way out into the rising heat.

"He'll do that once too many times," Momma said quietly as he walked past her with his face full of worry, and Dalton wasn't sure if she was referring to Robbie or to Daddy.

Kelly Granville and Fleda Mae Slaughter outside the home place, Church View, Middlesex County, Virginia.   Circa 1940.

Back row - Evelyn, Edward, Kelly, Dalton, Robbie, Wilson.
Middle row - Virginia Mae, Lucille, Fleda. Front row - Bobby, Sonny, Tommy.
Outside the home place, Church View, Middlesex County, Virginia.   Circa 1940.

Chapter 4

Accident on the Bridge

Virginia, up to December 1940.

Lucy Byrd Carlton was born 4th September '23 and when Dalton started dating her in the summer of '38 she was only fourteen. Typically, Robbie was dating the older sister, Elizabeth, two years Lucy's senior. When the boys acquired the 1929 Model A Ford, a two door sedan, they could take the girls further afield; to the movies at the Rappanna Theater in Urbanna and the Pine Tree snack bar for a sandwich or a cone on the way back. The Loving's Store or Pine Tree Store as it was more commonly called wasn't the only store in Pine Tree, but it stayed open later than Bob Green's over the road and even had a dance hall at the back, becoming affectionately known as 'the knock down and drag out club'. The Slaughter boys sometimes went there but not with the girls, they were too young and Dalton didn't want to lose Mrs. Carlton's trust. By day, the old men sat on the store's porch, chewed tobacco and shared tales and by night came the youngsters in their beat up old cars. The country store was a combination of post office, gas station, meat market and grocery, outfitters and snack bar. Some, particularly the youngsters, considered the country store more of a hub to the community than the local church, especially the Pine Tree and Kelly remarked that some wayward youngsters went there more often than they prayed to God.
Urbanna was where the Slaughters bought the bigger items of need which they couldn't get in the storehouse and where Kelly sometimes launched his fishing boat. When Robbie and Dalton took the girls out during the day, they would walk the quays and watch the watermen unloading their catch: the oysters, crabs and fish. Slightly further up river, away from where the Urbanna Creek met the

Rappahannock, was a roped off swimming area and in summer it was a popular spot for families and dating couples. The Urbanna carnivals with swings and rides and the once a year oyster festival were entertainments not to be missed. The boys still fished for oysters with their daddy to earn extra money as well as supplement the family's food, giving some to the Carltons when the occasion was right. Dalton had plenty to tell Lucy about his exploits as they walked the banks. How the tongs, shaped like post hole diggers, would be pushed into the mud, clasped together and pulled out time and again in the hope of grabbing at least one oyster at every ten attempts. Lucy had heard the story before, but still told him how strong he must be to do such work all day and 'from a wobbly boat'. The praise usually prompted Dalton to tell of how when younger he had cut his foot on a broken bottle pushing the 30 foot boat off the horse drawn trailer into the water, then had to wait till he got home to have it seen to. Lucy had heard that story too but always managed an 'oh you poor thing' and her sympathy made the pain worthwhile. She sure was a real loving, hugging sort of girl and Dalton could take as much loving and hugging as she could give.

Lucy's father, Rowland Carlton, had died in 1933 when she was ten, leaving six girls and two boys including William Henry Carlton who was closest to Lucy. Their momma brought the family up single handed and only permitted the dating because Lucy was going with Elizabeth. It helped too that the families knew each other from church, attending every Sunday without fail unless the roads were impassable. During the twenties the horse-drawn wagons, buggies and individual horses would be parked up outside the church with the few 'horseless carriages' and in winter the slow journey required hot bricks and blankets to keep the young ones from getting too cold. Lucy moved into the choir as she reached her teens and without fail Dalton would immediately search her out, giving her a 'big sweet smile' as he entered. Lucy considered Dalton handsome and very eligible. He became her first boyfriend and after dating for over two years, was likely to be her last she thought, for girls often married at sixteen.

During the service Dalton tried to catch Lucy's eye, paying less attention to the service and more and more as to what he might say to her afterward. It was only at weekends that they had the time to date and it was usually arranged at church the week before. The soda fountain at Marshall's Drug store in Urbanna was a nice spot to get 'real friendly' for it had booths down one side where you could 'get kinda cosy' and the Rappanna was just around the corner. But with both families not having much money, supper at one of their homes was more common than an expensive trip into town. When Lucy came to eat, Dalton's momma would always use her yellow, round croc bowl with the fine ridges and if there was potato salad on the menu, for sure it would arrive in the yellow croc bowl.

The Carltons lived in Dragonville just across the Dragon in King and Queen County and the shortest route from the Slaughter home place and from Urbanna was via Wares Bridge. One Saturday late in the year the four had been out on a pre-Christmas date and Robbie had opted as usual for the back seat leaving Dalton to drive. The winter had come early and with dusk approaching the insides of the car windows kept freezing up. The ruts on the country roads were fixed for the duration and the narrow swamp bridges appeared blurred through the frosted windows, manifesting themselves like giant hunting traps from the twilight air. The Dragon already had an inch of ice, perhaps more at the edge as the two door sedan slipped between the side rails. It rumbled across the boards and leaving Middlesex County entered King and Queen on Wares Bridge Road. They passed Wares Church and then the open fields beyond, established about the same time as Wares in 1772. In the failing light the two storey, clapboarded Carlton home could just be seen over the hedges and fences several hundred yards away to the right. But Dalton had to drive another few hundred yards to reach woodland again where the Water Fence Road dropped into its first hollow. At the bottom he slowed right up before pulling into the narrow track which led to the Carltons and the Chamblins. The Chamblins were coloreds who owned a place at the end of the track, where in summer, wheat met corn in the fields beyond a narrow band of trees.

As Dalton pulled up between the house and the barns of the Carlton home Robbie got edgy, "Can't come in, gotta run," he said in response to Elizabeth and Lucy's usual invitation. "You go in," Robbie said to Dalton as he quickly replaced his brother in the driving seat.

"I'll walk back then," Dalton offered, hoping Robbie might change his mind or come back for him, but a rev of the engine provided the reply. The car was soon lost from sight, its weak illumination absorbed quickly by the bastion of trees as it dropped down the steep slope just beyond the open fields and headed for the road.

Dalton stayed a while, had a late supper and tried to leave several times, but didn't step from the house until well after dark. With Mrs. Carlton and so many girls fussing him, it was mighty difficult to pull away but good manners prevailed. With a final kiss on the porch, he left Lucy to set off on his three mile walk. Guided by a waning moon, its light reflecting off a frost which had set with the darkness, he made his way across the fields; a quicker route than taking the track. Stepping onto the Timber Branch Road, the trees bristled with the cold and with no wind, their faint shadows were as lifeless as the bull frogs hibernating in the mud. Just before Wares there was a right turn, the Mount Olive Road which led to Truhart. It ran past the Ashley home where Evelyn now lived with her husband Steve, the logging boy. Dalton thought it so right that he was dating Lucy, for Lucy not only knew Evelyn from church, a close friend and now neighbor, but Lucy was also Steve's first cousin and thus already related to the family.

Several deer were ruminating at the edge of the woods where the Timber Branch Road met Mount Olive and neither man nor animal noticed each other until only shock could come of the meeting. The deer raced off into the undergrowth, snapping frozen twigs and crunching crisp leaves until they had run far enough to stand and listen to the returning silence. If only he had been carrying his shotgun, Momma would have been right pleased with the quarry.

Wares grew out of the grayness and the grave markers of the Fauntleroys sidled in as if greeting the young passer-by as Dalton strolled past, completely at ease in God's domain. A left onto the Wares Bridge Road took Dalton out of sight of the Baptist grounds. He could walk this route blindfolded; the long sweeping curve with the wheat and corn fields to the right, the Glenn family home to the left, then the final straight stretch with its gentle gradient down to the Dragon Swamp. Half way across the bridge he stopped in the faint crescent moonlight and considered that he must now be half in Middlesex and half in King and Queen. How often had he done that as a boy and still found himself doing it? Edging up to the eight inch high wooden verge which was all that separated him from a fall to the river, Dalton peered along the frozen surface. The way was misty and gray and seemed to reflect the uncertainties which now lay ahead of him. News of war in Europe kept creeping into the weekly editions of the South Side Sentinel, world events slowly filtering through the nation. Robbie had told him that the armed services paid a whole lot more than casual labor and Dalton considered that being drafted mightn't be so bad after all; might be able to afford to buy that farm a whole lot quicker. But wherever he might have to work, Dalton was determined that one day he would return here for good.

Dalton walked to the other side of the bridge and looked down at the ice, the pine needles and other less familiar shapes on its surface now indiscernible. Picturing the water beneath, his eyes fell upon a dark patch, as if of water, not more than a couple of yards from the bridge support. It was a few feet in diameter and as he continued to stare so the broken surface and sharp edges of ice became evident. Something had fallen through for sure, right in the middle of the river. Probably a deer, maybe stepped onto a thin patch Dalton thought as he craned over to see more clearly. Shivering at the thought of ending up in the swamp somewhere downstream, he stepped back, left the bridge and jogged the few hundred yards home. Momma had left an oil lantern burning and its light and the embers of the wood stove provided the welcome.

The dying embers and the deepening cold drove Dalton to bed where he waited well into the night for Robbie to come home. When he did so there was no sound of the car and the smell of booze was the only forewarning of his arrival. As Robbie began to fidget at what would become a long wakeful night, Dalton reached over and squeezed his brother's hand; they would talk when Robbie was ready.

There was no change in the weather by morning. The church service ran smooth as usual, like a blade across ice with only a few less in the congregation. The Preacher, Jesse E. Bowman, led the singing and played the pump organ at the same time, as was his skill and made his sermon just a little shorter in view of the cold. After the service, Dalton and Robbie stood and talked with the Carlton girls whilst amongst others, Mrs. Carlton, the Reveres, Waltons and Longests paid their respects to those who had passed away. The conversation amongst the folks was unusually prolonged in such temperatures, always an indication of things worth sharing; the War in Europe for one thing and the accident on the bridge being another. Members had different views about the war news, not that the local paper exactly gave good account of it, but Mr. Fletcher and a few others had a wireless and it was they who mainly shared their opinions. For the most part they concluded that if Hitler had taken a few more countries, then what did it matter? Denmark and Norway had been added to Poland and another with a strange long name which Dalton couldn't repeat. Countries that most folks had never heard of. "Tracts of land," as someone referred to them, which together amounted to no bigger than the state of Texas.

"So what is all the fuss about?" Mr. Ashley asked adamantly.

"And anyhow, another civil war in Europe isn't going to change life for us folks in Middlesex any more than the last one did," Mr. Fletcher suggested, quickly closing the debate. It turned out that the accident on the bridge occurred the previous night. According to one of Mr. Glenn's boys, Robbie and the driver of a truck coming the other way had both driven onto the bridge despite the other's approach. Panic and ice on the road combined to cause the fatality, the driver of the truck was thrown or jumped from his cab and was 'dead for sure' because he had gone straight through the ice on the river.

And as the conversation erupted around the throng with each having their interpretation of events, Mr. Glenn turned to Edward and asked quietly, "Has Robbie or Dalton said anything?"

Mr. Glenn knew the Slaughters well; he had known Robbie and Dalton since they were born. When they reached school age he had come across them every morning standing at the road side as he took his daughter Elizabeth to school. 'Mornin Mr. Glenn' they would say to him as he steered his horses past. Then watched by bright-eyed Elizabeth, they would run to the back of his wagon and hang on for a free ride to school. Elizabeth might turn round and chat to them in whispered tones, her father ignorant of the extra passengers, so the youngsters thought. Yes those boys got up to tricks alright, Mr. Glenn thought, thick as thieves.

Edward told Mr. Glenn that his brothers had been out in Urbanna with the Carlton girls last night, came back late and had said nothing.

"Well," Mr. Glen added as Kelly joined them, giving his next words much thought, "Guess the police will decide whose fault it was, or wasn't, as the case may be."

No one spoke for some seconds whilst the implication of the words sank home and Kelly looked across at Robbie and thought him 'a damn fool of a boy'. But even Kelly was thankful that the community would pull together to protect its own. Then moving the conversation on, Mr. Fletcher said, "Anyhow, I guess the body won't be found till the thaw?"

Chapter 5

A Yank learns his lesson

London, England, February 1927.

William James Eaglestone was proud he'd never been unemployed, not even during the depression which followed the Great War. Jim, as he preferred to be called, was a bricklayer now and making a decent wage working on the new builds in Wembley. Wet though the weather was in February, he braced himself against the elements, a grin on his face as he told the youngsters that the trenches made life on a windy scaffold seem like paradise.

Jim was born at 5, Foscote Mews, Paddington in 1894 within spitting distance of the Harrow Road. From a lanky youth he'd grown into a tall, powerfully built chap who could turn his hand to anything. He looked a man straight in the face, his eyes unnerving to the dishonest and his flat cap hid only a good head of hair. Like the rest of his siblings, and there were many, Jim had started out in the family fairground business touring the south-east, a good introduction to work if ever there was one, he thought. Sleeping under the caravan at night and pulling in the punters during the day, the family ran two attractions: the roll-a-ball table with the occasional narrower slot which won the punter a prize and the 'hair-raising' boat swing. After the allocated time period on the boat swing, it was Jim's job to stand with a board on his shoulder so that the heavy contraption, laden with two or three occupants, might just scrape along and slow down on each pass. At the end of the summer the Eaglestone family would return to Foscote Mews and the shoe repair business his father ran, leaving the fairground equipment down the side of the house ready for another year.

Grinning at the lads moaning about the weather, Jim adjusted his string marker and knew that the younger labourers would get some more ribbing that night. It would soon be time to knock off and kip down in the cabins and that's when the real banter began. Jim always had a joke up his sleeve and a good story to tell and likely that was what attracted Ethel Chapman to him.

Ethel Chapman had been a nippy, nippier than a nippy, so Jim had thought when he first caught sight of her at the Lyon's Corner House on Marble Arch in 1913. He'd taken to the habit of calling in there after a day's work on the railways, the Great Western Railway, where he worked as a carman before the war. Not so much to eat and drink, though he did so but more to watch the smart waitresses rush around serving customers amongst the sea of tables. The large wall mirrors, potted plants, chandeliers and background music making him feel somebody, even if he wasn't.

Jim was frugal with his wages and chose carefully from the menu; tea and sandwiches more often, just tea sometimes and when he had worked overtime, soup, followed by fried fish. He would sit where he fancied the waitresses most; serving at almost a run, taking orders and hurrying down the one-way production line to obtain the food for their customers. The 'nippies' wore black dresses with high white starched collars and white aprons all topped with a coronet hat. Perhaps it was Ethel's dark hair so befitting of the uniform which caught his eye, or perhaps that she seemed to be everywhere, serving everyone. He waited two hours so he could walk her home to Lanark Mews, not far, but the path led much further, to marriage and three children and little did he know then what it would mean to have Lucy Chapman as a mother-in-law.

Much to Lucy's surprise and some might have said annoyance, Jim came back from the trenches to marry Ethel in July 1918. A cheek wound sustained in the Spring Offensive on the Somme having provided him with the opportunity. A quick, cheap marriage at the Paddington Registry Office on the Harrow Road and a single picture afforded, of Jim in his uniform and Ethel in the best second-hand dress she could muster.

Returning to the army, Jim was finally demobbed in February 1919, surviving over three years in a war which took over 800,000 British servicemen's lives and 10 million in total. Not surprising that he adopted thirteen as his lucky number for having served three years in 1/13 Battalion of the London Regiment, his one and only wounding occurred whilst serving for five months with the 1/15, the Civil Service Rifles. It was on the 13th May 1922 that his second child was born, a girl, Hetty, named after his sister and the date of arrival told him that this was the child he might cherish most.

"Yes, a cushy number," Jim told the other lads on the building site as he breathed in the fresh winter air. "No mustard gas in this breeze," he said with a smirk to those who had little idea of what he was talking about.

"Ah the winter of 1917 'ey Jim," said Len, Jim's brother-in-law, who laboured for him. Len still lived on Lanark Mews, at Number 2, with Lucy next door at Number 1. "The mud and blood of the Somme trenches; thirty-eight gassed in your section one day, two hundred and ten missing the next. Am I right Jim?" Len asked, trying his best to get the conversation going.

"Too right," James Eaglestone replied, "fighting over the same patch for months, knee deep in mud."

The younger lads wanted to hear about glory and victory, but Jim could recall nothing but hardship and brutality.

"Germany pushed forward in 1914 and early 1915 but then for three years the front line hardly moved," Jim told the lads, who always seemed surprised. "We attacked them and then they attacked us. Pretty bloody predictable really," Jim said getting out his Golden Virginia during a break, a tobacco which he preferred and always used to roll his own. Jim usually told the lads stories which he made sound funny, of killing lice in the seams of his clothes with a candle flame, dreaded trench foot or falling into the tank trap in no man's land at night. But perhaps the wet weather was subduing his humour.

"All happened along a five hundred mile line of trenches stretching from Switzerland to the North Sea," he explained knowing that most of the lads had no idea where Switzerland was. The youth of today Jim thought, no respect for what the older generation had done for them. Most of them sat now smoking cheap Player's Weights, a school boy's choice he thought, one to be smoked in the dark of a picture house.

"Bleeding crazy weren't it," Len concluded, "and the government posters had said 'Back in six months' and 'Don't miss the excitement!' " Len told the youngsters and some actually laughed at that.

The posters had done nothing to convince Jim to volunteer, for not only had he seen thousands of black-edged telegrams coming off the mail train, but he also considered that the men who designed such posters were those he'd seen taking the Cornish Riviera Express from Paddington station to holiday in the West Country. Jim only signed his Attestation on the 22nd February 1916 after the government ran out of willing volunteers and introduced conscription.

Jim could see the youngsters losing interest now, one of them passed round his Player's Navy Cut, but when offered a smoke from the packet bearing the bearded sailor in his blue ratings uniform, Jim could only smile at the image portrayed of the happy, contented serviceman. Jim just tapped the tin of Golden Virginia in his pocket, "No thanks, prefer this," he said, "long and fine."

Too much of a thinking man, that was Jim; a bit deep, the young labourers might have said, but one who appreciated the simple things of life and fresh air always reminded him that life wasn't so bad after all. 'Breathe in the fresh air' he so often told his children, 'the best things in life are free'. And it was always Hetty who listened, whilst his older daughter Edith and Young Jimmy only pretended to. Like most of the youngsters on site, Jim thought. Yes, Hetty listened and learnt, possibly learnt too much, sometimes of the wrong things. But what could a man do when he had to work away all week on the buildings, the bus fare too much to return each evening.

Every Monday morning Jim took the tram out of the capital, the journey to Sudbury by way of the Harrow Road costing fourpence, whilst anything over thrupence had in his youth been an adventure. After the conductor had rung the bell punch on the machine that hung against his stomach, Jim would be carried out of the 'smoke', past Harlesden and its Jubilee Clock and the fields beyond to Stonebridge Park. Then crossing the grimy river Brent which separated Stonebridge from Wembley, the bus climbed the hill past Sudbury Farm, with Wembley Stadium under construction beyond it. When he reached the building site on Wembley High Street with the fields on either side, Jim felt he was really starting to get out of the city.

After the Great War, Jim found work with Mr. Small of Golders Green, maintaining Mr. Small's flats and later assisting in the building of two cottages at Brookmans Park. Now Jim's work came from the Abbey Road Building Society. The society offered mortgages for their houses in Sudbury, Staples Corner and now Wembley for the aspiring Londoner who wanted to get away from the city grime and ever-increasing traffic. Jim's dream was to one day move here; for if he could build them, then why shouldn't he be able to afford one. With his wage and Ethel working all hours, they were bringing home some decent money.

For Jim a good smoke always led to a deep discussion; the state of the country, the diminishing Empire, the 'bloody foreigners' who'd crept in after the war or questioning as to who could afford to buy the houses they were now working on. Slowly working as it happened, for February had proved wet and eighteen days of continuous rain caused flooding in the suburbs. Building work ground almost to a halt, hours were lost, even days and no work meant no pay. Patience was running as thin as wallets and that was when the argument with the Yank kicked off.

With his jacket done up and cap pulled down as far as it would go, Jim crouched down, protecting his work from the developing drizzle. A drizzle which seemed to return like clockwork whenever the breaks finished, as if determined to stifle the men's resolve to earn a decent day's wage. He was cutting a brick with a hammer and bolster, hoping that soon the worst of the bad weather might be over and wages improve. Turning the brick and striking it at least twice on as many faces, the yellow coloured London stock cleaved cleanly. Everyone was getting colder with the winds turning from the east, chilling fingers and making them cumbersome appendages. As the day's light dimmed, the short winter's day still shorter from the heavy cloud cover, Jim ran out of bricks. Len hadn't brought them; instead he, like most, was listening to a discussion with the Yank which was fast developing into an argument further down the scaffold.

Jim had already finished the soldier course above the first floor windows and was now near to where he would step the bricks out to reach the cast iron gutter position. Here he would create a dog-tooth by laying each brick across the wall at near 45 degrees. With the corners thus facing the street and hanging out past the front face they created a toothed effect; easier than some other patterns, he felt.

As the argument became heated, someone told the Yank to mind his own business, but he would not shut his 'big Yankee mouth' as someone else told him he should.

As a bricky, Jim was responsible for all the brick and mortar work from clay drain pipe joints and drain chambers to the roof. And it was always satisfying for him to reach roof level and to know that the structure was almost complete. A structure made up of so many small parts, each skilfully placed together such that a family and its descendants might be accommodated well past the end of the century.

The Yank was getting upset now, "If the brickies had laid the bricks frog down, the house would have been finished long before the God damn rain," he shouted. And of course, Jim always laid his bricks frog up, for that ensured it would fill with mortar and create a stronger wall.

"Face down saves on mortar," the Yank kept saying, stretching out the r to further annoy the Cockney ears about him, "it's quicker and still strong enough," he repeated adamantly, becoming increasingly frustrated by the men who'd become stuck in their ways.

"Since when were you the foreman?" someone asked and "How long you been a bricky?" asked another.

"Why don't you fuck off back home?" said Alfie. Alfie had lost two brothers on the first day of the Somme and the Yank annoyed him, always saying how great his country was and how they'd won the war.

The Yank got mad now and squared up to the 'foul mouthed ignorant Cockney'. Alfie always got under the Yank's skin and everyone knew it.

"You Yanks are cowardly bastards," Alfie went on, "you turned up three years after it all started, summer time of course, luvly, wait until you've got all the bleedin' food over to fill your fat stomachs and then didn't get involved until the Germans launched their Spring Offensive in 1918."

"Didn't know you were a historian?" the foreman joked, which put Alfie off his stride a bit.

"We lost twenty thousand men on the first day of the Somme and you had what, one hundred thousand men over here at the end," Alfie continued.

"Showing off now Alfie," someone said.

"Then you've got the cheek to tell us you won the bloody war!" Alfie exclaimed angrily.

"If it hadn't been for our money you...," the Yank tried to explain but he never finished his sentence. Alfie was as good at boxing as he was at hod carrying and caught the Yank with an upper cut that laid him unconscious.

"Bloody Yanks," Jim said straightening up and climbing down to stop Alfie from kicking the hell out of the man, prostate on the wet scaffolding boards. Every one of 'em's full of 'emselves and their country he thought. "Come on Alfie," Jim said forcefully pulling the angry Cockney back from the next boot. Alfie didn't argue; no one argued with William Eaglestone, the man had too much strength as well as respect.

"I've never taken a liking to the Yanks and probably never will," Jim said afterwards, as he flicked water onto the last mortar of the day. Jim knew exactly the right consistency he needed, a consistency to make it flow off his trowel and ensure his next brick sank just to the right level, creating the thickness of mortar joint he desired. And whilst Len started to wash off the tools, someone threw the remains of their cleaning water over the Yank's face but didn't get a response. Jim agreed with the Yank on the part about using less mortar, but didn't like what he considered to be a sloppy technique. He might have explained his opinion to the man, but the Yank never returned to work.

William James Eaglestone
marries
Ethel Lucy Chapman
23rd July 1918
Paddington Registry Office

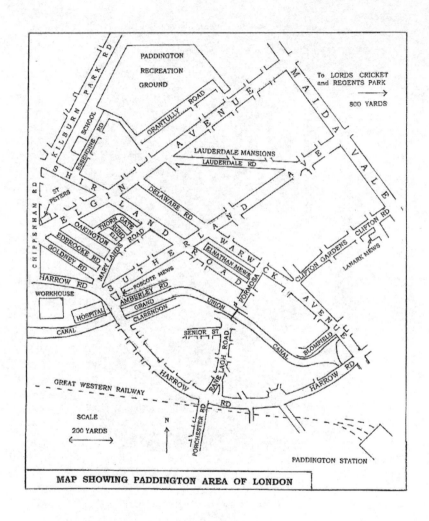

MAP SHOWING PADDINGTON AREA OF LONDON

Chapter 6

The Important Message

Paddington, London, May 1933.

Hetty walked past the grey terraced houses which lined either side of the street, the longer days and sunshine bringing a fresh look to them. Although the basement was still hidden from the sun, the three upper floors were basking in it and you could almost see the damp of winter evaporating from the once yellow bricks. Mr. Permy, one of the neighbours, had even left his motor bike uncovered, a sure sign of better weather. It was one of only two vehicles in the street and attracted the admiring eyes of almost the entire male population of Ranelagh Road. Jimmy, Hetty's brother, was playing cricket with the other boys, a lamp post for their wicket and Senior Street the 'four boundary'. He was getting exceptionally good at the game, much to the annoyance of the other boys. But Mum was very proud of him, Hetty reflected as Jimmy sneaked a couple of runs, having hit the hard red ball slowly along the gutter. Her 'litall darlin' she called him.

Hetty climbed the few steps to the front door and let herself in using the latch key around her neck. She would normally play with the girls but was late home and someone had to do the chores. Her sister Edith had asked her to call in at Senior Street School to tell the teacher that she was ill; it proved to be an embarrassing waste of time.

'What on earth is your sister trying to achieve by sending you in to tell me lies?' the form teacher had replied. He then placed several absent notes on his desk which Edith had written herself, forging their mother's signature. Thank goodness her mum was sending her to Essendine Road School when she finished at Amberley Road, Hetty thought as she stood before him. The teacher had made Hetty promise to tell her mum what was going on and that he needed to see her urgently. Edith was hanging around with Fred the car thief, always getting into trouble he was and he'd done time.

Hetty raced up the stairs to their top floor flat in record time; she never walked if she could run. She was determined to deliver the important message despite not wanting to get her sister into trouble, for a promise is a promise. There were four floors in the house, each with a different family, some with lodgers and all had to use the only tap and toilet in the basement. The move to Ranelagh had pleased her dad for it placed a healthier distance between him and Grandmother Lucy, but for the rest of the family it simply meant more walking. Their old flat on Crompton Street had been ideal for their mother for it was only yards from Gran's on Lanark Mews, but the two rooms left little space for the growing family. At Ranelagh they had three rooms and it meant that Hetty, her sister and brother had a bedroom separate from their parents and even better, the two sisters didn't have to share a bed with their brother. Unlocking the flat door, Hetty knew instinctively that she was again first home. The message will have to wait she thought as she picked up the water bucket and went down to the basement to fill it. She was always first home lately and ended up doing all the chores. Some girls were in the yard playing three balls against the house wall and Hetty would love to have joined them. Just a small backyard with an outhouse but it was ideal for ball games and hopscotch. Returning to peel the potatoes, she finally placed them in a saucepan on the gas stove ready to boil. The stove was their only means of getting hot water, even for bath day. Sunday was bath day, 'whether you needed it or not' her dad said and every bit of water had to be brought up from the basement, heated on the stove and then carried down again when they had finished. They all used the same water of course, for to fill and empty the galvanised steel tub once was effort enough. Some families didn't bother for weeks, but Ethel and James insisted their family would be clean.

Apart from the gas stove and table where they could sit and eat, the fire was the only other luxury in the parlour. It was the centre of family life and even baths were taken in front of it. The down side of having a fire was that it needed cleaning out every day and that was the job of the first person home. Hetty dutifully took the ashes downstairs to the bin in the back yard, threw a couple of hop scotch stones before carrying coal up to replenish the large wooden coal box that her dad had constructed in the parlour. They couldn't afford to have a fire in the bedrooms, unless someone was really ill and at that moment Hetty considered it a blessing that they were poor.

Eating at Grandmother Lucy Chapman's was a lot easier Hetty reflected as she started on the other vegetables, just the washing up to be done there. Gran cooked the beans and 'something' for it was always beans and 'something' with custard and 'something' for 'afters'. When they were younger they walked there every school lunch time to eat and even went back some evenings when Mum knew she would be really late from work. Play up though and Grandfather Thomas Chapman would throw their food over the balcony. They didn't play up - well not often. If they were good they'd be sent with a penny to Tregeser's bakery on Clifton Road to buy a dozen 'end of the day' stale cakes. But probably the best thing about Gran's was going to the Windsor Castle Pub later in the evening with a thruppenny piece and Gran's beer jug. James Whitaker, the landlord, always gave Lucy a generous measure and if they were lucky they might see Mr. Strange being carted off in a policeman's wheel barrow, blind drunk.

Hetty had finished the carrots and was just thinking of going downstairs to play when her mum came home, thwarting her plans.

"Don't tell yer farver!" Ethel shouted breathlessly as she entered the flat, startling Hetty from her thoughts. Don't tell him what, Hetty wondered, thinking that her mum might already know about Edith's skiving off school? Ethel allowed the flat door to slam shut in her haste, shut by the wind, an uncharged for extra which always seemed to be circulating the property. Quickly reappearing from her bedroom, Ethel was carrying something extra to the enormous bag she seemed inseparable from, something grey which hung limp over her arm, pressed and clean. Strange, Hetty thought, where was Mum taking Dad's suit? Forcefully gripping the banister as though to steady her tiring legs, Ethel negotiated the stairs back down to the street. "Oh, the message!" Hetty exclaimed, running to the window. Her rapping on the glass was lost in the traffic noise from the Harrow Road and by the time she had negotiated the ageing sash, her mum was well out of ear shot and heading towards the Grand Union Canal.

Had they had another argument about Mum always being at Lucy's, Hetty wondered. Was Dad's suit about to be thrown in the canal? Nell at number nine had thrown her husband's bicycle in the canal. He always left it in the hall instead of taking it through to the backyard and one day Nell 'lost her rag'. The canal consumed lots of things, the wanted and the unwanted, including children. Charlie from number eighteen had lost his older brother in the deep wide channel, drowned before anyone could fish him out. Hetty had felt so sorry for Charlie because being small for his age he was now 'bullied terrible' where previously his brother had protected him. Hetty hated to see the boys threaten to throw him in the water, 'To see if you can swim better than your brother' they taunted.

Hetty persuaded her mother to invite Charlie to tea one evening. But after eating every morsel of food, Charlie had licked his plate clean and wasn't invited again.

Hetty could just see her mother's head wobble its way across the canal footbridge as she strode purposefully onward, then disappear out of sight as she descended the steps into Formosa Street. So, Hetty concluded, Mum hadn't thrown Dad's suit into the water. But where was she going with it?

Just as Hetty was not always sure of the whereabouts of her sister, she was becoming increasingly unsure of her mum's doings. Everyone seemed to be hiding things from each other, well except her dad. Edith and Young Jimmy were even slipping off on those evenings Mum and Dad went to variety shows at the Kilburn Empire or to the picture house. Half the adult population of London seemed to be out watching the news reels, mixed with Laurel and Hardy clips and stage entertainment, all thrown in for a shilling. Mum and Dad gave them sweets and comics to keep them busy, but Edith and Young Jimmy were finding their own entertainment.

Hetty watched her mum disappear into the distance and wondered if she might not see her until very late. Ethel sometimes worked at Countess Droider's in the evenings for extra money when the Countess was entertaining guests. And what if Edith came home before Mum ... fireworks, probably never speak to me for the rest of my life, Hetty thought. Suddenly she came to a decision, it shocked her but Hetty somehow knew she must follow her mum, well not follow her exactly but catch her and give her the message.

Throwing caution aside and the knife into the bowl of vegetables, Hetty made off in pursuit. She ran up Ranelagh, crossed the canal bridge and leapt down the steps into Formosa. Her mother had sometimes left their flat in Crompton Street with family belongings and by instinct Hetty made for that direction. She reached the Edgware Road where the grocer's shop sat above the Grand Union Canal tunnel entrance and scanned the street. Hetty could feel the discomfort she so often felt there; her mother's bartering with the grocer, each purchase a clash of intent. The Edgware Road was busy, her mother lost amongst the shoppers, then a sudden glimpse of a familiar posture on the other side of the road heading for Church Street. Uncle Tom Harrison had a market barrow on Church Street and Hetty knew he sold all types of things, 'cut price' he often told her, 'just don't ask where they're from' he'd add, with one of his cheeky smiles.

Hetty ran now, crossed the street between the delivery vehicles and buses, passed the fire station and was within a hundred yards of her mother when Ethel stopped outside a shop. She took a quick look round, covert like glances up and down the busy pavement as if checking to see if she was being watched. Hetty slipped into a shop doorway out of sight and when she looked again, just caught the back of her mum entering Bosher's Pawn Brokers. "No Mum!" Hetty exclaimed, "Please no, not Dad's suit ..." - Dad looked so handsome in his suit, afforded from his demob money so he could look smart when he searched for work.

Hetty was crying now, upset that the family was in such need of money, blaming herself, believing that in some way it was her fault. With her right foot crossing and tucked against her left ankle, Hetty looked as though she was standing on one leg and swayed to and fro nervously. Twiddling her plaits, her fair hair tinged red by the watery evening sun, she waited hoping desperately that her mum would reappear with the suit still over her arm. But she didn't.

With just her enormous bag, Ethel stepped back out onto the pavement, crossed over the Edgware Road and hurried down Clifton. Hetty followed but held back until she was sure her mum was heading home, for at that moment she felt that her mum would not be pleased to see her. On the north side of Clifton and almost at the Warwick Avenue, her mum turned and walked down the steps into the area of one of the houses. A dark entrance, paper and old leaves the welcome and a tabby cat lazing in a diminishing patch of sunshine on the coal bunker. It was the betting house, as the seemingly private residence had come to be called.

Hetty walked past without a glance. She knew exactly what happened in there, for a school friend's uncle ran it and made lots of money out of people. Horrible place she thought, horrible. Hetty was almost as upset with her mum now as she had been when she first saw a bucket of blood leaving her mum's bedroom. When the door had opened she had seen the crochet hook, then Gran carried the bucket out past her. She took it downstairs and flushed what was left of the baby down the toilet. Lucy seemed to visit them for just two reasons; to borrow money and to help her mum abort a child.

Hetty decided to go home and with head down, watched as the gaps between the paving slabs passed beneath her. Passing as did her thoughts and with each gap becoming the thing she disliked, so she made sure her feet didn't land on them. Her mum came home later and helped finish the food. Jimmy came in from his cricket game sometime afterwards and Edith's late arrival went unnoticed. As they all sat down to eat in a deeper silence than normal Hetty quite simply forgot about the teacher's message, for it just didn't seem important any more.

Chapter 7

The Game for Gentlemen

Paddington, London, 1934.

From Ranelagh Road the Eaglestones moved to a second floor flat at 117, Kilburn Park Road. A wide road lined with terraced houses on either side, built from the same yellow brick which had turned grey with the city. Along the length of the road and several feet beneath it ran the Kil Burn; a stream with its source on Hampstead Heath and which once flowed past Kilburn, the Village on the Burn, and on finally into the Thames. Like the Fleet under Fleet Street, the Kil had been bricked into a tunnelled channel to form part of the capital's underground sewerage system in the mid eighteen hundreds.

The flat at 117 was one floor up from the street level rather than two and luxurious compared to Ranelagh for it had a small sink on the landing with running water and the waste actually flowed away on its own. The parlour was situated on one level and up six steps were the two other rooms; one a bedroom for the children and the other, supposedly a living room, acted as the bedroom for Jim and Ethel. Not self-contained and with no locks on the rooms, the hall and stairs were a thoroughfare to the other flats, but it cost an affordable fifteen shillings a month. Although there was still no electricity, there were a number of things about Kilburn Park Road which changed Hetty's life for the better.

At Ranelagh, her dad's sister Hetty had lived on the next floor down and Ethel and Aunt Hetty were always fighting. Not just pulling hair and scratching but punching and biting each other. More than once her mum had arrived upstairs with her skirt torn off, the fight often stopped by the men from the other flats. Hetty found it so embarrassing and it would all start over something stupid, like her mum cleaning their stairs and just one of Aunt Hetty's to make the point that Aunt Hetty's were dirty.

Another change for the better was when her dad purchased a two valve wireless, bringing information into the household and transforming conversation. When the accumulator needed recharging, its delivery by Hetty to Bowden's Electrical Shop, on the other side of the road, became a priority.

The other main aspect which changed life for the better at Kilburn Park Road was the view the flat gave over the Paddington Recreation ground. Behind the wall of the backyard lay the cricket pitch and beyond that, the cinder running track. The view from the kitchen window was like a window upon the world, free entertainment, of other people's doings and pastimes. Of mothers who spent time to play with their children, boys playing cricket with their fathers and couples strolling under the trees together.

At the weekend Young Jimmy and Hetty would sit with their dad and watch the adult teams play on the well-tended pitch below their window. With the players dressed in their white flannels, the batsmen with their pads and the fielders chasing around at the direction of the captain, it all seemed very serious and complicated. Jimmy was fascinated by the tactical, hard fought games.

"Like draughts," their dad said. "Move your players carefully, tempt your opponent and then catch 'em out."

Jimmy was always playing cricket now and getting as good at fielding as he was at batting. He had even abandoned his bike, the new bike that Mum had bought for him from the bike shop on the Harrow Road. Hetty and Edith had never had a bike, yet despite it gathering dust in the hallway, Jimmy wouldn't allow anyone else to use it.

Jimmy watched intently as the cricketers on the recreation ground would be sent further from or nearer to the wicket and to different places on the field; the captain moving his fielders strategically according to the strengths and weaknesses of the bowler and the batsman. Jimmy started talking about the mid on, square leg, long stop and other positions that were meaningless to Hetty. As meaningless as the different types of bowling he talked about to his dad.

The best part of Saturday afternoon for Hetty was being sent over to Frenche's to get a jug of milk in the interval when the cricketers took their tea. The shop lay on the other side of the road to number 117 next to the Shakespeare pub, the Willesden Borough side. Kilburn Park Road separated Paddington Borough from Willesden. The shop sold sweets, chocolates, biscuits, milk and probably other things which Hetty hadn't noticed; a most delightful place to visit because she could buy her favourite Peek Freans custard cream biscuits there. The tuppence worth would be put into a cone made out of an old newspaper or telephone directory and by the time she had crossed back over the road her slender hand had dipped into the cone at least half a dozen times.

On finishing her custard creams, it would usually be time to help her mum with the food preparation and so Hetty always laboured over the last one. She took off one side, licked away the cream and started to nibble both sides to oblivion until her mum eventually insisted she get started. So as men chased red leather-bound balls, struck by willow across short cropped grass, Hetty would pull herself away from the window to join her mother and leave her dad and brother to watch the game for gentlemen to a conclusion; a game that would influence Hetty's life as much as her brother's.

Hetty Elizabeth Eaglestone

Circa 1935 - about 13 years old

Chapter 8

Langridge's Farm

Paddington to 1938.

Porchester Hall in Porchester Road, on the other side of the Harrow Road from Ranelagh Road, was a regular forum for dances and attracted many of the local youngsters from London W9 and W2. Its wooden boards were a sea of tiny dents from the stiletto heels and the bar portrayed, as it had for decades, the rows of beer taps and racks of glasses. Youngsters stood up all evening, drank, smoked and flirted as they had always done. With girls talking and pretending not to notice the men and men who said little, stared a lot and made their move often too late in the evening.

At sixteen, Hetty had blossomed into a slim, curvaceous young woman and was starting to attract the attention of many of the young men. She always borrowed a party dress from Edith, the pink one, for her sister had two and preferred the white. But it was the first time Peter had seen her in it and he was quick to tell her just how pretty she looked. Stan Kirby, her regular dancing partner, thought she looked pretty too. He had always thought her pretty, right through Essendine School, for they had been in the same year together. But Stan and Hetty had become 'mates' and good 'mates' didn't tell each other things like that. When Peter asked her to dance, Stan graciously stood aside saying, "Of course I don't mind." But he did mind, he minded a lot and despite being given the come-on by more than one of the local girls, the tall, handsome and very good dancer left Porchester Hall early and on his own that night.

Hetty liked Peter's confidence, the confidence which came from having been in the army and as a policeman making the streets of London a safer place. He worked with Tom Duckett, also ex-army on reserve pay and following recent developments in Europe their army skills would likely soon be needed again.

Edith was dating Tom, although it hadn't started out that way. She had previously been dating George, another of Tom's army friends. But George couldn't write and unbeknown to Edith, his letters were being written by Tom. Several weeks of correspondence had passed when Tom found an excuse to visit Edith at 117, Kilburn Park Road, saying that he had a message from George. During the conversation, Tom 'accidentally' let it slip that he was writing the letters.

He had only just left the flat when Hetty's mother told her to run after him and invite him to tea. Tom, of course, accepted and that was the beginning of Edith and Thomas Duckett's relationship. It also led to the end of Edith having to conceal her party frock from her father, slipping out the house with it tucked up under her coat and Hetty having to cover for her.

As Peter and Tom walked the sisters home from the dance, James Eaglestone waited for his daughters just outside the front door, the glow of the street lamps sufficient to warn of his presence. "Get back by ten," Jim told the girls as they had left the house and both knew that if they failed to do so they would receive the rough edge of his belt. The two young men nodded to Mr. Eaglestone as he stood looking at them, seemingly like a sentry mounted at the top of the street steps and, "good evening" they said politely, keen to keep on the right side of the man who permitted the friendship.

James approved of the company his daughters had acquired - army reservists and policemen, solid sorts. The sort of men Britain had for centuries proudly sent overseas to win wars and gain an empire. How long would such a world-standing linger James wondered and how long before such men would be needed again? For James didn't trust the 'Hun', never had. Just twenty years earlier 'millions of soldiers were killed because of 'em and for what?' he often asked. Now they grew again in such strength. 'Absurd, absurd, unbelievable' were the frequent utterances of his army mates of the Great War, utterances over a pint as they pondered the state of the nation.

"Can I see Hetty on Saturday?" Peter asked Mr. Eaglestone.

"Alright with me," James replied and looked at Hetty hoping she would agree. But in response she simply smiled, which Peter took as a yes,

"See you at one o'clock then," he concluded and walked off with a spring in his step as he retreated towards the Shirland Road with Tom.

"Why didn't you answer him?" James enquired of Hetty as the men turned the corner and passed out of sight.

"Too embarrassing Dad."

"Not if you just said yes. And what do you want me to tell him when he turns up on Saturday?"

"Don't know Dad, just don't embarrass me," she said and kissed her father lovingly on the cheek. He was her rock and would not let her down.

The lorry arrived outside the Eaglestone home in the early hours of Saturday morning and to Hetty's further embarrassment it was an open one. They hadn't travelled down in an open backed lorry for years. There were already two other families loaded on and the more sheltered places behind the cab were taken. Like her father, Hetty thought fruit and hop picking degrading. James Eaglestone had never gone down with the family and preferred that his children didn't. Hetty felt she had no choice but to go with her mother and her mother felt she had no choice but to go with Lucy. Lucy had been going down to Kent ever since the eighteen hundreds and when Lucy said you must come down, her children obeyed. It was Lucy's escape from the city, several weeks in the country to lord it over her children and usurp the partners, for whilst fruit and hop picking, she was the governor.

So there Hetty sat 'like a refugee' clutching her coat for warmth, whilst around her the family's belongings, the kitchen utensils, table and chairs, bedding and clothes were exposed for 'all the world' to see.

Whilst it was still dark they crossed the Thames via Vauxhall Bridge, headed for Sidcup, then Sevenoaks and reached the countryside beyond as day was breaking. Hetty sat next to Gran who looked slightly sinister with her big coat and head scarf, huddled over to keep warm. In the dawn light Hetty could just make out the facial lines that once represented rebellion, but which a combination of ageing, tobacco and alcohol had carved into permanent features. Funny, Hetty thought, that Gran had shunned her parents and siblings yet held so firmly onto her own children. Born a Hitchcock, Lucy had seven brothers, but it was only Samuel who ever visited her. He came twice a year, at Christmas and on her birthday to give her money. A lot of money so Hetty's cousin young Lenny said. 'A bear of a man' so Lenny described him. Lenny could mimic Samuel perfectly, 'and with the palm of his hand still resting on the envelope Samuel would say, 'something for you Lucy'.' Hetty smiled at the thought of Young Lenny's face as he told the tale; also telling her that Lucy claimed Alfred Hitchcock, the famous film director, was her nephew – and of course all the family believed it. Living next door to Gran, Lenny saw it all. Samuel Hitchcock always arrived in a chauffeur driven car with his wife, but Mrs. Hitchcock would never go inside the flat. Hetty wondered why with all that money in the family, Gran had led the life she had. 'Nothing as strange as folk' her dad often said and with that thought Hetty tried to prop Gran up for she had fallen asleep. She didn't look sinister anymore, just frail and a little bit sad.

As dawn progressed to morning, more people were on the move but fortunately no one knew them here and Hetty could relax save for the knowledge that Peter would be calling at her home in a few hours time. What would her father tell him she wondered, for James Eaglestone would not lie.

They reached the Seven Mile Lane and thundered along it with the slip stream buffeting the passengers, crossed the Medway by the narrow stone bridge at the Leas where the weir was in full flow and finally rattled into Yalding Village.

With London and the Thames estuary on one side and the sea on two others, the county of Kent, 'the Garden of

England', was but a few miles from the encroaching suburbs of the capital. Yet its chalk hills and cliffs and lush green valleys provided for a picturesque escape for the city dwellers. Well known for its production of fruit and hops where intensive labour was needed, it was the only kind of holiday many Londoners could afford to take.

Lucy didn't pick but expected half of Ethel's book at the end of the season. Hetty's mother thus started picking early in the morning so that she could pick her quota and still prepare the evening meal for everyone. Often a pot roast with suet pudding, cooked on an open fire outside the hut. There was always enough to eat for the ten or so and sometimes more family members who would join them later in the summer. Lucy's daughter Doll, with her children, usually stayed for two weeks and Lucy's son Len always arrived at the weekend by bicycle. Her other son Sid came down not to pick but for the fishing and almost as importantly, to keep his mother happy.

'Best spot to fish' Hetty's Uncle Sid would say whilst standing on the 'Fishing Lane' bridge over the River Medway, rod in one hand and sandwich in the other. His sandwiches and flask safely delivered by one of the younger members of the family. Though once not so safely when it was carried on the back rack of a wobbling bike to fall off and break the flask and spread the sandwiches across the lane.

For all the embarrassment it gave Hetty, fruit and hop picking brought her close to her mother's family; playing with cousins, being treated by uncles and aunts and sleeping all together in the one hut. The highlight of retiring to bed for the children was watching grandmother Lucy getting undressed. She always wore 'old fashioned clothes', long dresses with a white or black apron. But of particular interest was the shark boned corset which pulled her in at the waist and 'puffed up' her breasts. When that came off she would look so relieved and transformed, but not for the better.

When Peter arrived at Mr. Langridge's farm it was a terrible shock. Hetty saw his car drive down the road and turn onto the track towards the farm house. 'Gone down to stay on Mr. Langridge's farm in Yalding for a few weeks,' her father had told him when Peter called by on the Saturday afternoon, omitting to mention anything about picking. Hetty saw Peter go to the large front door of the farm house and watched as Mr. Langridge opened it and started pointing in her direction. Getting back into his car, Peter returned to the road and headed for the picking fields and that was when Hetty made a run for it. At full pelt she headed for the family's hut in the raspberry field. Passing the younger ones at play she slammed the ill- fitting hut door behind her and lay on the bed, her face hidden in the blankets. Even though the Chapmans were privileged and didn't have to share a hut with another family, Hetty knew that Peter would not approve of her gypsy-like existence. The other family huts were nearer the hop fields, a long row of them, with two or even three families in each big hut, smoky, dirty and not very clean faces so Hetty considered. But because Lucy Chapman had been coming down for decades, Mr. Langridge let her have the round hut situated on its own in the raspberry field.

With her hair dishevelled and eyes tearful Hetty listened with baited breath to the sounds outside. The thin tin sheets conveying even the sound of long grass brushing the sides as a summer breeze rolled across the farm land. The younger children who had to pick a certain quota of fruit before they were allowed to play were now quiet, the game of hide and seek seemingly placed on hold. Hetty running from her boyfriend was better entertainment than hide and seek or even a family game of cricket, though it might not equal a picnic and swim in the Medway on a balmy summer's day.

Hetty was still lying amongst the blankets upon the faggots and straw when she heard the car arrive with her mother sitting in the front passenger seat, for how else would Peter have found his way to the raspberry field?

"She's in the hut Mister," said one of the children.

With her face reddening deeper with embarrassment, Hetty heard the door open as Peter stepped in, the bright summer light illuminating the stark interior, half burnt candles in saucers sitting on the dirt floor, milk crate seats and belongings stacked as best they could against one wall. Peter had never seen a bed like it, a bundle of twigs at the bottom held the straw between them and the wall. Bedding was placed over the straw to create one large bed for the whole family. Normally Hetty found it very comfortable, but she was far from comfortable as she looked round to see Peter staring at her.

She got up awkwardly, brushed herself down and went over to him trying to look pleased to see him. "Why don't you two go for a walk along the fishing lane?" Ethel suggested and that's what they did, followed by the younger ones. Peter didn't say very much; there was no suggestion of a walk through the fields or a jaunt by the river and it wasn't long before he made some excuse about having to return to London. And in her heart Hetty knew it would be the last time she saw him.

"Don't worry luv, plenty more fish in the sea," Ethel said as her daughter returned to the raspberry field with Peter's car disappearing into the distance. But Ethel wasn't thinking of fish in general, more specifically the cricket boys of Middlesex County Cricket Club.

Chapter 9

The Cricket Boys

Paddington to 1940.

James Eaglestone quite enjoyed his time in the family house at fruit and hop picking time - 'a bit of peace'. But six weeks was quite long enough and some years he might have to write to say that if Ethel didn't return that week, then she needn't bother. About five years earlier Ethel had said she was leaving to go picking but instead she took the three children to live at Lucy's so that she could do all the chores for her mother. James only found out when he caught her wheeling a pile of washing to the baths: Lucy's, Len's, Sid's and probably others. At least when the picking lorry turned up outside the house, James could be confident of the real destination of his wife and children.

The Eaglestone family made a big step up the property ladder in 1937, for having moved from 117, Kilburn Park Road to 22, Rundell Road for several months, they finally moved to 43, Thorngate Road. A block paved street lined with terraces having small front yards above coal bunkers and several steps down to the area where a door provided access to the basement. At the street level, four steps up from the pavement, there was another front door, recessed to provide a small covered area. Bay windows rose from the basement to the middle floor at the front with concrete lintels to represent the best house the family had ever lived in.

At Thorngate they rented the whole house, living in the basement and sub-letting the other two floors, making it easy for Ethel to pay the agent, Mr. Harris, when he called on a Friday. With both parents working full time, there was money to spare and although Ethel wasted money on gin, betting and secretly siphoned off some to Lucy, James's thrifty, careful approach ensured that cash started to accumulate. Not trusting the banks, he engineered secret hiding places; drawers made shallower with an extra layer of ply to compact the notes, removable panels on furniture and strategic floor boards where he placed tins of cash at arm's length and entrusted no one with the knowledge.

Ethel was as good at collecting the money as James was at hiding it and when it was not forthcoming, judged the right time to call, pressurise and persuade her lodgers. When coercion failed she used other methods. When Mrs. Morris became overdue by two weeks Ethel invited herself into the flat with Hetty 'to talk.' Whilst Hetty continued to engage Mrs. Morris and prompted by her mother to hold her attention, Ethel slipped behind the woman, picked up her hand bag and searched around inside for the woman's purse. Although the blood drained from Hetty's face and her mouth became so dry that she found it difficult to speak, Mrs. Morris never realised the deed being carried out behind her, at least, not until it was too late.

Over time, Ethel prioritised more and more of her money to Jimmy to assist him in cricket. He had become an exceptional school cricketer and was subsequently selected for the All London Schools Cricket Team. Cricket was mainly a middle and upper class sport and Ethel was determined to ensure that her son would not stand out as the poor member of the team. Instead of the cheaper kit bags she bought him the real leather variety to carry his pads, bats and gloves in and bought the top quality flannels.

Playing with the best of the all London schools against teams from other regions in the country, Jimmy's ability again stood out and he was soon appointed captain. Fast on his feet with sharp reactions, Jimmy was as good at fielding as he was at batting and talented youngsters would be picked from the All London Schools side to join the Middlesex County Cricket Club, the centre of English cricket. The home ground was at Lords on St. John's Wood Road, just one mile from the Eaglestone home on Thorngate Road. Jimmy and his friend Paul Brooks were sent for trials there. Both were successful and thus on leaving Essendine

School at fourteen years of age, the two boys joined the ground staff of the most influential and successful cricket club in the world.

In that same year of 1937, Pelham Warner became president of the club. Nationally renowned and a star player of the Middlesex and England teams, Warner received a Knighthood in '37 for his services to cricket both on and off the field. Affectionately known as 'Plum Warner' and 'The Grand Old Man of Cricket' he was a fantastic character. Jimmy and Paul were very fortunate in joining Middlesex at such a time in its history; it provided them with an unprecedented opportunity to make it to the top of the most highly respected sport in the land.

With her son likely heading towards first class cricket and even the England team, Ethel was presented with a still heavier financial burden. But for her youngest child and only son, she would do anything, stealing money from her husband's wallet if necessary rather than letting her son down. And visits to Bosher's pawn shop on the Edgware Road became a regular weekly event, dropping off something on a Monday when her money was short and buying it back on pay day, if finances allowed. The one bonus for Hetty of her mother's obsession was the arrival of the cricket boys every Sunday for tea, which Ethel encouraged by putting on the best spread she could muster. Some weeks the boys might go to Paul Brook's home in Oakington Road, but always came by 43, Thorngate afterwards saying they were hungry. Ethel was only too pleased to present the right social environment for the class to which her son aspired. Dick Martin, Eddie Routledge, Roy Harrington and Paul Brooks were among the regulars, together with Stan Kirby who wasn't in the cricket scene, but as Hetty's old school friend and long term dancing partner he was always welcome.

It was Dick Martin to whom Hetty first took a real liking, for 'he was lovely' and much to Stan Kirby's annoyance, Dick told Ethel that he was 'in love' with her daughter. Hetty received so much attention, sitting amongst the young men, playing cards, laughing and chatting. She would flit around and get drinks for the boys whilst they would comment on each other's cricketing talents, or lapses of. The easy catch that was dropped, Eddie being foolishly stumped or Jimmy out for a duck when previously he had hit half a century. Hetty was always included in the games and omitted from the jibes. Her sense of fun was an attraction to equal her curvaceous figure and good looks and as the boys vied for her attention, Hetty soaked it up and couldn't decide who she fancied most.

"One day I shall marry your daughter," Eddie Routledge said to Hetty's mother as he left the house one Sunday evening. Everyone laughed in the knowledge that the comment was half meant, and Dick Martin was the first to say there were others already ahead of Eddie in the queue. As there were in the batting order so someone else added and so the banter ran with the boys who jostled noisily down the street; imprints of energy at every foot fall, their rhetoric whipping into the night air. Paul Brooks was always the last to leave, being sure to say goodnight to Hetty's parents and finally to Hetty, with whom he would linger, his glances portraying more than friendship. And as she watched Paul catch up with the rest of the cricket boys, Hetty wondered if he could ever become more than a friend. For when you have grown up living around the corner from each other, playing in the street and attending the same school, how could touching be anything other than chance encounters at play?

Paul's confidence in sport hadn't manifested itself with women and when on the next Sunday evening Eddie Routledge announced he had given up his fiancée in order to date Hetty, everyone laughed and then cheered. Stan Kirby, Paul Brooks and even Dick Martin cheered with the rest for how could they do otherwise and how could Hetty refuse?

When Hetty had first left school in 1936, she worked as a shop assistant for Jordan's department store on Church Street, a busy shopping area just off the Edgware Road. The store was owned and run by Mr. and Mrs. Jordan and their two grown up sons. Hetty started work at 9a.m. but once a week arrived at 8a.m. to take part in the company keep fit class. Provided free, the class was usually held on the flat roof of the building but once a month would meet in Regent's Park for rowing lessons.

Outside Jordan's on Church Street, market barrows lined either side of the road and during her break Hetty might pop out to Uncle Tom Harrison to see what he was selling, perhaps glassware or linen, and be entertained by his rhetoric. The stall next to his, sold new and second hand comics and did exchanges, which attracted many of the local lads.

Uncle Tom told her that some market traders handled goods that had fallen off the back of a lorry, 'but not me of course' he'd say emphatically.

Of all the different departments within Jordan's store, Hetty was by chance allocated to ladies' fashions, her favourite; 'far more interesting for a fourteen year old than furniture or china'. The jewellery department would have been fine had it not been for the employees. They were all at least forty years old, plastered in makeup and the smell of their perfume seemed to spread even out to the market stalls.

When a customer presented Hetty with a cheque she would have to get it authorized by one of the Jordan family members, who during opening hours did not hide in the office but patrolled the shop floor, helping customers and employees alike. Company cheques were the only way some families could afford to buy things. Hetty's mother used Bravington's, £2, £3 or even larger amounts when the need arose. The store received the money from the company, whilst a representative of Bravington's would visit the Eaglestone home once a week to collect half a crown until the debt was paid.

Working 9a.m. till 6p.m. during the week and 9a.m. till 9p.m. on Saturday, Hetty earned 12s 6d, which seemed a lot when she first started. But a slightly better wage could be earned at the more prestigious stores in the West End and so in September 1938 she moved from Jordan's to John Lewis on Oxford Street, again in ladies' fashions.

Dresses, coats, suits and all the accessories a lady needed to go with them. The takings increased when Hetty arrived for it was almost with a skip that she moved around the clothes racks, searching for that extra special fit to satisfy the customer's desire to look younger, slimmer, more alluring. And Hetty did it with diligence, attentiveness and most importantly, with a smile.

A few months before Hetty moved down to Oxford Street, in the March of 1938, Hitler arrived in Vienna to the cheers of the Austrian crowds and the ringing of church bells. The annexing of Austria was yet another violation of the Treaty of Versailles, a provocative gesture and a grave warning, for Germany was devoting one fifth of its industrial output to the preparation for war. When the bells stopped ringing in Austria, the silence spread not just over that country but lay heavily across the continent, like stifling air before the onset of a major storm. James Eaglestone shook his head with despair as he listened to the news and then later in September scoffed when he heard that the mountainous, heavily fortified Sudeten region of western Czechoslovakia would also be annexed to Germany; because the German speaking Czechs were being oppressed, so Hitler claimed.

"As if that's a valid reason to enter another sovereign state!" James declared to his ex-army pals down at the Shirland Pub.

On meeting Hitler in Munich, Neville Chamberlain agreed the Sudetenland be handed over in return for the Fuehrer's lasting promise of peace. 'I believe it is peace for our time', the Prime Minister said on his return to London. And not for the first time, James wasn't so sure he believed his government's message and Hetty's elation at Chamberlain's words was dampened by her father's scepticism.

Under the agreement, by relinquishing the Sudeten Region, Czechoslovakia was guaranteed that the rest of their country would be protected from aggression. But by March 1939, German troops marched into Prague, the capital city, and the people wept as they were forced to salute the Fuehrer.

"I've seen it all before," James said to Hetty as the news of Germany's incursion was announced to a tense nation. "And at the end of it, millions died!"

So whilst ladies slipped money out of their handbags to pay for the expensive fashionable clothes so well presented to them by Hetty and with John Lewis's cash tills ringing to the tune of their purchases, in German territories the windows of stores belonging to 'undesirables' were being smashed, staff hit with metal bars and stock looted.

When Hetty came from work one night in May '39, her father told her that the Germans might finally have a fight on their hands, for he considered that the Poles would not roll over like others had done.

"Made of strong stuff the Poles," James said.

Hitler now had his sights on the Polish Baltic port of Danzig and even more serious, Britain and France had committed themselves in March '39 to backing Poland in the event of an invasion. Thus as the promise of an approaching summer filled the streets of London, a shiver of anxiety ran down the spines of men who knew the true meaning of events. Whilst Chamberlain publicly brokered peace, his preparation for war increased with earnest. Farmers were encouraged to create more arable land, conscription was fully introduced, 750 planes a month started to come off the production lines, whilst shipyards and armament factories worked flat out. Four months later on the 1st September Germany invaded Poland and on the following Sunday morning Hetty, with the rest of her family, sat by the wireless tuned into the BBC. It had been announced that the Prime Minster would make a speech sometime after 11a.m. Likely the whole nation was waiting. Thorngate Road was deserted, no traffic could be heard even on the Shirland Road and the only background to the family's thoughts was the lady talking about tin food recipes on the wireless. When Neville Chamberlain finally started his delivery, Hetty dared not breathe. Britain had called for an undertaking from Hitler to withdraw his troops from Poland. "I have to tell you now," Chamberlain said, "that no such undertaking has been received and that consequently this country is at war with Germany."

"That's it, my Tom will be called back up," Edith declared after her father turned off the radio with an action that said 'told you so'. Tom had spent seven years in the Duke of Cornwall's Light Infantry before entering the police as an army reservist and within days Ethel was proved right, all reservists were called back into the army. Poland was attacked by both Russia and Germany in a pact to divide the country between them and with no military support and little time to prepare, Poland's brave efforts to counter overwhelming odds failed with terrible losses. The country was occupied by the end of September, the Germans in the western half and the Russians in the eastern half. The rest of Europe held back to leave the Poles to their fate, what else could they do, they were weak by comparison to the mighty Germans. Britain was as yet unprepared for direct conflict and its declaration of war had failed to sway Hitler's intentions.

As the country prepared for war so life in London carried on to be merely inconvenienced. Travelling to work on the red double decker, Hetty would be carried as before on the number 6 bus down the Shirland Road to Warwick Avenue and along Clifton. Turning right onto the Edgware Road the bus approached Marble Arch before finally heading down Oxford Street. Hetty loved the Arch, the white marble so majestic, so solid looking like her country once seemed, as her life had been before the declaration of war. Although scared as most were of developments, shoppers still came down to the West End and John Lewis department store was as busy as ever. Hetty flitted about trying to keep everyone happy, whilst annoying the older women with her turnover.

White had become very popular with the blackout restrictions, a demand which manufacturers had manipulated into a range of fashionable accessories. Yet walking in London was still a dangerous activity after dusk and as the winter nights of 1939 drew in, the number of fatal accidents increased. The blackout meant that there could be no street lighting, vehicle lights were forbidden, windows were blacked out and double blackout curtains were placed across commercial entrances to ensure light did not escape onto the street. Wardens even told people to put their cigarettes out.

Despite driving very slowly, vehicles mounted pavements, collided with each other and pedestrians were run over by unseen vehicles driven by drivers who hadn't seen the pedestrians. By December, 4,000 deaths had occurred because of the blackout, yet no military losses had been incurred for there had been no military engagements. Hetty, like her fellow travellers, started to wonder what all the fuss was about. Two million Anderson shelters had been distributed even before the war. Civilians had been carrying gas masks since September and reporting for their stint on Air Raid Patrol. Children had been evacuated to the countryside, trench shelters had been dug in parks, brick shelters constructed on the streets, yet not a single German plane had she seen or heard over the capital.

Whilst British folk referred to the seven months between September '39 to March '40 as the phoney war, it was not seen as such in the occupied countries. In Poland the Russians were rounding up hundreds of thousands of German speakers, teachers, civic workers and anyone else they mistrusted and sending them off to Siberia along with 200,000 Polish servicemen, many of whom never returned. In March '40, they killed 15,000 Polish Army Officers at Katyn. Mowed down standing at the edge of the mass grave they had dug for themselves. And the Germans were committing similar atrocities in their western sector, creating the beginnings of the concentration camps which received Russian speakers, intellectuals, Jews and anyone else they happened to dislike or mistrust. With hundreds of thousands of German and Russian troops forcing themselves into the homes of ordinary people, to be fed and looked after by the women folk, everyday family life became a terrible ordeal. Nothing phoney about such actions even if unreported; this was no phoney war.

Tom Duckett, like many of his army reservist pals, had panicked when they were first recalled for duty. Active service meant leaving girlfriends to the mercy of the civvies and marriage was seen as a way of protecting the goods. Worried that he might lose Edith, Tom gained James Eaglestone's permission and proposed to the nineteen year old within days of Chamberlain's declaration of war. Six years older than Edith, Tom married his girl on November 28th at the Paddington Registry Office, in the same room where Ethel and James had married during the previous war. A room befitting the dark times; bleak, gloomy and as cold as the war would become for many newly-weds. Not the romantic setting Hetty dreamt of. Hetty wanted the perfect day, a sunny day, a lovely church, perhaps St. Peter's on Elgin Avenue filled with friends and family, flowers, hymns, bridesmaids in pretty dresses and a big black car to deliver her there. Pat, Tom Harrison's daughter, would be one of the maids, they had already agreed to that, but as to who the knight in shining armour might be, she hadn't yet decided. Eddie Routledge didn't seem the same once she started courting him 'and anyway' he volunteered for the RAF at eighteen. Ethel favoured the local boy Paul Brooks as the most suitable choice for her youngest daughter. The families knew each other well, Paul was an exceptional cricketer and not least, he was Jimmy's best friend. In Ethel's view Paul Brooks was the perfect choice for everyone.

County Cricket was suspended during the war years, but Middlesex kept on some staff and nurtured youngsters as best it could with the hope that one day, sporting life in Britain would return to normal. When Dick Martin reached eighteen, he too joined the RAF, the service of choice for such men, whilst Paul Brooks who was a year older than Hetty entered the fire service. Paul was thus able to keep in touch with the Eaglestones and maintained some level of cricketing practice. He trained hard when he could and even had an offer to play in Australia. But Paul loved his family and secretly loved Hetty. He would leave neither and after all he had already played in the young professional side for the best club in the world.

The seven month 'phoney war' in Britain ended in April 1940 when Germany invaded Denmark and Norway. With Denmark a lost cause, there being no substantial resistance, British, French and Polish forces tried to support the embattled Norwegians. The attempt proved amateurish but German naval losses hampered plans for the invasion of Britain and Norway's occupation tied down extensive German resources for the duration of the war. British forces were again involved in mainland Europe when the Germans attacked Holland and north Belgium in May '40. The German's 'right hook' and their bombardment of the Maginot line pulled the British and French forces north. This left the Ardennes weakly defended, however the allies assumed them to be impassable by armour. It was a move predicted by the enemy, who subsequently unleashed 45 divisions to quickly penetrate the Ardennes, swing west to the channel and sever the Allies cohesion, communications and cut off hundreds of thousands of Allied troops.

Thus began the biggest military evacuation of troops the war would witness and a major body blow to the confidence of the British nation. 200,000 British and 140,000 French troops were evacuated from the French port of Dunkirk on any available vessel; from naval ships, to ferries, river cruisers, fishing boats and even small yachts. The London newspapers tried to make the best of the bad news and talked of the true British Bulldog Spirit; citing the bravery of 'our servicemen' and that of ordinary civilians who sailed whatever vessel they could to bring back the boys. An indication they claimed that the nation was not about to roll over and surrender.

But bad news was difficult to conceal. On June 14th German troops marched down the streets of Paris as the German flag was hoisted to the top of the Eiffel Tower. A symbol of power, a reminder to the people, should they need one, that their country was no more. France signed its ceasefire with Germany in the same railway coach in which the Germans received the armistice terms in November

1918. Naturally Hitler was present to relish the French humiliation. Germany occupied the northern half of France and its Atlantic coast and established a puppet government in the south.

"It doesn't look good," James Eaglestone commented after listening to the BBC nine o'clock news. Hetty watched her father gravely, knitting needles in hand and a jumper half made trailing into her lap. She sat in one of the armchairs to the three piece suite, the front room clogged with furniture: dining table and chairs, gramophone and glass cabinet to show off the family best.

"Worse than last time," James said as the mantelpiece clock shifted towards an early bed time and earlier still if the air raid sirens sounded. Hetty's needles continued to click, breaking the silences as James paused for thought. Plain and purl, her usual, smooth on one side and ribbed on the other.

"Who next?" he asked out loud, though speaking to himself and got up to adjust the heavy blackout curtain which hung across the still intact window. He pulled the thick material taut, almost caressing it with the back of his hand, ensuring that not even the faintest slit of light be seen from the outside. It was as if the action might secure his family a little longer against the threat of enemy soldiers on English soil. In just three months, Denmark, Norway, Holland, Belgium and France had been captured. With Poland, Czechoslovakia and Austria already consumed and Italy joining forces with the Germans, Britain was isolated. James left the room to put the kettle on, leaving Hetty to ponder what she might make next, perhaps a dress if her mother could acquire the material.

When the cricket boys next came to Sunday tea the jokes still ran with the cards and James Eaglestone played as if he was one of the boys. His 'wise cracks' just as sharp as the bright youngsters he entertained. But doubt now crept in behind the humour. History would have it that the British were invincible, the Empire unequalled, yet all knew their armed forces had taken a beating. They were weak and Hitler might invade before they had time to prepare.

For Hetty however there was no doubt. The new Prime Minister, Winston Churchill, would look after the country just as her mother would look after their regular Sunday visitors, and it was she who sent Paul Brooks to help Hetty in the parlour.

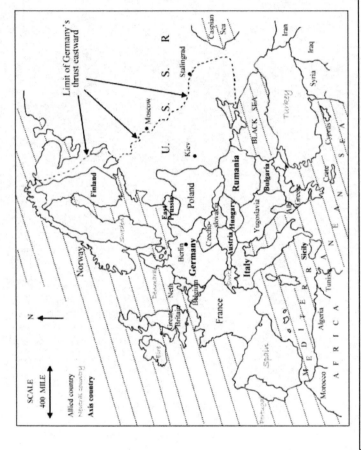

Map of Europe showing Allied, Axis and neutral countries and the extent of Germany's expansion.

Chapter 10

September 7th

Paddington to September 1940.

After Dunkirk, James Eaglestone was convinced Britain would be next on Hitler's list. Where else was there for him to go apart from against his friend, Stalin?

"They didn't invade us last time Dad," Hetty said hopefully as her father boiled his morning egg and made ready to leave for work.

"Things have changed sweetheart. This is modern warfare, armies move quickly with countries taken in weeks," he explained.

Hetty was about to say something of Churchill's assurances but James anticipated his daughter's thoughts. "And don't believe everythin' you hear on the news or read in the papers. They told us the Great War would be over in six months, join up for an adventure, see Europe!" James laughed in spite of himself.

In June, Prime Minister Winston Churchill had reassured the nation that Britain was well placed to repulse an invasion. That the Navy was quite capable of cutting off the huge supply chain needed by an invading force and there was some truth in the latter, so James thought. But as for land defences and military deployment, they were hopelessly disorganised. Friends and relatives in the army and Local Defence Volunteers were testimony to that.

"At the closest we're just twenty miles from the French coast," James said trying to educate his daughter. "German occupied coast," he said, correcting himself. "And once they arrive, what's going to stop 'em making it the sixty miles to London?" James knew from his travels that there were no major physical obstacles between London and the south coast and nothing had been built. "Won't be months fighting over a few yards of mud, like we did last time," he said.

With the troops barely home from France, everyone had started talking about an invasion, as were the German high command. General Milch wanted to invade immediately. He knew that with every day's delay the British would regroup, their defence made stronger. We need our paratroops to land in southern England immediately, he said, followed by an invasion force. The Luftwaffe would provide air cover whilst simultaneously attacking the British Navy.

Instead, Operation Sealion, the invasion of 'England' was developed at Hitler's request with landings planned for the end of July. But by July the initiative had already been lost. Sensibly, most German navy and army commanders opposed 'Sealion' until air superiority could be guaranteed. Then Britain's navy and land defences could be neutralised and troops and equipment pass safely across the channel.

Hermann Goering, Air Minister and Commander in Chief of the Luftwaffe, was confident he could annihilate British Fighter Command within a few weeks. They had downed 1,000 RAF planes in the battle for France and Goering was sure they could do the same in the battle for 'England'. Britain's fate would thus be decided in the air and America, who remained neutral, awaited the outcome. For Roosevelt did not want to supply a doomed nation only to find at some later date, the arms they had supplied be used against them. Many Americans predicted that with or without their help, Britain would be overrun within twelve months anyway.

In July the London newspapers reported that the Luftwaffe were attacking British ships in the Channel, playing down German successes and upbeat about the RAF's response. Unbeknown to most, Goering was teasing out the RAF who must surely come to protect their ships. But Goering underestimated the importance of the developing British RADAR system and Air Chief Marshal Hugh Dowding's intuitive use of fighter planes; prioritising their assignment and never losing sight of 'the need to fight again tomorrow'. The Battle of Britain stretched into August and by the 11th the Luftwaffe had lost 274 aircraft compared to the RAF's 124. Fighting the RAF over their home patch wasn't the same as fighting them over France. James read the papers avidly and even reading between the lines could see that the boys in blue were at least holding their own. When Dick Martin, Eddie Routledge and others came home on leave they were positive about their chances of beating the Luftwaffe, despite their exhaustion. And the mood of the nation changed ever so slightly towards optimism, with faith growing in their armed forces.

With a measure of disbelief, Goering threw his net wider, attacking airfields, aircraft production and radar stations. He attacked further and further inland, gradually crippling the entire structure of Britain's air defence. Day after day runways were cratered, command centres and radar masts damaged and British fighters destroyed both on the ground and in the air.

Hetty's Uncle Tom Harrison said that Churchill should get help from the Americans and Hetty wasn't sure if he meant it or was just trying to wind up her father. For James's fondness for the Yanks hadn't grown with his years.

"What and let them say they won the war for us again? No thanks, we don't need 'em," James said, "But you wait, once we get the upper hand, then they'll come in and say it was all down to them. Just like last time." And Tom mouthed 'like last time' before James said it. "We'd been fighting for three years," James continued, not spotting the gesture, "then in the last few months they threw in a couple of battalions and claimed victory for themselves. No, we can do it without 'em, we're the ones with the Empire."

Tom really knew how to wind her dad up Hetty thought and felt sorry for him. 'Good to have opinions' her dad would say and 'stick by your principles' he often told her and he was always right. Anyway, she said to herself, I don't like the sound of the Yanks either.

With Goering's net spreading wider, bomb attacks on London intensified and the capital's death toll mounted. In August, unaware of the increased threat, Hetty moved from John Lewis department store to work right in the heart of the city, at the Black and White Milk Bar. It was situated on the corner of Leicester Square and New Coventry Street. Hetty worked not so much in the milk bar but in the wooden kiosk partitioned off from the rest of the milk bar. Facing the square, the kiosk had a counter onto the street from which Hetty sold cigarettes and tobacco to passers-by: Players, H. O. Wills and St. Julian.

The main part of the milk bar had windows onto both New Coventry Street and Leicester Square and sold ice cream and milk shakes. A mixture of milk and ice cream, the flavour of choice, were whisked before being placed in a cold glass and consumed on the premises. Hetty's best friend Maud worked there and that was all the encouragement Hetty needed to take the job, plus the fact that the pay was even better than at John Lewis. With two pretty girls fronting the business, sales outpaced those at the other milk bar on the square, Fortes, situated next to the Ritz Cinema. The owner of Fortes sent his son over to check out what was going on, for glancing across the road, the opposition always seemed crammed with servicemen. The economic espionage resulted in the son falling for Hetty and buying his milk shakes and tobacco there whilst pursuing her for a date.

Leicester Square presented Hetty with a view upon life which she had never previously enjoyed, not even at John Lewis. For Piccadilly Circus, Leicester Square and neighbouring Covent Garden attracted all the servicemen from home and abroad. Men of the Commonwealth: Canadians, New Zealanders and Australians as well as those escaping from the German occupation of Europe: Polish, Czechs, French, Norwegians, Belgians and Dutch.

Unlike America, within days of Britain's declaration of war on Germany, Canada stopped being neutral and sent 23,000 of her troops. They were joined by 35,000 French, 25,000 Polish and thousands of other servicemen who had escaped to the sanctuary that the British Isles represented, and at some point all wanted to visit the famous capital; the seat of power for a great empire and which was fast becoming a cosmopolitan city.

During Hetty's first weeks there she had many offers of courtship; from cheeky 'old' men whom Hetty thought were 'just kidding', to the younger servicemen and not least Pat the local beat bobby.

When Hetty left home to go to work on Saturday September 7th the weather was warm with just a few clouds casting shadows over the city. She walked to Warwick Avenue underground station, the summer dress she made ruffling in the wake of her quick stride. There she caught the train to Piccadilly Circus, with plenty of time to be at the Milk Bar for her afternoon shift starting at 2p.m.

She intended to catch the number 6 bus back and pop in to see her cousin Pat Harrison, but it proved to be no ordinary Saturday.

A few weeks earlier on August 24th, German bombers hit civilian areas of London when they unleashed the rest of their bombs returning from a raid. In response Churchill ordered an attack on Berlin. Whether in retaliation or as a strategy to goad Hitler into changing his tactics is open to debate, but within days Hitler made a decision not to focus solely on Britain's Fighter Command. The tactical change would have terrible consequences for Britain's city population and the 7th September marked the beginning. But it was also one more nail in the coffin for Hitler's attempt to win the Battle of Britain, for the Luftwaffe had already lost 900 planes to the RAF's 500. Losses which might have been unsustainable had Churchill not appointed Beaverbrook as Minister for Aircraft Production in May 1940.

'We must work without stopping' the Canadian newspaper magnet said 'to save the nation' and thence produced fighters at double the rate they were being produced in Germany. Thus every time the Luftwaffe arrived in the skies above Britain they were met by still more Spitfires and Hurricanes, though often flown by replacement pilots with ever decreasing experience.

Arriving on the Bakerloo line, Hetty climbed the stairs from the platform and passed the government posters reminding travellers to carry their gas masks and that 'Careless Talk

Costs Lives' as if people needed more reminders. The deepest tunnels at Piccadilly Circus Station lay some 200 feet below the city's streets, an ideal haven from the bombing, though not permitted, at least not until the 7th unfolded, for not long after Hetty stepped out into the sunshine, East Enders at Liverpool Street Station would force the authorities to change the rules.

The streets were buzzing with traffic and the pavements full with window shoppers; women in hats and cotton summer dresses walking arm in arm with their partners. A sailor fresh from the London docks winked at Hetty as she passed, an airman did the same but she noticed neither for just down from them Hetty saw the first 'coloured' man she'd ever seen, a Canadian Air Force boy. She had previously only seen coloured people at the pictures, often chanting around mud huts. He reminded her of the black doll she once had as a child. As then, Hetty didn't question the colour, he was black as she was white; as her black china doll broke just like the white ones - dropped on the concrete steps leading up to Grandmother Lucy's flat at Lanark Mews and then taken to the doll hospital on Edgware Road to be mended. The coloured man was quite handsome she thought, he smiled at her, perhaps wondering why she was staring at him and she sheepishly smiled back.

Middle aged men sat in smart attire eating food in the Perroquet Restaurant on Leicester Square, full plates and white table cloths; reminding Hetty of when her mother came home with more than the family's rations and excused it by saying 'the rich still eat out in the city, so why can't the poor eat well at home?' And even James Eaglestone found his wife's argument difficult to counter, despite the example it set for his children.

The queue for the matinee performance at the Leicester Square Odeon jostled forward as Hetty slipped through the narrow entrance of the wooden kiosk, ready to sell her tobacco and cigarettes to the throngs of people out to enjoy the late summer sunshine.

"How old are you?" asked Pat the Irish bobby as he stood by the kiosk, nodding to the locals who passed him.

"Eighteen," Hetty replied shyly as she finished serving a young lad with a packet of Players Navy Cut, not for the cigarette cards but to smoke whilst watching 'Gone With the Wind' which was still attracting big audiences at the Ritz Cinema on the north side of the square. "Thanks luv," another interrupted as Hetty held out the man's regular purchase of Kensitas before he ran off to catch his bus.

"Why don't we take a stroll tomorrow if you're free," Pat suggested between the interruptions, "perhaps meet here and head for St. James's?"

Hetty needed time to think about the sudden but flattering proposition. Her father would approve of a policeman, although perhaps not an Irish one who was at least ten years her senior. But Hetty wanted to date him. He looked handsome in his uniform and walked with such authority, a glance being all that was needed to sway a person from illegal intent, or so Hetty thought.

Perhaps she would tell her father that she was visiting Maud. That wouldn't be a lie for Maud would be working at the milk bar on Sunday. And after all, the weather was beautiful and the lake in St. James's Park a magnet for wildlife as well as courting couples. Mind made up and with her face slightly flushed, Hetty gave Pat the answer he had been waiting for. And with that, he strode off to complete his beat, the black and white striped band near the end of his left sleeve flashing in the sunlight - warning, if warning was needed, that the long arm of the law was on the move again.

A couple of hours later, perhaps around 4p.m. the air raid sirens sounded, the streets filling with the oppressive noise and emptying of people. Even the traffic reluctantly stopped. Another nuisance raid and likely over before it started so Hetty predicted as she quickly served the last of the still waiting customers; a pack of fags more pressing than the call of a bomb shelter. Nonchalantly Hetty pulled down the shutters and made for the back of the milk bar, where together with Maud she would sit out the raid and wait for the all-clear.

As they sat and gossiped in the spot beneath the stairs, the increasing drone of aircraft engines told the girls that this was no nuisance raid. An hour later great swathes of the East End and the Thames frontage were ablaze; factories, warehouses, barges, people's homes and even the blocks of paved roads were set alight. The heat so intense that paint blistered on ships passing down the river. Victoria and Surrey Docks were devastated along with the homes, warehouses and factories densely packed around them. With the dark of evening so the conflagration could be seen from sixty miles away on Brighton Downs.

Hitler had sent 300 bombers, escorted by hundreds of fighters to cover 800 square miles of air space as his first token of what was to come.

After the all-clear sounded around 6p.m. people emerged from the bomb shelters whilst fire engines and ambulances raced towards the inferno, their bells ringing and with crews still buttoning their tunics. The West End had also been hit, but nothing like the docklands.

"Back to work then," Hetty said to Maud, as people looked in, seemingly determined that life would go on, the draw of nicotine strengthened rather than weakened by events. But even as Hetty started to raise the shutters on her kiosk, German air crews were making ready for the next wave, arriving over London just after sunset.

When the air raid sirens sounded for the second time, Hetty decided to walk home; believing that once she got there she would be safe.

"No use waiting for the all-clear again," the two girls agreed, for it would be "too late to reopen."

Thus with the search lights scanning the night sky to illuminate the specks that were Dorniers and Heinkels, the firing of anti-aircraft guns too few in number, and the rumble of explosions, Hetty used her torch to help find her way through the blacked out streets. Regulations dictated that her torch be covered by a paper bag with a slit in the end and it was about as inadequate as the ack ack guns.

Dust and smoke rolled through the darkness from damaged buildings and a severed human head lay by itself at the kerbside. Hetty only realised what it was when she was within inches of it, placed her hand over her mouth and stumbled on into the blackness.

"Where do you think you're going Miss?" a voice asked her.

"In the name of God what are you doing?" Pat asked in disbelief as he realised it was Hetty.

"I am going home," she said with a tone that asked where else would I be going. "I'll be safe at home," she added confidently. Pat just stared at her, not sure if he was hearing right.

"Where's home?" he asked.

"Thorngate Road ... off Shirland," she added, seeing that he had no idea where Thorngate was.

"That's over four miles away," Pat informed her, not that she needed informing.

"Not far, I walk quickly," Hetty said smiling.

"And do you have an air raid shelter at home?" Pat continued, ignoring her smile with some difficulty.

"No!" Hetty replied dogmatically, wondering what difference it made.

Pat said nothing, he just looked at the young, foolish girl before him and felt very protective of her.

"Here," he said giving her his war issue helmet, "wear this and don't argue."

"I wouldn't argue with a policeman," she said grinning. Pat guided Hetty past the rubble and then insisted he walk her all the way home.

With her secret date firmly fixed for the next day in St. James Park, Hetty closed the street door at 43, Thorngate and joined her family. They were all huddled in the basement front room, including James Eaglestone's sister Aunt Nine and her husband Frank who always felt safer at the Eaglestones than in their own house on Rundell Road. James kept the family entertained with his stories and joke telling, the same old ones as Hetty recalled but they laughed all the same. Midnight came and went with no respite in the bombing and with the early hours slipping by,

James reflected that long bombardments in the trenches always preceded an attack. Everyone looked at him aghast, was he suggesting that this might be the start of the invasion, that German soldiers might soon be on English soil?

Suddenly they didn't feel quite so safe. British soldiers guarded the capital, Stan Kirby was one of them. There to do whatever was required of them and likely out now, keeping order, helping the trapped and injured, watching out for looters and the like who 'took advantage' of the noise and distraction. But could they repel an attack by thousands of German paratroopers? Wouldn't want to be out there now, Hetty thought.

People who didn't have a shelter at home sometimes used a public shelter, but not the Eaglestones. Ethel often left for work before the all-clear and had 'looked in' on a few. Overcrowded, noisy, people sitting on the bare floor, babies crying, some being breast fed in front of everyone, 'disgustin' Ethel recalled. Most had just a bucket for a toilet with no privacy, 'not a place for my family' Ethel would say adamantly.

The brick and timber shelter for Thorngate was right in front of the Eaglestone's house but few took refuge there. James was a builder, he knew about structures and he wouldn't recommend it over his own house, save it didn't have a chimney to cascade down upon the occupants. It was used more as a wardens' station and James used it when he carried out his Air Raid Patrol duties. He was often on duty for he did Ethel's, Hetty's and Edith's as well as his own. James wasn't going to have any of his women folk patrolling the blacked out streets.

The Eaglestones were still waiting for their own shelter but likely the proximity of the communal one, placed them as low priority. One night during August they had been invited to share Mr. Ashton's air raid shelter. Mr. Ashton's garden backed onto the Eaglestones. He was a friend of James and had installed an Anderson early on in the war. The Anderson was named after John Anderson, Lord Privy Seal in charge of air raid precautions. The shelters started to be distributed as early as February 1939 and consisted of six curved, corrugated tin sheets supposedly providing enough space to comfortably shelter six people. The night the Eaglestones joined them there was Mr. and Mrs. Ashton and their daughter, James and Ethel, Hetty, Edith and Jimmy as well as Hetty's Aunt Nine and Uncle Frank.

Mr. Ashton was proud of his endeavours to protect his family. Although the council delivered the shelter, it was up to the residents to dig the pit, against the edges of which the ends of the curved sheets of metal would sit. The council then came back and poured concrete into the pit providing a floor and sandwiching the sheets at their base. Mr. Ashton had dutifully piled the excavated soil against the sides and from other areas of the garden took more soil to cover the roof to a depth of eighteen inches.

Some neighbours built steps down and tried to make their shelters homely with rugs and curtains, but Mr. Ashton's contained just bare wooden benches and seemed cold and damp. After a few hours of gossip and the conversation dying with the onset of midnight, Ethel had made some excuse to return home. It wasn't long before the rest of the family followed her over the garden wall and all returned long before the all-clear sounded. Grateful as they were to Mr. Ashton's further invitations, they always found some reason not to go.

With thoughts of German soldiers on Thorngate Road and bombs still falling despite the unearthly hour, the supply of cigarettes was running low in the Eaglestone's basement front room. It wasn't until around 3a.m. that someone thought about the family's piano, recently moved into the middle front room and at that moment situated right above their heads. Looking at each other in the semi darkness, silently at first as the significance registered, they burst into laughter, the cigarette smoke from half filled lungs bursting hysterically into the darkened room. 'How we laughed!' Ethel said the next day to one of the neighbours when recounting the tale.

The bombing finished around 4a.m. but started up again later that day and lasted another nine hours. By the end of the weekend 1,000 Londoners were dead, 2000 seriously injured and tens of thousands homeless. The bombers came back day and night and by the Wednesday of that week the Eaglestones learnt of the close hits they had heard: 23 houses were destroyed on Lanark Road, the Lauderdale Mansions were seriously damaged and the mansions on Delaware Road destroyed. Yet Hetty and her parents went to work every day, her father to shore up houses that could still be inhabited, board off those that couldn't and help demolish those which were dangerous.

Chapter 11

The Parachute Mine

Paddington to May 1941.

Following the 7th September, the Luftwaffe blitzed London day and night for eight days. But on the 15th September they lost 56 planes, bringing their total losses for the week to 174. It was too high a price to pay and on the 16th Goering cancelled all further day time raids. The next day, Hitler indefinitely postponed the invasion of England.

The RAF had prevailed and Germany had lost the battle for Britain, their first failure of the war and as could be expected, Churchill concluded the British success in eloquent style. 'Never in the field of human conflict was so much owed by so many to so few.' The few being 3,000 pilots, but in truth, the effort spread to a vast ground based support structure. Of the 3,000, 250 were 'Wild Men' Polish and Czechs who gained by far the highest kill rates, 100 New Zealanders, 100 Canadians, 100 other nationalities and 7 Americans.

Churchill had used his best diplomacy to obtain military support from across the Atlantic with little success but winning the Battle of Britain became his ace card. In December, despite its continuing neutrality and strong isolationism, US Congress finally approved the Lend Lease scheme, allowing Britain to have billions of pounds worth of supplies and military equipment on credit. It was fifteen months after the start of hostilities but at least Churchill could now take the war to the enemy. In January '41 he sent a large British tank force across the north African desert at night to surprise half a million Italian troops massed in Libya. The Italians panicked and Tobruk fell by January 21st with the capture of tens of thousands. Then in March, Churchill sent 50,000 troops to help the Greeks halt the Italian invasion in the north of their country and thus temporarily curtailed the Axis Expansion in Europe. Unbeknown to Edith, one of those British troops was her husband, Thomas Duckett, who Edith had last seen in October 1940. Little did she know then that he was destined for such danger and equally unaware that she was already four weeks pregnant.

Hitler was seriously disturbed by the sudden British successes and in particular their proximity in Greece to the oil fields of Rumania. In response, he sent German troops under Rommel to Africa and delaying the invasion of Russia for six weeks, ordered the attack of both Yugoslavia and Greece on the 6th April. Within eleven days Yugoslavia was completely overrun but Greece was more of a struggle, cut short when the Greeks refused to adopt British tactics. By the end of April, Britain was forced to evacuate 43,000 men from Greece to Crete and leave 11,000 New Zealand, Australian and British troops behind.

When the letter came from the War Department declaring that Thomas Duckett was missing in action, Edith was almost eight months pregnant. In July 1941 Georgina was born and Hetty became an aunty, her sister a mum and possibly a widow.

The nightly bombing of London and other major cities continued through to the end of 1940 and on into 1941. It was motivated by Hitler's belief that he could now bomb and starve the nation into capitulation, thus rendering an invasion unnecessary. Thorngate Road was in the middle of West London's railway network. Eight hundred yards south lay the Great Western line running into Paddington Station with its marshalling yards at Acton, and fourteen hundred yards north was the London Midland Southern line into Euston with its Willesden Junction marshalling yards. Bombing was inaccurate, particularly the parachute mines drifting in the air currents and many destined for the railway system fell on the densely populated terraced streets between.

On the 20th September a bomb dropped on number 11 Elnathan Mews, completely destroying it and seriously damaging the two adjoining houses. Elnathan lay between

Shirland Road and Warwick Avenue and on the 24th it was Warwick Avenue's turn with eight houses left uninhabitable. The next day The Express Dairy on Clifton Road was seriously damaged, a house on Edbrooke Road 100 yards from the Eaglestones was hit and houses left uninhabitable on Kilburn Park Road and Shirland Road. It was Elgin Avenue's turn on the 28th. By the end of September over 6,000 civilians had been killed in the bombing.

On the 1st October Elgin Avenue and Shirland were hit again. Kilburn Park Road and Sutherland were hit on the 9th and eight houses seriously damaged on Edbrooke on the 12th. That same night, on Goldney Road a bomb landed right on number 13, also taking out the two houses on either side.

"Unlucky number 13!" Ethel said to her daughters but James was quick to point out that Fred Ready who lived at number 13 Thorngate wasn't doing 'too bad for himself'. He owned all the odd numbers on the street from 5 to 17, plus numbers 49 and 65 and likely others no one knew about.

"We'll own this house one day," Ethel said, seemingly confident of the fact.

James Eaglestone didn't know it yet, but Ethel had approached the owner via Mr. Harris the agent, about buying number 43. Not surprising that the owner Mr. Rust was considering her low offer. For living in the relatively safe backwater of Minehead in Devon, Mr. Rust considered the sale of a house at serious risk of being destroyed to be an attractive proposition. Already by mid October 100,000 buildings had been seriously damaged across the capital, over 20,000 beyond repair. Whilst many people rented in Thorngate like the Childs at 45 and the Cooks at 47, Ethel wanted to be like Mr. and Mrs. Hall next door at number 41 or the Cretchleys at 33 who owned their own. Maybe one day, Ethel thought, she would be like Fred Ready, own others and rent them out.

Hetty was shocked when John Lewis department store was completely destroyed in September as if how dare the Germans hit such a lovely shop. Then on the 16th October,

Thurstons the snooker table manufacturer and the Perroquet Restaurant both on Leicester Square were bombed, Thurstons being on the same row as the Black and White Milk Bar. By the end of November another 6,000 people had been killed and finally it struck home to Hetty that everything around her was at risk: her home, her family, her job and even perhaps the relationships she had considered so dependable, as if overnight they might all disappear. She still insisted on walking home if the siren sounded whilst still at work, believing it would be safer there, but by November she was doing so alone. For Pat the policeman just wasn't on his normal beat one day and she never saw him again.

With so many air raid warnings at all hours of the night, the Eaglestones decided it better to die comfortably resting in bed, snatching what sleep they could, than to die tired and uncomfortable. If the bombs came close they would all go down into the front basement room.

After the 8th December when 400 tons of bombs and 120,000 incendiaries were dropped causing almost 2,000 fires across the capital, there was no bombing anywhere over the Christmas period. This allowed the Eaglestones to sit down to a peaceful festive dinner, silly hats adorning their heads and paper chains hanging across the ceiling; the type you made yourself by looping one strip round the next and sticking the ends to form a chain of loops. Ethel made sure plates were full with chicken, brussel sprouts, carrots and potatoes in plenty. But the vegetables were not from James's garden. James didn't dig for victory he just worked hard for it. The back yard at 43 Thorngate was James's escape from the war; beyond the paving stones, the outside toilet and the roses climbing on the trellis lay his domain. The trellis demarked its beginning, the few square yards of garden, his oasis, lying no more than a rake's distance from the house. Except for the chicken coop it was covered with flower beds between which James had built neat, narrow, concrete paths to provide access for planting and weeding. In warmer times roses were in abundance, pink predominantly, Ethel's favourite and red for Hetty.

Hetty and her red! And dahlias, James loved dahlias. He carefully dug up the tubers after they finished blooming each year, washed and dried them and put them away in the small cupboard beneath the drainer, to separate and replant the next spring. 'Of all the things that could be kept in the cupboard beneath the drainer,' Ethel would say.

On the 27th and 29th December the Luftwaffe returned and on the next morning fires still smouldered from the thousands of incendiaries. Bitterly cold with a smattering of snow, Paul Brooks and thousands of other firemen worked all night to fight the devastation. With smoke smudged face and freezing wet clothes he arrived at number 43 that morning to see if the Eaglestones were okay and present them with a freshly laid egg from his parents' hens. A gesture soon to become a ritual but more to tell Hetty of his endeavours and be admired by the woman he secretly loved.

On the 16th April '41 came the heaviest raid of the Blitz so far with 900 tons of bombs and 150,000 incendiaries dropped onto the capital over a period of eight hours. It stretched the fire services to breaking point. The Plaza Hotel on St. Martins Street off Leicester Square was hit at about 11p.m. then Bear Street, also just off Leicester Square, was devastated by a high explosive bomb around 3a.m. The air raid refuge trenches in the square were hit the same night and the entrance to the air raid shelter blocked with six people trapped and one dead. More stores on Oxford Street were hit together with nineteen churches destroyed and eighteen hospitals damaged. 1,200 people were killed and 2,200 seriously injured including many firemen attempting to put out the thousands of raging fires. But no night was quite like that of the 10th May.

Hetty, Jimmy, Paul Brooks and Stan Kirby stood at the area front door at number 43, watching tracer bullets rise up into the night sky. The search lights flashed this way and that, illuminating mostly barrage balloons and just occasionally a loathsome grey shape beyond, an intruder upon the London sky. It seemed to the youngsters that aircraft engine noise emanated from the very roofs of the terraced houses, which sadly deflected only sound, not steel. Shirland Road was hit and then shortly afterwards, Warwick Avenue, so the youngsters thought; the thunderous, crashing sound indicating close proximity to experienced ears. The earth trembled, the house creaked, an object once thought to be so immoveable, so secure. Yet Hetty was feeling safer in her own home again for it had been lucky for them. Seven months of bombing and still it stood with mere windows missing. Fires sprung up from the bomb sites throwing an orange glow into the night, dust and smoke of different shades according to their composition, wooden joists, linoleum, furniture or clothing. Capping stones and chimneys were silhouetted by the fires and still the city's defences fired blindly back, the ack ack sound punctuating the explosions that crushed people's homes; homes with families that proudly stood one moment and were gone the next. Then as if in a lull, that lasted but a split second, the youngsters heard a flapping sound, the distinctive flapping of a parachute. The surrounding cacophony returned to quickly block it out but it was definitely a parachute mine and the realisation slowly entered their consciousness to freeze their stance. A parachute mine meant only one thing - widespread destruction. It didn't embed itself in the ground to create a crater and wipe out a couple of houses, it exploded on the surface. The associated shock wave could wipe out a whole street. Yet still the youngsters stood at the open door, as if mesmerised by the developing battle, of magnitude even London had not previously experienced.

Oppressive, heavy air preceded the impact of the shock wave; air that was like a brick wall into which they had run. Hetty, Jimmy, Paul Brooks and Stan Kirby were thrown twenty feet down the hallway, falling into a pile of intertwined limbs at the foot of the stairs. Tiles crashed down into the area, plaster dislodged from ceilings, the water mains severed, gas and power cut. But number 43 remained standing, its walls bearing the roof timbers and remaining tiles. The adults, who had been sitting in the basement front room, quickly lit candles to search out the youngsters, but like James they were already checking around the house. In the semi gloom of candles and run down torches, dust spread across broken glass, the last tenacious panes that had survived lesser nights, dispensed with. Embers from the coal burning stove had been blasted across the parlour floor to smoulder and start a fire, but James knowingly went straight into the kitchen to douse them. And on checking his room, Young Jimmy found pieces of glass the size of daggers sticking out of the mattress of his bed.

Aunt Nine wanted Frank to go and check on their house in Rundell Road. The blast from the land mine, as they referred to the parachute mine, had seemed centred there, at their end near Marylands Road. She was frantic about losing her false teeth. Had forgotten them when the air raid siren sounded; left them on the mantelpiece to weather the storm. Thus out into the chaos Uncle Frank was bustled to negotiate the debris, the fire engines and ambulances. Frank stumbled upon ruined homes and couldn't make sense of the scene. Another terrible explosion shook the ground as twenty homes on Essendine Road were struck, breaking them like a hammer hitting upon a porcelain pan. An air raid warden told Frank to 'bugger off' and get into the public shelter. But Frank was still trying to convince himself that this was where his house once stood; like losing something about one's person and convinced it must be somewhere. There were no windows, no street door, not even a roof; the chimney and all that was once upstairs lay on the ground floor. Curtains flapped in the uncanny chill breeze and only the walls remained to define what was once his home. Worse, there was no sign of Nine's teeth.

Frank returned to report that all was lost, everything gone. All their belongings, the furniture they had worked so hard to afford, clothes, keepsakes and trinkets; the collection of a lifetime's labour gone, money and all. "But what about my teeth?" Aunt Nine shouted.

The parachute mine had landed on Marylands Road at the junction with Rundell Road, 120 yards from the Eaglestones. Twenty houses on Marylands and four on

Rundell were demolished and fifty houses made uninhabitable including some on Oakington and Thorngate. That same night Clarendon Terrace, Clifton Gardens, Clifton Road, Shirland and Warwick Avenue were all hit and the ten houses on Lanark Mews destroyed; Grandmother Lucy's home at number 1, Uncle Len's at number 2 along with the other homes and garage businesses. Fortunately the Chapmans were in a public shelter at the time. 1,500 Londoners lost their lives on the 10th May 1941, 5,000 homes were destroyed and 12,000 people made homeless.

Chapter 12

Next of Kin

Virginia, December 1941 to the Summer of 1942.

The tires of the Model A Ford sank deep into the farm track as Dalton left his sister Evelyn's place; rain and snow followed by more rain having transformed the roads into quagmires. Turning right onto Mount Olive Road and drawing up at the T junction with the Timber Branch, Dalton could just see the Carlton home way over the fields. He hadn't visited there in a good whiles and wanted to call in now, but thought better of it. As he turned right to head away from the Carltons and pass Wares Church it started raining again, and Dalton just hoped it would turn to snow, so they might have a proper Christmas.

Dalton always slowed down as he passed his church, perhaps out of respect for those who lay in the grave yard, or perhaps because he just liked the location so much and wanted to linger there awhile. Anyway, racing past in a car just didn't sit right.

The white painted wood of the church glistened as water ran down its clapboarded sides and the granite grave markers appeared still grayer in the wet. Not a house in sight, just the comfort of the surrounding trees and fields; so many good memories and many more to come he hoped. Dalton remembered the gossiping and heated debates outside the church and the more recent topic about getting involved in the European war. Well they were sure involved in war now, in the Pacific as well as in Europe. In a few weeks thousands of US servicemen were going to Britain, the first since the Great War and likely many more would follow. Roosevelt must have been planning for something, because Dalton had been drafted May 8th 1941, seven months before Pearl Harbor, the first peacetime draft in the country's history.

The Selective Training and Service Act adopted by Congress 16th September 1940 eventually led to more than ten million men being called upon. Initially, those aged twenty-one to thirty-six were drafted for one year of military service. But after Pearl Harbor all men between eighteen and forty-five were required to register and the term of service was extended for the duration of the war plus six months. Dalton was inducted in Baltimore of all places, at the 5th Regiment Armory. A massive hall, the biggest building Dalton had ever seen with tables all around: doctors, dentists, interviewing officers and the rest.

Like the others drafted early, the extension of service for 'the duration' could mean anything for Dalton. So make the most of the time at home was all he could do. And the membership of Wares prayed for the war to be brief and that Dalton and the other boys come home safely and soon.

The Christmas furlough would pass all too quickly. After seeing Momma, Daddy and Edward at the home place he'd visited with his baby sister. At twenty-five, Evelyn was three years older than Dalton but with Myrtle at the grand old age of thirty-two and Bertha thirty, Evelyn sure was his baby sister. Her three boys were growing fast; the oldest Sonny would be seven in a few days time!

Dalton stayed at the Ashley's longer than planned, ate plenty, talked about his training then ate some more. Finally, around late afternoon he pulled himself away from his nephews to drive home and eat his momma's food.

After the church he turned left onto the Wares Bridge Road and at the Dragon Run stopped and got out despite the rain. He missed all this, he reflected as he looked from the bridge to see the swamp spreading far into the woods on either side of the open water. Must have had three or four inches of rain he judged by the height of it. The rain drops caused ripples which fanned out across the flat surface, slipping over the slow, steady flow of the stream as if oblivious to its movement. The ice which had started to grip the river was being washed away, but it would come back; winter had yet to take full hold upon the landscape. He remembered that terrible night when Robbie had come back so late after the accident. Thank God, Dalton thought, that Robbie hadn't been drinking when the accident happened and equally that the bad conditions were blamed for the collision.

It had been over twelve months since Dalton left Middlesex and next spring would be his second without working the Virginian soil. Been away too long already he thought and how long would it take to beat the Japanese? He had worked six months in the city before the army, like Wilson, to earn some real money. But unlike his brother, had intended to save what he could. 'Save for a farm' he'd told his family and Wilson had made fun at his younger brother's naivety. Yet right he was, for Dalton had saved nothing; simply spent the hard earned dollars surviving from one day to the next.

Dalton gave his address to the draft board as Route 6, Towson, Baltimore, Maryland, but hadn't belonged there. He belonged right here amongst the woods and farmland, hands working the soil. Although delivering ice from a Charles Hoffberger ice truck, he told the induction officer that his civilian occupation was 'farmer' and it had sounded real good. Dalton couldn't understand how his rebellious brother coped with working on the trams amidst the noise and fumes of the city. But then Wilson would stay in Baltimore just to prove a point to his daddy.

Wilson hadn't been drafted and Dalton wondered if the draft board had something against ice delivery men. For they had even called upon Preston's services despite him being thirty-five years old with nine children. Maybe ice delivery was a bad choice of job, but what did a farm boy do in the city?

Moving to Baltimore had not only taken Dalton away from farming, but also from Lucy. Lost a lot and made nothing he reflected. Lucy had married a local boy by the name of William Hall, July 26th 1941. Dalton intended to go see her before he was posted overseas, for rumor had it that the 29th Division would be leaving next year, probably to the Pacific.

Dalton was soaking wet by the time he got back into the car and when he reached home his momma fussed him just like she always did; warm, dry clothes and food on the table for the son who visited her as often as he could. Robbie wasn't home, he was either at Camp Lee, Virginia or Fort Bragg, North Carolina, no one was quite sure. He didn't write much. Drafted into the catering unit of a Signals Battalion. "How in the world had he gotten to be a cook?" Kelly kept asking, "The boy can't cook!"

Dalton had no idea for there was no choice as far as he could tell. He had walked into Fort George Meade, Maryland as a fresh faced recruit and simply followed orders. No choices, no voice, did what he was told and just pleased to be earning decent money.

Dalton's lean, solid frame, toned from years of farm work had stood tall and proud for the B Company photograph in front of the hastily erected barracks. One hundred and twelve men standing shoulder to shoulder in four reasonably neat rows, mostly fresh recruits sprinkled with a few experienced National Guardsmen. All plucked from the farms, small towns and few cities of the mid eastern sea board; to be made into soldiers and certain of three good meals a day and regular monthly pay. As a private, Dalton received $21 a month, a fortune by comparison to that which he had earned working for his daddy. But Fort Meade was empty now, the men at home, maybe for the last time, for who knew what the next twelve months would hold.

Dalton loved Christmas at the best of times and this year was even more special. The long nights with the wood fire, candles and oil lamps glowing and Momma's cooking. The snow came back, just a few inches, but it made things right and searching for a Christmas tree more fun. For inside the army uniform was a heart that still belonged to a boy. With Virginia Mae happy to ride on his shoulders, Dalton brushed through pines to cover them both with snow. And as she pointed out trees she thought were best, he went the wrong way accidentally on purpose. Until finally both had laughed so much that coming upon a cedar with the right shape, a shape that Momma would think real pretty and being not too high for the house, Dalton shook the snow from it and with an axe, chopped it off at its base. Firmly roped up, Dalton carried the tree back to the farm house, Mae skipping behind him with excitement. As long as there were uncles to mess and tease her, Bertha's daughter might never want to go back to her mother.

Nailing the Christmas tree down to the wooden floor, Dalton started to decorate with Mae's help and the occasional bit of unwanted advice from the others. The few balls to hang on the tree this year were courtesy of Edward, bought from the 5 & 10 cent store in Urbanna right opposite Bristow and Son's clothing. Adding bits of cotton wool to create a snow effect and some homemade decorations, Dalton stood back and asked his momma what she thought. "Real pretty," she said and Dalton gave her one of his lovely smiles. It was good to be home.

With darkness across Europe, Dalton sat down to his momma's Christmas dinner, the light outside still illuminating the youthful footprints in the virgin white snow. Momma had been up early preparing and now, with sweat on her brow, was finally able to get away from the stove and sit awhile, albeit briefly. The long wooden dining table was filled with family members as the wood stove blazed and thanks given to God for the food they were about to receive. Then with the last words of the prayer still hanging in the air, the boys started to devour the hours of planting, nurturing, picking, food preparation and finally cooking which Fleda had so painstakingly performed. As she performed for every meal time, every day, year on year, without thanks, save that her family left nothing on their plates. And she too gave thanks, for many things, but especially for the turkey, well fattened for the special day and hardly a fiber left for soup.

Dalton just sat at the table afterward, looking at the Christmas tree in the flickering light of the candles and listened to his daddy's view of world events. Smiling as he recalled how they had all gone with him to Virginia Beach the day after Pearl Harbor was attacked, shotguns at the ready, just in case of an invasion. Five battleships and fourteen smaller ships along with 200 aircraft were destroyed and 2,400 people killed at Pearl Harbor; 'an aggressive act' which Roosevelt had expected, although its location was a surprise to all. Expected because on November 26th he had demanded that Japan withdraw from China and from their alliance with Germany, knowing full well that his demand would not be met and likely instigate a military response.

Sometime after the sun had slipped behind the trees on the other side of the dirt road, Evelyn and Steve arrived with their three boys to visit Mamma and Papa, as they called Fleda and Kelly. They knew only too well that they were in for a treat and not just from the older members.

Kelly soon brought the conversation back to the war and Fleda took the cue to entertain her grandchildren. Kelly just couldn't understand America getting involved with Germany. "Japan is where we need to head," he declared, unable like most, to predict the tide of events. And looking at Dalton said "Guess that's where you'll be going son."

Kelly slung a bunch of papers onto the table, mainly the South Side Sentinel printed in Urbanna. But there was also a copy of the Baltimore News Post which Dalton had brought down from Fort Meade. Even the local paper had less on its front page about Christmas than normal, making way for articles on the war. That the fire siren would sound short blasts for two minutes in the event of air attack and two long blasts for the all-clear; that units were being established in Urbanna to cater for the after effects of bombing and collections being made for the Red Cross war needs. But because of its earlier date and wider circulation, the Baltimore paper was more focused on the war. Above the short reports of events in the Pacific, the sinking of the aircraft carrier Lexington off Hawaii and of developments in Manila, Singapore and Java, there was a huge attention grabbing headline in large capital letters stating
'U.S. DECLARES WAR AGAINST GERMANY, ITALY'.

Then explaining that the 'action came a few hours after Germany's declaration of war against this country …' and that 'the vote in the Senate was 88 to 0'.

"Well it ain't gonna stop us enjoying our Christmas," Kelly declared, dismissing the paper and hoping that Roosevelt would remember that it was the 'Japs' who had attacked the US, not the 'God Damn Germans'.

"Soon be time for some whiskey, hey boys," he said, pulling thoughts from the headline; his whiskey distillery producing an uplift to dreary times and cold weather, the temperature dropping to twenty Fahrenheit outside.

Later, Dalton sat next to Evelyn, his arm across her shoulders, whilst she picked her way through the newspapers, skipping first over the Sentinel's pages. Adverts for three-wheeled bikes her boys might like, ranging in price from $1 to $3.50. The film 'Wide Open Town' featuring William Boyd, was showing at the Rappanna Theater in Urbanna. Then in the Baltimore paper, adverts which touched Evelyn's sense of humor. Brager Eisenberg 'Baltimore's Dominant Thrift Store' as it declared itself, occupied a full page spread for 'perplexed Santas'.

"A page of timely gift suggestions that should solve that-what to give question," Evelyn read aloud to those who might be listening.

"Well I declare," Fleda responded on cue, surprised by the 'what to give question', "No trouble there" she said, "just give the things people need."

The best present for Fleda of the entire year, was Dalton's summer gift to her of a wireless. The first and last one she would own, bought out of Dalton's first army pay. It was one of two main purchases he had made, the other being the greyhound bus ticket to bring it home. And from his second month's pay, Dalton bought himself a watch and 'my, he was so proud of it'.

Evelyn started to read out some of Brager Eisenberg's offers; "Candlewick robes at $1.99, electric train sets at $6.77 and gay colored Christmas balls at 3c … and the shop stays open till 9p.m. … oh my lands, what do you know!" Evelyn concluded.

"What did the boys get?" Dalton asked Evelyn.

"Nothing," she joked. Where upon Sonny spun round and ran off a list and more besides, ready for his birthday.

"Spoilt!" Dalton joked, grabbing Sonny and tickling him in the ribs, his hard fingers sending screams of laughter through the house. Bobby and Tommy stood watching, anticipation in their eyes, hoping that Uncle Dalton might turn on them next. Spotting their open, innocent, happy faces calling for attention, Dalton picked Bobby up and pretended to throw him out into the snow.

"Do that to me," the other two simultaneously cried out, everyone getting excited, not least Uncle Dalton.

When the night closed in and the whiskey came out, Evelyn and Fleda cuddled up to Dalton. The Christmas tree with small presents beneath, seemingly breathing a sigh of relief that the children were at last fast asleep; temporarily tucked up in the beds upstairs until they were taken home. With a lull in the talking, Fleda reached over to gently clasp Dalton's Dog Tag. It had received much attention from the boys, particularly when Dalton had barked like a dog. 'It's my dog tag' he'd said and told them that they would bark too if it was placed around their necks and of course they did, just as soon as it was on and before in Tommy's case. With Dalton almost asleep beside her and in the low light of the diminishing candles, Fleda began to caress the shiny metal surface, thumb and forefinger running over the rounded edges, as if the action might sooth her worries. Dalton's number, her son's number, 33043230 and the next of kin inscribed beneath, 'Fleda Mae Slaughter, Church View, VA'.

As the end of a lovely day loomed, its memory starkly contrasting with the bare, cold night outside and the wicks of the candles finally faded and died, Fleda silently prayed for the safety of her sons.

The family had no idea of the history to which Dalton had been attached. And could not have foreseen or likely even imagined the sacrifices men of his unit would make or the role they would play in determining the outcome of the Second World War. Dalton Roy Slaughter was now a

Stonewaller, of General Jackson fame, a soldier of the 116th Regiment, 29th Infantry Division, the 'Blue and Gray'.

When in the Great War President Woodrow Wilson signed the declaration of war on Germany, April 6th 1917, the US regular army had just 128,000 men, plus 8,500 part time soldiers in the reserve National Guard. The rapid recruitment drive placed new recruits and National Guard units into newly created divisions, the 29th being one of them, activated in the August. It was composed of men from states which had fought on both sides in the American Civil War. From Virginia where Richmond had been the capital of the confederacy and from the 'Yankee' states of New Jersey, Delaware and Maryland. It was fitting therefore that the 29th Division be referred to as the 'Blue and Gray'.

Arriving in France in May 1918, the division saw six months service and was deactivated twenty months after its creation. But in February 1941 it was remobilized at Fort George Meade Maryland and in a changed US perspective on the world, would stand the test of time.

The 116th National Guard Regiment was again absorbed into the 'Blue and Gray' and together with the 115th and 175th Regiments formed the new triangular system introduced by the new division commander, Major General Leonard Gerow.

The 116th Regiment had started its long distinguished life in 1760, originally the Second Virginia Regiment. Having been involved in the Colonial and Revolutionary Wars it became known as the Stonewall Brigade during the Civil War of 1861-65. 'Stonewall' because of General Bee's last words to rally his Confederate troops when he was facing defeat at the first battle of Manassas; called the first battle of Bull Run by the northern Union. 'There is Jackson standing like a stone wall. Let us determine to die here, and we will conquer,' Bee said.

Bee was killed, but General Jackson's men held firm to win the day for the Confederates and the name Stonewall became firmly attached to both the 116th and Jackson. Thus twenty-one year old Dalton Roy Slaughter had become a 'Stonewaller' eighty years later. And like many thousands of men before and after, proudly wore the 29th insignia on his shoulder, a swirl of blue and gray merging to signify the unification of a once divided nation. And in the course of time, the 'Blue and Gray' would contribute to military successes of which the American people would again be proud.

The Christmas and New Year of 1941-42 proved cold, with more snow and the Dragon Run freezing over. Robbie showed up on the doorstep sometime after everyone had gone to bed on Christmas night and Dalton stayed up with his 'little' brother well into the early hours. Robbie made the days more fun and the nights even more so and the Christmas furlough seemed to be over in the blink of an eye.

Training at Fort Meade was tough in the wintry conditions of early '42. When the boys of the 116th hit the ground it felt as if their bones would break and the cold showers were like ice. They received all their basic training, fitness work and marching drills at Meade. How to keep bedding, belongings and themselves in order, kitchen duties, guard duty lasting around the clock and barrack duty, ensuring the coal fired boiler kept up the temperature in their block. How to clean down their M1 Garrand rifle and put it back together in quick time and blindfolded; that to care for their weapon was to care for their life.

Dalton soon revealed a youthful anxiety to please; perhaps his new buddies might have said 'a naivety', easily exploited by lesser men. But by chance or destiny, Dalton was absorbed by a small group who recognized compassion and honesty for the blessing such attributes offer a friend. Dalton would make a fun and loyal army buddy as he had a brother - and in the years together until their parting, so their friendships became as such.

There were rogues and those who might be frowned upon by more fortunate folk, but as the months passed, civilian backgrounds mattered less and less. The men learned that by pulling together achievements could be made which would otherwise be impossible. Fort Meade taught those who needed it about team work, discipline and respect for authority and transformed civilians, the mild and the aggressive, into soldiers.

After three and a half months Dalton was promoted to Private First Class, a consequence, so his staff sergeant said, of his fitness and determination. Dalton wasn't the best at the written tasks; he had left school in the seventh grade. But his positive, stoic personality, despite the conditions or hardship, made him stand out as a good soldier. Unquestioning obedience and a capacity for physical endurance were sometimes the only credentials a team needed when the chips were down, and Dalton had plenty of both.

Furloughs became even more important as the months of training dragged on, the weekends into Washington and Baltimore helping to maintain morale, boosting resolve and further uniting the men. In the big cities they would hit the 'honkey-tonks' at the beer joints; painted-up ladies with tight clothing, matching the tight grip they took upon the infantry boys' arms and it sure made the men feel better. They ordered whiskeys for the ladies and paid whiskey prices for the iced tea that the bar tender served and considered it a small price to pay for the company.

In February '42 the 116th moved from Fort Meade, Maryland down to Camp A.P. Hill in Virginia, a large military area occupying most of Caroline County and taken over by the War Department in '41. The men were housed under tents, six allocated to each, in a barren landscape which became their new home. Sandy soil encroaching into everything, cold outdoor showers and a routine of work, eat and sleep. Live artillery attacks, simulated US fighter attacks, long combat patrols, 18 miles with 40lbs on their backs and then as the hot summer days approached, sweated buckets doing the same. Staged twenty-four hour battles with part of the regiment attacking and part defending, walked twenty miles in the process with no sleep and the noise of a mock battle for a lullaby.

In July '42 the whole 29th Division headed to the swamps of North Carolina, the large maneuvers area close to

Albemarle, east of Charlotte, involving thousands of troops, artillery and armor units. They spent a whole month with base camp being moved all the time, digging in then moving on again just for the hell of it, or so it seemed. Sometimes they upped camp late, walked several more miles before wading through a deep swamp and bedded down, soaking wet, in what remained of the night. The heat and humidity, insects and dirt mixed to irritate the skin beneath material that felt too heavy but which couldn't be shed for fear of being eaten alive.

The routine became predictable until one day everything ground to a halt. They had just done an early morning boat crossing, followed by a twenty-five mile march in pouring rain when the company was told to dig in and wait for orders. But as the evening passed so nothing happened. The morning brought a further absence of marching orders and it was as if the military clockwork had faltered, a cog jammed or a spoke obstructing. All further maneuvers were cancelled. The 29th Division was on hold.

Unbeknown to the men, the 1st Division was being sent overseas and the 29th would replace them at Camp Blanding, Florida and be made ready. They would be next.

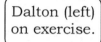

Dalton (left)
on exercise.

Dalton with Sonny,
Evelyn's eldest child.

Dalton, after training exercise.

Dalton with his momma.

Chapter 13

Hetty Will You Marry Me?

Paddington, May 1941 to the Summer of 1942.

About an hour after Frank came back from Rundell Road to report on Aunt Nine's teeth, Paul Brooks' family arrived to swell the numbers, their house on Oakington Road having been badly damaged. The arrival reminded everyone of how close the two families were and not least of Paul's attraction to Hetty, something even the least observant had begun to notice. But unbeknown to most, including the man himself, she was developing a fondness for someone else.

When the all-clear finally sounded, Ethel discovered a bottle of gin and with glasses and souls filling with spirit, those gathered made the best of what was left of a terrible night. After two glasses and possibly a couple more from her secret supply in the parlour, Ethel got on the Old Joanna and played a few favourites. 'Maybe It's Because I'm a Londoner' and 'Don't Dilly Dally On The Way'. And Aunt Nine's singing displayed healthy gums if not so her ear for notes, with only coughing fits interrupting her flow.

The gathering developed into one of celebration, though quite how no one could later explain, but the reason was likely simple, house or no house, they were alive. Perhaps there was also a feeling that whatever Hitler now threw at them, they would prevail. After the 10th May, bombing was light and infrequent, barely equalling the nuisance raids of the previous spring. It was the end of the Blitz. Forty-three thousand civilians were dead and two and a quarter million homeless.

The reason for the lull was that in June, having at last dealt with Greece, Hitler turned his attention on Russia, believing that he must take them before finally suppressing the British. For whilst he had been focused on France, Stalin's 'Red Army' had taken Lithuania, Latvia, Estonia and

Eastern Rumania and he feared being stabbed in the back by them. The Red Army's mediocrity in Finland the previous winter made Hitler believe he could easily crush them, likely by the autumn; after which he could finally deal with the irksome 'English', finish them off and bring Churchill to heel. But the six week distraction in Greece that the British and Commonwealth troops had caused him would upset all his plans.

On a calm September evening in London, when the Germans were crossing Russia in a desperate race to reach Moscow and Leningrad before the autumn rains and the early Russian winter, Hetty headed off with Stan Kirby for the Hammersmith Palais. She was still only nineteen and her father normally expected her to be accompanied by another family member. But not this night for Pat Harrison was poorly and James Eaglestone had placed, as an exception, his trust in Stan. After all, he had become like a brother to Hetty, James could 'trust Stan'.

They walked to Paddington Station and took the underground to Hammersmith. From Hammersmith station, the Palais was just a few yards up the Shepherds Bush Road on the left hand side. It was reasonably priced, especially on normal nights when two less well known or resident bands would take turns entertaining the huge gathering of young people.

"Are you sure you wouldn't prefer to go and see a film," Stan asked Hetty as they stepped out onto Shepherds Bush Road. "Moon Over Burma is playing at the Hammersmith Regal," Stan explained hopefully, knowing Hetty had always wanted to see the film, especially because she thought the lead actor, Robert Preston, very handsome.

Stan loved dancing, especially with Hetty but would have done anything rather than share Hetty this night with the others he knew were coming.

"No let's dance tonight," Hetty said, quickening her step as if eager to have fun.

"Ok, but let's sit downstairs by the dance floor," he interjected as he caught up with her, which Hetty found strange, for they always sat downstairs.

On one particularly memorable night Hetty and Stan had enjoyed the music of Victor Silvester at the Palais. Together with perhaps over a 1,000 other dancers Stan had led Hetty around the nationally renowned, maple sprung dance floor to tunes such as 'By Candle Light', a waltz and 'I Wonder Where My Baby Is Tonight', a foxtrot. It was always fun dancing with Stan, Hetty thought; a film she could watch anytime.

After leaving their coats in the cloakroom, Stan pulled Hetty's chair out for her at the small round table which she had made a bee line for. Centrally placed, she could see both bands well, each now setting up on their respective lower stages. The lower stages were situated on either side of the central open staircase which led up to the main stage which wasn't used on a small band night. One hundred feet of maple stretched out either side of Hetty's prime position, eighty feet in width. Plenty of room for even the most energetic ballroom dancers.

Hetty was a little surprised to see the Cricket and RAF boys arrive, taking up their seats at tables situated on one of the balconies. Five staircases led up to one long and two shorter, wide, curved balconies. They created a theatre-like arrangement where people could interact whilst having a good view of events below.

Perhaps he should have suggested the Covent Garden Dance Hall instead, Stan thought as he saw their friends arrive.

Each band had the use of a grand piano and it was the pianist who often warmed up first whilst the others sorted out their instruments; the violin, sax, horn, trumpet and cello players and the all important drummer and double bass players. Hetty counted ten, possibly as many as fifteen players in each of the bands; it was going to be a good night of dancing she thought as Stan came back with their first drinks from the bar.

When the Cricket boys came to the dances, Stan could easily have refused their requests to dance with Hetty. At six foot two with a physique to match his army training, they wouldn't have argued. But Hetty would have thought less of him; after all they were officially just friends. Around midway through the evening Paul Brooks asked Hetty to dance; a fox trot and the dance floor was soon brimming with happy, smiling couples out to enjoy life whilst they still could. Stan tried not to watch but he couldn't help it. He pretended to look at the other girls who vied for his attention, but his eyes kept searching out Hetty. He easily followed her, her style unmistakeable, he knew it so well. Transfixed almost by the way she bobbed up onto her toes with such poise; and how it made her dark shoulder length hair bounce, a lovely bounce so Stan considered. Full, flowing hair which moved just as it had always done. Except now it had darkened to a luscious brunette from the fair, almost blonde it had once been when they were kids. Hair that Stan wanted to run his fingers through and tell Hetty how he really felt about her.

Paul was speaking to Hetty in a way that Stan didn't like, the two of them smiling, sometimes laughing and it sent a feeling through Stan as if he had just been thrown from a cliff with no life line. But then she always smiled, smiled at everyone, so Stan reassured himself.

Perhaps he had fallen in love with her long ago, even as far back as Essendine School. They had both lived on Kilburn Park Road for a time and walked to Essendine, not exactly together, but amongst friends. After school and at weekends they had played in the Paddington Rec; tennis, rounders and silly kid's games like whip and top, back and four stones. Memories which brought a smile to Stan's face despite Paul becoming ever more confident as he led Hetty around the dance floor.

Hetty used to hit the rounders ball with such determination that her head moved with the swing of the bat. Her hair chased in pursuit of the movement, before her fast running legs took her safely to first stop. Quick on her feet, won all the sprints, as far as Stan's memory could recall. She even came back from fruit picking for school sports day, held annually in the Rec. Travelled by train with one of her uncles she did. Missed weeks and weeks of school, but not sports day!

Stan was not the only one to notice Paul Brook's increasing confidence with Hetty. Paul's work in the fire service had changed him. There were constant reminders in the local dailies of how indebted Londoners were to the men who risked their lives night after night fighting fires, with bombs and buildings falling around them.

The foxtrot finished and the band took quick drags from cigarettes, swilled down by beer whilst introducing their next number - a slow waltz. Slow waltzes came ever more frequently as the end of the night approached and men, often too late, made their moves for the girls they wanted to walk home.

Hetty and Paul remained on the dance floor, talking, Hetty animated, her hair bobbing. Stan's heart almost stopped when they stayed there. Had Paul's team mates made a special request to the band? A chill engulfed him, his heart momentarily frozen. He could hear nothing and see no one except Hetty with Paul. He must go onto the dance floor now, claim his dancing partner, his Hetty before it was too late, before the band started playing. A melody to hold someone close by, to pull them to within a hair's breadth, to feel their warmth, and Hetty was all woman.

There was a delay; the drummer had spilt beer over his trousers. The double bass player kept strumming a few strings, warming to the next number, but the drummer wasn't ready, his beat missing. That underlying drum beat, the rhythmic guide to set the flow had been replaced by frantic mopping of cold alcohol from warm, fleshy places. No one could start and Stan remained frozen. And then Hetty turned to look his way, motioned towards him and began to leave the dance floor, Paul followed and left her at Stan's side. The beat started up, consistency again, the band took its lead and begun to play, the dancing resumed.

Hetty's hair cupped her face, just as it had done when she was younger and Stan wanted to trace its curve with his hands; that face which looked no older to him than of a mere child full of energy and mischief. 'How long before someone proposed to her?' Stan asked himself. He knew Paul Brooks wanted to, everyone knew Paul was in love with Hetty. You didn't have to go to the Eaglestone's for Sunday tea to know it. But "Hetty's my girl," Stan whispered into the music filled air of the Palais, yet not exactly, he hadn't ever asked her to date him. Yet they had dated all the time really. Hadn't they? Hetty surely considered it that way too. He should ask her when they were dancing. He had meant to the night of the parachute mine, but once the Brooks family arrived it just hadn't seemed right, what with everyone losing their homes and all. But now he would ask her, he was determined.

Stan didn't have the opportunity to lead Hetty onto the floor, "Come on," she said, taking his hand and pulling him. "I want to dance with the best dancer this side of London."

With the floor already crowded they pushed through to find some space. The music flowed, the beat slow and rhythmical, 'Waltz of My Heart' a Victor Sylvester number and they knew it well. They came together, their steps second nature and as Stan looked into Hetty's eyes she said, "Paul just asked me to date him."

Stan was dumb struck. He tried to look happy for her but the grimace pre-empted the concealment. He couldn't bring himself to ask if the offer had been accepted and simply said nothing. The movement subconsciously carried him, his mind detached from the music. Hetty moved closer to him, but he wasn't aware of the change. He could not feel her warmth, yet her warmth still flowed. And Hetty took his silence as quiet acknowledgement of what most of her friends and family had repeatedly stated; that Paul Brooks and her were meant for each other.

Paul not Stan walked Hetty home, a long slow walk holding hands. They had never held hands before except in play. And at the corner of Thorngate, assisted by the blackout, Paul pulled Hetty slowly to him. And with her compliance and seemingly the culmination of much waiting, he kissed her. A small lingering kiss at first, placed neatly close to her lips. Less cautiously then and with growing confidence he pulled her in at the waist, to feel her warmth upon him, to embrace her, longingly, tasting her, as though absorbing the closeness he had so long desired.

And as they moved together to continue the last few steps of that walk, the touch of Paul's hand in hers seemed strange, no longer that of children, but of adults on a new shared path.

As number 43 came into view, the front door opened and James Eaglestone stood waiting; waiting where he always did for his daughters, in the shadows at the top of the street steps.

"Good night," Hetty said to Paul softly.

"I'm dating Hetty," Paul said to Hetty's father, who stood upright and alert like the sentry he once was. "I hope that's alright with you?" he added submissively.

"Of course it is," James replied with a smile - and about time too he thought.

It was official. Hetty was dating Paul Brooks and the story ran around Paddington full circle and arrived back at Stan Kirby's ear, now Lance Corporal Stan Kirby, of His Majesty's Army. He could wait, Stan told himself, it won't last, she'll soon get bored.

Paul Brooks possessed all the virtues that James Eaglestone respected in a man; a job of which to be proud and a sporting career to match - a worthy combination for a son-in-law. Paul played for the best cricket club in the country and was likely destined for the National Team. A real gentleman playing a gentleman's game, James considered. Not a gentleman in the cricketing sense, for like Jimmy, Paul was a player. A gentleman played for fun not for money. No, Paul would never use the gentlemen's entrance to Lords but in all other respects he was a gentleman.

For Ethel it was like a dream come true, the culmination of years of subtle and at times not so subtle manipulation.

"Do you love him?" Ethel now asked almost every time he left their home.

"I think so Mum," Hetty unfailingly replied.

"Well you had better know when he asks you to marry him," Ethel said, seemingly confident that the question would one day be asked.

The Christmas of '41, the third Christmas of the war passed with plates again full and spirit in plenty at the Eaglestone home. Ethel knew shopkeepers who kept a little something under the counter for 'special' customers. If you knew the right person, and many did, then you could pick up another ration book or two; robbed, forged or looted from a bomb damaged building. Many like Ethel also frequented markets where coupons were 'unnecessary' and food plentiful by comparison. Ethel wasn't going to let her family go hungry and certainly not at Christmas.

The gramophone lovingly situated in the front room was only used on such special occasions and James or Ethel were still the only ones allowed to touch it. If it was James's choice the first 78 to be placed on the turntable would be 'If You Were the Only Girl in the World' with 'My Blue Heaven' a close second. And as Christmas Day unfolded, with interruptions only for the wireless news, so the games and fun extended with the arrival of family and neighbours. Hetty's Grandmother Lucy, Uncle Sid, Uncle Frank and Aunt Nine less her teeth, Patsy Harrison, Paul Brooks and his family. Then sometime later, Stan Kirby came by 'just to say hello' and when a waltz was played, someone encouraged him to dance with Hetty, for they 'were dancing partners.' There wasn't much space in the front room what with everyone filling the easy chairs as well as the dining chairs and the two youngsters strayed out into the hall. And whilst Ethel's gin and Lucy's Guinness oiled the atmosphere in the room, Stan and Hetty negotiated their narrow hallway dance floor. Intoxicated only by the atmosphere of Christmas and the fun of dancing together again, they laughed and talked like the good friends they were. But for Stan, they had been 'friends' for long enough.

James Eaglestone didn't drink much, slowly downing his pint of bitter, flavoured towards midnight by a touch of whisky. And as the mantelpiece clock indicated the approach of Boxing Day, the red linoleum flooring with its black square pattern seemed less well worn, glistening from the small spills that had spread across it. The bronze firemen ornaments had been witness to many family events, both happy and less so; and if they could have moved to catch the latest intrigue, they surely would have gone out to the hallway. There, as the two brushed past the small snooker table which Ethel had lavished upon her son, Hetty had stopped laughing whilst Stan said what he had come to say. Some minutes after the waltz had been changed to someone else's favourite, Paul Brooks came out into the hallway. He touched Hetty's arm, reminding her he was there and with that Stan wished everyone good night and a Merry Christmas and made his departure. "Merry Christmas sweet'art," Ethel said to the boy they all knew so well. The dancing had come to an end but Stan's affection for his dancing partner had not and it was with an element of sadness and churning inside that Hetty watched him close the street door and walk alone into the blackout and the cold Christmas night.

When the dread of 1941 closed, the arrival of 1942 brought greater optimism. For the Yanks had been forced or some might have said, played into the war. Pearl Harbour had been bombed by the Japanese on December 7th and 'the United States was in the war up to the neck and in to the death'. After two years of fighting alone Churchill now knew that 'England would live, Britain would live, the Commonwealth and the Empire would live' to emerge, 'however mauled or mutilated, safe and victorious'. Britain declared war on Japan the next day and by Christmas Day had lost Hong Kong, by February Malaya and Singapore and by mid May, the whole of Burma. Outnumbered and with inadequate RAF support, surrendering forces were left to the mercy of the Japanese.

Over the road from number 43, Fred Bowen had been declared missing in action against the Japs in Burma. Yet years later his family still set a place for him at meal times; the table arrangement not reorganised, the chair not removed, even though to have done so would have given them more room. It was for their son to come home to, to sit and eat with them. To remove it would have been to have given up hope.

The vicious, brutal treatment with summary executions that the Japs inflicted on British forces made life in Stalag 18A seem tolerable by comparison. 18A in Yugoslavia had been home to Thomas Duckett since his capture almost twelve months earlier. 'Out of the blue' a letter addressed to Edith in Tom's hand, landed on the hallway mat in March. He had been captured in Greece and imprisoned. Life was hard, food scarce and without the Red Cross he might have starved. But then it was the Germans who allowed the Red Cross access and unlike the children of men captured by the Japanese, eight month old Georgina might yet have a daddy come home to her.

With just nuisance raids and intermittent air raid sirens interrupting the flow of London life, the first Americans started to arrive in the country. Initially to build the bases and airfields that would eventually hold over 1.5 million of their servicemen - airfields in the counties of Norfolk and Suffolk and army bases in the south and west of the country. A vindication of Churchill's diplomacy and rhetoric, that he had persuaded Roosevelt to put Europe first, despite the US being attacked in the Pacific. Their arrival wasn't to James Eaglestone's liking and he wasn't alone for most disliked the Yanks, except perhaps Tom Harrison.

One evening as the summer of '42 approached and with Americans adding to the cosmopolitan nature of London, Paul Brooks called by at the Eaglestones. The terraced house was like a second home to him. The concreted front yard above the coal bunkers, the steps down to the area, everything unchanged, even from when he had visited years earlier. The black painted front door seemed never to have been repainted but of course it had, Mr. Eaglestone made sure of that. Gloss black paint, to be pushed against by familiar hands and some less familiar as time would tell.

Paul looked agitated as if on fireman's work. He hadn't even changed out of his uniform and as Ethel opened the street door to greet him, he asked not of Hetty but of James Eaglestone.

"In the front room," she said grinning, beckoning him in as if frightened he might go away again.

Ethel ushered Paul into the front room and closed the door behind him. James seemed unsurprised to see him. "Cup of tea son?" he asked.

"No thank you Mr. Eaglestone," Paul replied not wanting to delay in case he stumbled further.

James Eaglestone motioned towards an easy chair so that Paul might sit down, settling in his own, proud of the house he would soon own and proud of the quality of man his daughter had attracted.

It was without reservation that he gave his consent to Paul's request for Hetty's hand in marriage and with a smile and a firm handshake welcomed Paul as his future son-in-law.

"I'll call Hetty," James said and left Paul alone with the ticking mantelpiece clock and the watchful bronze firemen.

No one was quite sure how long the firemen had stood so dramatically upon the mantelpiece. When Countess Droider, whom Ethel had worked for, moved abroad she had given Ethel many things: the leopard skin rug, children's annuals, beautiful wooden boxes and perhaps the bronze firemen. But no one was quite sure, for they seemed to have stood there since time began, or at least since the mantelpiece clock.

"Hetty will you marry me?" Paul said as soon as she entered the room. Then looked into her pretty face, searching for the expression he so dearly hoped to see.

"Oh Paul!" Hetty replied, her insides churning with the anxiety of indecision. The proposal was expected, her mother had so often warned her. But still it seemed sudden, as if dropped from a height and with but a split second to accept or step aside.

Feelings, fears and memories raced through her, each of differing colours, like a river in flood carrying ribbons of dye. Of shared times as children and as teenagers, of their families so close and Jimmy as Paul's best friend and the approval of parents.

Paul was a considerate, honest and lovely man and she was very fond of him, of that she was sure. But marriage? She didn't feel deep love, not like the romantic novels she had read or as the films portrayed. But then that was 'pure fantasy' so her mother often reminded her.

And it wasn't just her mother who kept saying how right Paul was for her, there were others and Jimmy often said it too. Marrying Paul would be right for everyone, she thought. Paul was the right choice. How could there ever be anyone else? Of course she loved him, how could she not love him? Paul was the kindest, most generous and respectful man she had ever met.

Paul still watched her intently, hopes dimming as each millisecond passed, the instantaneous response sought but not forthcoming. But then the answer came and it was the one he had dreamt of for so long, "Yes, I would love to marry you," Hetty said and she meant it with all her heart.

Hetty

Circa 1942 - about 20 years old

Chapter 14

55.50N, 08.56W and the True Meaning of War

To October 1942.

Clayton's daddy dropped Dalton where Route 360 crossed Route 14 in King and Queen County. It would be a quick visit home and when his brother Edward arrived in the farm truck to take him there, Dalton slouched down to grab some sleep which he had avoided whilst in the company of Clayton's family. Clayton's momma was sick and Clayton had wanted to see her because it now looked certain that the 29th Division would be moving overseas before the fall. Dalton had gone with his army buddy 'for the ride' and it had been a long, long journey, Florida was much further from Virginia than Dalton had thought.

Whilst the 29th stayed at Camp Blanding, so the vacation feeling continued, for never before had Dalton and his buddies seen such white sand or sat in the shade of a palm tree. The tans were good, the bodies well toned and the women in Jacksonville found it hard to resist them. Blanding offered the easiest drills, the easiest exercises and the best surroundings. There was a lake to swim in, the big city night clubs just forty miles away and the Jacksonville and St. Augustine buses ran right by the camp every half hour. Unlike A.P. Hill and Fort Meade, Blanding offered plenty to do. Several canteens, two theaters and a service club providing dances, games, reading and educational facilities. Even the wooden huts were a cut above previous barracks with electricity and running water. The guys just hoped that their military services wouldn't be needed too soon and that they might have the fortune of 'wintering in the Orange State'.

When Dalton arrived at the home place with Edward, Fleda Mae hugged her son as though she hadn't seen him for a lifetime. She didn't even take the time to brush herself down as she hurried from the vegetable garden toward the front yard. A good wholesome dinner was in preparation and Dalton could all but taste the salted ham as his momma's arms pulled him in close. For a moment he hung there, longer than he might normally have done, for the safety and security of her embrace seemed suddenly more comforting than he could remember since being a boy.

"Everyone at church has been asking if you had gotten home and Mrs. Carlton told me to tell you, make sure you go see them," Fleda said as she held him at arms length to take in the sun kissed face and full chest of her second youngest child. He looked so handsome she thought and the intensity of her love almost prevented Dalton's mind recalling memories of Lucy and arms that once held him with a different passion.

"I'll go see them before I leave," he promised his momma. He'd promised to visit the Carltons at Christmas, but hadn't.

Dinner tasted real good. Evelyn and Steve with their three boys joined Robbie, Edward and Dalton to make seven adults and three children at the kitchen table. Just like old times Dalton thought and smiled when the potato salad arrived as it had always done, in the round yellow croc bowl with the fine ridges. How could potato salad be served in anything else? Dalton sat next to Robbie, pleased that he'd gotten a furlough at the same time. Robbie told everyone he was convinced they both would be going to Europe and the comment soured the atmosphere for their momma and their daddy, but for different reasons. Kelly still felt that his boys should be heading to the Pacific to fight America's war. But then the 1st Division had been sent to Africa, so anything was possible. Before the dish washing had barely finished, Dalton and Robbie drove off in the family's newly acquired Chevrolet, a 1933 4dr Sedan; to pick up a couple of girls whom Robbie knew, but they didn't mention that to their momma. Driving to Urbanna, the boys bought four tickets to the movies and as they had often done with the Carlton girls, stopped for ice cream cones at the Pine Tree Storehouse on the way back. The Slaughter boys sure knew how to give the ladies a good time, but then it was hard to lavish money on a woman so far away from the city lights.

Whilst most 29th Infantry boys heard the announcement, Dalton returned to Church View oblivious that the division had been recalled. He and Robbie spent a relaxed night under the home place lying on the cool dirt. Not that it was too hot and humid to sleep inside, but for old times' sake. Both felt the reality of world events creeping into their hearts. It filtered even into Church View, its routines and family rituals so long established colored and flecked ever so slightly, changes which were obvious only to those absent for a time. Robbie and Dalton were still as close in friendship as they were in age and this night something told them they should not part. And as they talked so the night slipped by and gradually the background of croaking frogs and the cicadas faded as darkness and sleep overcame them and took brother from brother.

When Dalton stirred he found himself alone, the floor boards transmitting the sounds from the kitchen. Sounds of his momma's movements, of cleaning ashes from the stove and stoking it anew and sounds from the wireless he had given her. Robbie had woken early and had been gone for several hours when a lad from the post office arrived with the message for Dalton. All 29th Div. soldiers on furloughs were being ordered back to Blanding immediately. Perhaps there was a national emergency or perhaps this was it and the 29th were going to war. It was kinder on everyone not to assume the latter. Dalton hadn't the time to find Robbie. Driving to the Carlton home to say a quick hello and goodbye, Dalton dragged himself away from the family he had known so well to stand on the porch, alone with Lucy for the last time. Lucy Hall as she was now. Both were unable to find the words to fit the occasion, another yet final parting of their ways and equally unable to imagine the bigger changes to come. Silence encircled them, like the Carlton farmland, stretching out to the woods where a hint of summer's end lay in the changing colors. Then, when he could stay no longer, Dalton assured Lucy that he would come back, be her friend and neighbor and farm his own land, bought from the good rate of pay he would earn. And looking into her eyes, as though searching for memories of times they once shared, Dalton gave her one small last kiss on the cheek before turning and walking away.

Edward was waiting with the truck's engine running when Dalton got back. His momma had purposefully started to busy herself scrubbing clothes in the wash tub with water she had hauled from the well. Stay busy she told herself, for her son's sake as much as for her own. Dalton gathered together his few things and then took a moment to stand motionless in the yard and look at the home place. All that was dear to him now seemed precious. His momma where he had so often seen her, strong hands kneading and manipulating the same clothes for the uncountable time. She raised her head to look back at him, mother and son, their bond so strong, it could never be broken, not by mere distance and not even by death. She was first to pull away from the fixation, he must leave and leave quickly and she told him so. With gestured hugs and tears as always, no more or less so as with all Slaughter family departures, she handed him 'food for the journey'.

"See you soon," Fleda whispered as she ushered her son toward the gate. "See you soon," she said again.

"See you soon Momma ... bye Momma," Dalton called back as he jumped up beside Edward.

As Edward drove him away, Dalton hung out of the window, looking back and waving until the trees finally closed everything from view. A long uncertain journey had begun, but the image of his momma standing alone in the yard would remain in his memory forever.

When Dalton passed out of sight, Fleda's tears became a flood and she wept more than she had done since the death of Annie Ruth. After the laundry was done, through bleary eyes and blotched cheeks, Fleda made jam and by night fall and long before Dalton reached Camp Blanding, a few more jars were added to the line of jars and pies on the stairs.

Edward drove Dalton down toward St. Stephen's Church through the woods where Edward remarked as to the changes. The new logging tracks, the crop yield, fields yet to be harvested for lack of manpower with so many boys being drafted and the land they might be working next spring.

"It will all be over in six months and you can come home and start on that first field for me," Edward said with a gesture and a smile for his little brother.

Back at camp Blanding the reason for the 29th Infantry Division's recall was obvious though still unofficial; they were going to war. To the Pacific Theater most likely or perhaps North Africa in support of the 1st Division, no one knew, yet everyone had an opinion. The division was on alert, all men were confined to camp, pay phones disconnected and mail prohibited. Equipment was packed and crated; each man had two barrack bags 'A' bag to keep with him and 'B' bag to be put in the ship's hold. Each bag was packed, unpacked for inspection, then repacked for departure and final inoculations given. By mid September the camp was cleared and the division was on the move. With the train heading northward and not westward, the Pacific Theater could be eliminated.

Dalton shared a compartment with Clayton, Ted, Paul Kennedy, Austen, Allbritton, Smiler and a couple of other B Company men with whom he had become close buddies. Excitement selected their words and the banter came thick and fast, except for Ted, who didn't say anything for hours.

Like some of the other families, Ted's parents had come down to Florida a few days before departure. Ted's sister had come with them and to Ted's unease they also brought a pretty young thing who Ted assured his buddies was his sister's friend. "The girlfriend sure had a crush on Ted," Dalton observed as they crossed the Florida state border into Georgia. And Smiler told Ted to find a picture of his sister's friend so that he too might have something to look at in his top pocket. A reference to the picture of his parents that Ted always carried in his left breast pocket. But nothing could cheer him up.

When B Company had marched to the station from the camp, Ted's family had kept pace with them, trying to catch a glimpse of the son and brother of whom they were so proud. Right across Georgia, Ted just stared out of the window and it wasn't until they were half way across South Carolina that he finally joined in with the card games. Clayton usually won when money was at stake but the others still played, for best lose to a buddy than anyone else.

The train was packed with soldiers, their insignia removed in case spies tried to report on the movement of the division and at each station, guards prevented interaction between the men and members of the public. Yet despite the intensity of the departure and the prospect of entering the war, the B Company men were in good spirits. The war would 'soon be over' - the 'Virginian Boys' were coming.

After North Carolina they started into Virginia and it felt like coming home and leaving again all at once. The place names became familiar, then all too quickly less familiar and Virginia was left behind. Rattling across the Potomac River into the state of Maryland, then Delaware and across the Delaware River into New Jersey, the train finally reached its destination. The men would be temporarily based in Camp Kilmer, a staging post for the boys posted to the British Isles and thence Africa so they thought. Dalton and his buddies walked into Kilmer during the dark, early hours of the 19th September, wet through from a downpour, to be 'sealed' in camp with a high wire perimeter fence and armed guards, no one to leave and no visitors.

During their first day at Kilmer, Ted confided in Smiler that the girlfriend who had come down to Blanding was actually his childhood sweetheart and her last words to him were that he had to come back to her, for she could 'never fall in love with anyone else'. Ted asked Smiler not to tell anyone. And almost true to his word Smiler told just one person and within the hour Dalton heard the story, the last member of the platoon to do so. Yet not a soul mentioned anything to Ted for everyone liked the big man too much.

On the morning of the 26th September, Dalton threw his second kit bag into the allocated truck and carried his travelling bag with him to New Brunswick train station.

From there to Hoboken and after dark crossed the Hudson by ferry to a quayside on Manhattan.

The B Company men stretched out in a long line which edged forward along the quay as each soldier was checked off. Surnames being called out, Padgett, Sales, Torrence and Holmes; Holmes like the rest replied with his first name and was one of the few exceptions for he could not then give a middle initial, for John didn't have one. Paul Kennedy and Dalton shuffled forward to approach the Transportation Corps, the chalked numbers on their helmets identifying them. A few yards further on and suddenly the ship for which they were bound manifested itself out of the darkness. The silhouette against the Manhattan sky was of the largest ocean liner plying the seas. There lay the one thousand and twenty foot long Queen Mary, the pride of the Cunard White Star Line, waiting for the country boys. Not for the cruise of a life time, but for a journey from which many would never return.

Looking up in awe, the ship dwarfed the soldiers. It dwarfed everything save the sky scrapers behind. Eighty-one thousand tons floating in the Hudson, rising 181 feet from keel to the lip of her funnels, with 2,000 portholes. The prestigious ocean liner built on the River Clyde in Scotland for the rich to sail the Atlantic had been converted to a troop ship. All the luxuries were gone and in their place the basics, mainly bunks stacked four high with barely twenty inches between them.

On September 27th 1942 the ropes binding the ship to American soil were unleashed and the Mary with ten thousand, two hundred and thirty-nine soldiers of the 29th Infantry Division pulled away from the pier and headed down the Hudson River. The four thousand or so remaining men of the 'Blue and Gray' would follow a few days later aboard the Queen Elizabeth, Mary's sister ship.

By the time Dalton made it onto the open deck and had pushed through the mass of milling men to find a space to get a decent view, the sky scrapers of Manhattan were already shrinking in size. Like wooden painted models graying in color under an overcast sky and setting sun. It was a view most had only ever seen in the newspapers. So unreal did it appear and so powerless did Dalton feel being carried away from the only world he knew. No control and no defined destiny save that somewhere he would do battle, survive or not survive and return or not to see this view again. Heading below decks the night before when arriving on the ship, all the men had been handed a letter from President Roosevelt stating simply;

> *'You are a soldier of the United States Army,*
> *you have embarked for distant places where*
> *war is being fought.'*

The unsettled weather seemed to reflect the hearts of the men on board as the Queen Mary ploughed out to sea. Staring westward, the coast gradually slipped from the men's view and when the pencil line of land was no more and remained only in their imagination, it was replaced with butterflies in the stomach and a longing to go home. Dalton felt 'edgy' for this was not the ocean he could remember from his visits to Virginia Beach. Then, the sun had been shining brightly, the surf methodical, the water inviting; now the water looked dark, menacing almost. A poor swimmer, Dalton knew he would have little chance of survival should the ship be sunk by a U Boat. They had no escort, no defense and thousands of miles to cross. With the ocean stretching out before him, Dalton peered over the side and imagined having to plunge the several storeys down from the stricken ship and concluded he would not survive the fall.

The US entry into the war helped German U Boat operations against ships bound for Britain, since they no longer had to adhere to Roosevelt's one thousand mile neutrality zone. Thus as 1942 progressed, not only did the number of U boats in the Atlantic increase to over two hundred, but so did the number stalking the eastern seaboard of the US. There might have been a U Boat waiting beyond the mouth of the Hudson. The Type VII Unterseeboot had a range of six thousand nautical miles and after the German occupation of France in June '40, had direct access to the Atlantic. No longer did they need to creep around the UK to gain access to the shipping lanes and during 1942 alone, over six million tons of Allied shipping would be sunk. The allies tried to counter the menace by crossing in convoys with a naval escort, but then the U boats started to work in packs, 'Wolf Packs' so called. Thus vital supplies for the beleaguered British; food, ammunition, vehicles and medicines carried on cargo ships from US and Canadian ports frequently ended up on the ocean floor.

"Soon I'm going to be further from home than I've ever been," Paul Kennedy said to Dalton as he pushed through to his best buddy standing at the rail.

"Me too," Dalton replied.

Before being drafted, Dalton had travelled no further than Virginia Beach and Baltimore to the north and considered they would be lucky if they now made it further from home than Florida, the sea was so rough and the threat of war seemed so perilously close. The two stood in silence with their thoughts as the waves continued to thud against the bow and rush past, moving with such determination as if on an errand. Had the waves been able to carry the thoughts of the ten thousand soldiers on board, then spilling onto the beaches of America would be the hopes, fears and desire upon desire to return home soon and in one piece.

With the mighty 160,000 horse power engines pushing the Mary deeper into the Atlantic, she soon reached her cruising speed of over 28 knots, a phenomenal speed by any comparison. And it was speed that formed her main defense, for the Type VII U Boat had a surface speed of only 17 knots and just 9 knots under water. However, if by chance a U Boat lay ahead of the Mary, then a couple of well placed torpedoes might sink her and take the 29th Infantry Division and nine hundred crew to the bottom of the cold Atlantic Ocean.

Perhaps two hours after leaving the US coast behind, Paul and Dalton still leant against the promenade deck rail. The deck that before the war provided exercise and entertainment as travelers excitedly left ports and headed for adventure. The best buddies looked from the gray camouflaged ship across the gray ocean, an ocean which seemed to spread forever in all directions. White surf topped the waves to break the uniformity whilst the friends said nothing but simply used the fresh air to quell the unsettled feeling in their stomachs. They had gone below decks only briefly to find the ventilation wholly inadequate for the concentration of men now housed there. The Mary had been designed to carry less than two thousand passengers. Worse, many soldiers were vomiting and the concoction of body smells and partially digested food was not conducive to relaxation. Paul and Dalton chose the chill breeze, the sea spray and the occasional rain to the alternative below. So long did they stay in fact that when each finally looked at the other they almost fell hysterical to the wooden deck, for spray after spray of sea water had dried on their face and each had left a thin coating of salt to build up to a white encrustation which transformed their appearance into old men with white hair and white eyebrows.

Every four or five minutes the Mary altered course by twenty-five or fifty degrees, the zigzag bell providing the stimulus to ensure her angle of heading was always changing. But the great bow wave was forever thrown in an eastward direction, sliced by the tall raked stem. And as the days passed she came closer to the conflict in Europe, to the home of the U Boat and to the danger of aerial attack. Five days of sailing and still the liner was alone and pushing eastward, yet an escort was not expected until the sixth day. The Mary survived the fifth and entered the sixth day without incident and came within a few hundred miles of the British Isles. The risk had been taken, she had been left with her speed alone to protect her and it appeared that the risk had paid off. A naval escort across the vast Atlantic would have encumbered her, for there were few vessels able to maintain the Mary's pace in the encountered swell. Slowing her would have been counterproductive. But on the 2nd October and within one hundred and fifty miles of the

Outer Hebrides, the Mary needed a different protection, protection against the German Luftwaffe. She was now within range of the German Heinkel 177s and the Focke Wulf Condors. The day started bright, sunny and too warm for the time of year. Men strolled around the promenade deck, threw dice and played cards, whilst others hung onto the rails with the expectancy of sighting something. What they expected to catch sight of, few soldiers could have said. However Illingworth, the Mary's Captain, was very much expectant and looked eastward in search of his British Naval escort - six destroyers and one cruiser who with their anti-aircraft guns would shadow the Mary for the rest of the way. At about 8a.m. a Flying Fortress found the liner and provided welcome air cover. Then some twenty miles later, Captain Illingworth spotted his escort to the south-east.

Captain Boutwood of the cruiser HMS Curacoa was overall commander of the escort fleet and on catching sight of the Mary's funnels poking above the horizon at fifteen miles distant, positioned his fleet to lie directly ahead of her. The cruiser dropped behind the six destroyers to be the first contact and allowed the fast liner to catch up. Still zigzagging, the Mary closed in and on doing so, finally gained the protection of the Curacoa. Intent on providing effective air cover and with the departure of the Flying Fortress, the Curacoa had to closely shadow the liner.

At 1p.m. men lay on the promenade deck still soaking up the unexpected sunshine, whilst others leant on the rail to watch the intense and well timed maneuvering. The complicated, though supposedly predetermined changes of direction of the Mary and the strong ocean swell made it extremely difficult for the slower Curacoa to stay close to the liner yet keep out of her path. What happened just after 2p.m. was subject to protracted Law Court hearings and finally a Judgement by the House of Lords. But to the 439 men on the Curacoa and the watching GIs, the matter was simple, it was an avoidable tragedy. For within a few minutes, 338 men lost their lives.

The promenade deck of the Mary was becoming more and more crowded with GIs as word got around as to how close the Curacoa was approaching. It was their first sight of a British warship and men crammed the guard rail to get a better view. Dalton stood next to Clayton who had been at the rail for some time. "I think she's coming in too close," Clayton said to Dalton. Both watched as the cruiser, a few hundred yards forward and to the right of the Mary, seemed to be heading across their path.

The safety of the eleven thousand men on board the Mary and the crew of the Curacoa ultimately rested with the two captains, yet Illingworth and Boutward were not communicating, merely making assumptions. Boutwood on the Curacoa didn't know the zigzag pattern or leg of the zigzag the liner was following, whilst Illingworth assumed Boutwood knew Zigzag No.8 was being operated. Boutwood considered that to have found out would have indicated to the Mary that he was able and prepared to continuously change direction to allow for the zigzags. And he wasn't able and prepared to because the only way the slower vessel could keep up was by maintaining a straight path. Boutward felt that Illingworth must surely know this to be the case.

However Illingworth considered that under the circumstances and as the escorted ship, the Mary had the right of way. Yet according to seafaring convention, Boutward knew that his slower vessel had right of way and the faster overtaking Mary must steer clear. As the Mary continued to zigzag in front and behind the cruiser, so the Curacoa's proximity became more worrying.

Dalton lost sight of the cruiser as she moved in front of the liner, or rather, the liner headed straight for the Curacoa. Then perhaps thirty seconds later, after frantic actions by both crews and interaction between the ships made the situation worse, Dalton felt no more than a slight judder pass along the railing and deck. Within another few more seconds the stern section of the Curacoa passed down Dalton's side of the Queen Mary, the propellers sticking up out of the water, still rotating.

At 30 miles per hour, the 81,000 ton Mary had sliced right through the 4,290 ton Curacoa, a minnow by comparison.

Tearing through the three inch steel armor, the Mary sent steam, smoke and debris in all directions to create a chaotic scene. The 100 foot stern section and 350 foot fore section washed down either side of the Mary and as the two sections fell behind, men still clung to the structures or struggled for their lives in the north Atlantic water. They would get no help from the liner. The Mary maintained its course, merely blowing its whistle as though in farewell.

Quick thinking GIs threw lifebuoys over the side. But the gap between the Mary and stricken men was increasing rapidly and so soon did the stern section tip and sink and the fore section follow her into the depths, that likely many men had already drowned or were too far away now to reach the buoyancy aids. Covered in fuel oil and with little to hang on to, the few who initially survived languished in the water with friends and debris washing around them. Bits and bodies appeared from the depths as the broken ship made its way to the ocean floor 6,000 feet below, surrounding the survivors in more carnage. The living grew cold, were dispersed by the currents and choked on the fuel oil which blanketed their faces. The swell was fearsome and with each passing wave crest, they could see the Mary slightly smaller than a time period earlier, for Illingworth still maintained his course. Many could not hold on, the cold and the oil made hand-holds slip from their grasp and survivors soon became victims.

It was a terrible sight, not just of the event and of the men in the water, but knowing that the survivors were being left to their fate. Dalton was speechless, men around him gasped and some pleaded to God to help those in the water; for all knew that the sailors were being sacrificed for the safety of the soldiers. And at that moment, at 55.50N 08.56W, the true meaning of war fell into place and Dalton didn't like the feel of it.

HMS Bramham, Cowdray and Skate, three destroyers from the escort convoy turned back, but it was over two hours before they reached the scene. The Mary's damage was minor, just a 'hole the size of a house' in her bow and at reduced speed, she continued toward the River Clyde in Scotland.

Several hours after the collision, land came into view and just a few miles then remained between the 29th Infantry and the British nation; the last bastion of freedom in Europe. Most nations had been consumed and the few that had declared neutrality were no more than caged animals being spared the hunt. In the dying light of the 2nd October, the band of Islands making up the Hebrides could just be seen in the distance. Less friendly waters, those of neutral Ireland lay to the south. Then, as the day moved to night and the 3rd October dawned so the land closed in, Northern Ireland to the right and the mainland of Scotland to the left on the port side. The Queen Mary rounded the Mull of Kintyre and passing the Isle of Arran entered the safe waters of the Firth of Clyde. The deep natural estuary some fifteen miles wide cleaved its way into the heart of Scotland and some forty miles later, narrowed to under two miles where the liner turned eastward for the final slow approach to the Scottish port of Greenock. With the big city of Glasgow some twenty miles further up the Clyde, a river abounding with docks and ship building yards racing to replenish the quarry of German U Boats, Greenock was as far from the ocean as the liner was going to go.

Dalton

1942 - twenty-three years old

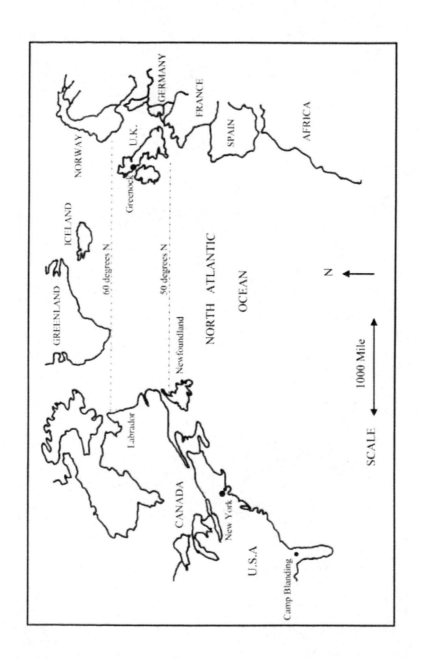

Chapter 15

Tidworth, England.

October to December 1942.

It was a miserable overcast day and raining, for this was Scotland and the day has to be chosen carefully to receive a different welcome. With a draft of thirty-nine feet, the Queen Mary could not dock at the Greenock quayside and thus the men had to transfer onto passenger ferries normally used for crossing the Clyde. From the quayside where the British Red Cross welcomed the GIs with coffee and doughnuts, it was a short walk to the London Midland Railway train and another stage in the journey. The carriages were cold and crowded. Compared to Virginia it was very cold for October, but then the 56th latitude cannot be expected to match the 37th. Dalton found a space on the floor and with his kit bag as the only comfort, tried to get some rest. Like so many, Dalton felt dispirited: by having witnessed the death of hundreds of servicemen, by their own circumstances and by the climate. It sure was a long way from home and getting further.

With a whistle and the exhalation of steam, the Duchess of Montrose strained at the couplings and pulled the long train of carriages away from the quay and out of Greenock. Smoke rushed past the dirt covered and smeared glass, past the sliding window that no one could quite close properly. The chill air pushed inward through the gap and brought with it the smell of combusted Clydesdale coal. The grey Scottish day cleared, then grew even darker than before and a strong westerly wind started to buffet the carriages bringing still more rain off the ocean. That same vast ocean the men had just crossed. By the time the train reached Kilmarnock, the first bodies from the Curacoa were washing up on the more remote Scottish islands. The droplets of ocean rain hit the right hand side windows, then pushed by the drag of the air, created jittery, withering trails along the glass. Looking past the grimy surface, trees, hills and lakes slipped by together with the occasional hamlet, stone wall and country lane. With a full sixteen carriages to pull, the 462 loco slowed significantly on the longer inclines, gasping air and blasting steam in a slow repetitive rhythm.

Having left the Clyde Valley, there seemed few people brave enough to inhabit the light starved countryside. October! 'What would winter be like?' The windows on the other side were strangely dry and beyond them the rain fell across scenery that on a different day could well have been beautiful.

Ted did not rest and for the most part stood by the door, pensive, as though he were about to jump from the train. Dalton joined him there and the two young men stood together as the engine pulled them onward to a place that would mean nothing to them.

"Do you feel empty, like something has been wrenched from you?" Ted asked Dalton.

"My belly sure feels empty," Dalton joked. But then, putting his arm around the big man's shoulders, he said "Be home before your momma and daddy start to miss you," being careful not to mention Ted's childhood sweetheart.

"Glad to get rid of you, you eat like a horse," Clayton butted in, having heard the conversation.

With the break of a smile across Ted's face, Clayton offered round the last of his Camel cigarettes, the second packet the train journey had already consumed.

When Dalton woke, his back was aching and his skin moulded to the ridges of the train door. Blackout blinds were being drawn down to prevent light escaping from the compartment, yet outside it seemed just as much like dusk as it had done all day. Through the night the train made its way ever southward. Travelling through cuttings, along embankments and across bridges in a war torn country and battle hardened nation. Just one bomb might be all that was needed to derail the train or demolish a bridge and send the cargo plummeting into a river below; the Esk, the Eden or another of the enemy's choosing.

On his way home from air raid patrol, Nicholas McNeal stopped where the lane crossed the tracks. A train was approaching through the darkness. Unusual he thought at such a late hour and stood to watch as the locomotive eased its way across several points and slowly made its way towards him. Hanging out of one of the door windows a couple of GIs called to him, "Hey, how far to Richmond?" they joked.

"A long bloody way!" Nicholas replied, yet he was thinking only of Richmond, West London, not Richmond, Virginia. And as a fastidious ARP he was going to add, shut that window and pull the blackout blind down, but words failed him as one of the GIs flicked a half smoked cigarette into the shadows. Nicolas just stood and watched, watched as the glow from the window painted a broad line on the darkness of the undergrowth, the undergrowth that bordered the stones, sleepers and rails. By the time the last carriage passed him and the engine started to pick up speed again, the unusual accent slotted into place. "The Yanks have arrived," he declared to the night, "bloody Yanks, as cocky as them on the films." And with that he pulled his collar up against the night air, crossed the line and made for home. His wife would have placed a log on the fire before retiring and he might just manage to brew a cup of tea before catching a couple of hours kip.

By the next afternoon the troop train had passed Birmingham, Oxford and reached the southern counties. Then, after the town of Swindon it started to make its way across Salisbury Plain. The plain stretched out in all directions for two hundred and twenty square miles - rolling hills of several hundred feet covered for the most part by grassland. Had the carriages been left stranded, the engine departed, then the most notable aspect would have been the silence, not even the sound of surface water for the porous chalk bedrock absorbed it to its depths. Featureless, except for the occasional cluster of trees, the landscape offered little protection against the elements. Bleak in winter, potentially hot and dry in summer and although the men didn't know it yet, the plain was to be their new training ground for the next seven months.

Fifteen miles and almost as many stations south of Swindon, the troop train passed through the cutting across Widgerly Down and reached the village of Ludgershall. Here it moved onto a branch line built specially to service the military camp to which they were headed. At the turn of the century the branch line had carried all the building materials needed to construct the camp, then over four decades many thousands of British troops and in October 1942, the US, 29th Infantry Division.

At Perham Down signal box the second track was lost and the pace of the engine slowed further as the train skirted Windmill Hill. The crawling pace of the engine, the change to a single track and glimpses of an army camp down in the valley to the right hinted the end of a very long journey. Many stirred from their passiveness to survey the scene. Some like Smiler hastily gathered their things, whilst others nonchalantly remained where they had been for hours, stretched out on the floor.

Dalton watched as the train crossed an embankment and from fields bordering either side, rattled under a road bridge where several English school boys hung over the low wall, laughing and waving. Beyond the bridge, Tidworth sidings sprawled out to the right. The ordnance depot, goods wagons, numerous army wagons capable of carrying large vehicles and three or four trains each of several coaches; more in keeping with a busy terminus than a small country village. A few yards on, the track became two again and points sent the train to the left, towards the troop platform. As the engine chugged slowly towards the buffers, Tidworth Station building slid past the right hand windows; its canopy overhanging the narrow platform, hanging in readiness to shelter travellers heading back to the main line. With a final screech and exhalation of steam the engine stopped and shouldered the nudges of each of the carriages that came to a halt behind it. The line went no further and Paul Kennedy looked across at Dalton as if to say, I guess we're there.

With their kit bags and rifles, the soldiers disembarked onto the broad platform, widened forty years earlier to accommodate the arrival of large numbers of troops. To their left lay the station master's house and the small terraced railway cottages, then nothing but countryside decorating the hill beyond. On the other side of the tracks and behind the station building lay the village. No more than a row of buildings down one side of Station Road with fields on the other and cottages beyond. The local bobby had stopped what little traffic normally used this main street so that the men could assemble there and Captain Zappacosta brought B Company to order. Ted was last to join them. Having finally fallen asleep after dwelling on his emptiness, it had been difficult to rouse him. Kicked by each passing buddy, Ted had eventually pulled himself up to full height and staggered out into what was a brighter day. Then to the sound of a military band and watched by interested villagers, the GIs were marched down Station Road.

Dalton looked at the villagers looking at him, English people. A little girl waving, a mum smiling and an old man perhaps an old soldier nodding at the young men who happened to look his way. No different to the folks back home, Dalton thought, paler perhaps but just as lean and hardy. Some were clearly shop workers for they wore the uniforms of their trade, others may have been shoppers, yet all were there to witness the event. The dairy workers, people out of a shoe shop called King's, waitresses from a restaurant called Annett's with its clean white table cloths and glistening cutlery behind very clean windows. The mechanic from Garrison Motors, 'established 1921' said the sign behind him, then clearly bank workers from a grand building declaring itself as Lloyds Bank, ESTD 1834. Yet what stood out most were the marble slabs supporting fresh fish in front of Shaw Porter and Co, the contrasting dark green tiles lining the walls inside presenting the impression that this was once a comfortable place to live with no shortage of food. And so the Americans marched on with the accompanying music, past an occasional delivery lorry with the steering wheel on the wrong side and facing the wrong way down the street. And to their equal surprise witnessed none of the bomb damage they had expected, for the German strategists had 'til now overlooked the military significance of Tidworth.

B Company passed the last row of cottages and crossed the Pennings Road to enter the camp, simply an extension of the village but which multiplied its population by several fold. A few hundred yards into the camp, B Company was directed towards its new barracks and the end of a five thousand mile journey.

There had been a settlement at Tidworth for over three thousand years, though the name stemmed from the Anglo-Saxon word 'worth' meaning an enclosure of land around a homestead. In Tidworth's case the enclosure had belonged to Tuda, a tribal chief. Thus when B Company first walked out of the camp to exercise on the plain, they followed not only in the footsteps of many decades of British soldiers, but also of those Britons who roamed and settled the plain thousands of years earlier. Ancient burial mounds and earth works lay no more than a few feet from the camp and at dusk one eerie night, Captain Zappacosta led B Company right past Stonehenge. Stonehenge had first been established around 3,000BC as a religious site, but the linteled circle of standing stones that the GIs saw in the half light were a thousand years younger. These Sarsen stones were massive, weighing 50 tons and 30 feet in height and overshadowed the older ditches, banks and smaller stones. Clayton had read about Stonehenge but few of the other men had any idea of its significance. The company had continued up the incline along by the A303 and taken nervous glances at the ominous and isolated site. Four thousand years earlier, the Sarsens had been hauled twenty miles across the plain from Marlborough Down. After twenty miles, Clayton was pleased he only had to haul himself up the slope, not a fifty ton rock as well.

Aliwal, Assaye, Candahar, Mooltan, Jellalabad, Delhi, Bhurtpore and Lucknow; the names of the different Tidworth barracks also meant nothing to most of the GIs. But then the British had an empire and battle history that stretched right around the world and across the centuries. Tidworth camp was extensive, occupying 460 acres of a shallow valley below Clarendon Hill. All the buildings were constructed of the same red brick and there were hundreds of thousands of them, for the barracks alone covered 220 acres. Bricks made from clay discovered in 1902 at Dodsdown, kilned at Dodsdown and then carried by train the eight miles to Tidworth. With sturdy walls and grey slate roofs the barracks seemed so substantial compared to the timber structures back home and with plaques dating them as 1905, some wondered if the British might cope in Europe without US help. The barracks even had verandas so that the men might walk along the front of the building without getting wet; more in keeping with the monsoons of India than the British drizzle.

B Company was allocated to Candahar Barrack, which like all the others had four barrack blocks, each of two floors. 3rd Platoon was directed to the first floor of one of the blocks and climbed the external staircase to reach the veranda. The white, wrought iron pillars and railings of the veranda embraced the smooth red brick face. The Dodsdowns had been laid with each alternate row lying at right angles to the previous one, to form a pattern which never settled on the eye.

Entering the vast dormitory from the veranda, Dalton grabbed the nearest bottom bunk and Paul Kennedy the bed above him. But being near the doorway and with just a single fireplace at one end of the cold, damp, chamber like room, Paul suggested they move nearer the fire. It proved a good idea for early October soon gave way to a typical British winter - cold and wet. The bunks had either seen better days or been constructed by a poor carpenter for they didn't match the solid surroundings. If one man rolled over, 'the other sure knew about it' and Paul on the top got the worst ride.

After the 1,000 mile train journey up the east coast of the United States, the 4,000 mile sea crossing and their 330 mile journey down this comparatively small island, the young men of B Company had taken but the first steps along a hazardous path - a path which few would have freely chosen and one which many would not retrace. If Ted felt he was a long way from home then so did most of the others and as they grabbed a bunk and unpacked their few belongings, hearts and minds focused on families, wives and sweethearts who were now just images of another time and place.

Having filled their three 'sack' mattresses with straw, known as biscuits, which had a habit of separating when the men turned over, Dalton and Paul walked out onto the veranda and watched the activity as more soldiers arrived and settled into Candahar; the banter, the swearing, the orders and the requests.

Two eighty yard long barrack blocks were situated down each of the longer sides of a rectangular area, with the verandas facing inward to the central area. The shorter sides of the rectangle had no buildings but within it lay the latrines, kitchen and canteen blocks. Just behind their barrack, 3rd Platoon had a railway track which passed within a few feet of the barrack wall. The track came right through the camp from Tidworth sidings and brought all the supplies necessary to keep such a large camp functioning. Looking across the top of the kitchen and canteen blocks, men could be seen walking along the verandas of the two blocks opposite. Instead of a railway line behind them, they had the parade ground, the quarter master's stores and the guard house. They would no doubt be spending a lot of time on the parade ground but hopefully none at all in the cells of the guard house.

Captain Zappacosta was housed in the Officers' Quarters, a building still more impressive than the barracks. Situated beyond the quarter master's stores, it separated the rest of Candahar from the road and civvy street. The pillared entrances of the officers' quarters were soon augmented by the Ford and Wiley jeeps to present an appearance as far from Kandahar as it had ever been. Perhaps Kandahar, the town in Afghanistan after which the barracks were named, would never come closer than this to the soldiers of the US. The British Army however had been in action there during the first and second Afghan Wars of 1840 and 1880; defeating the 'native' Afghans in a major battle at Kandahar to close the second Afghan war.

If the parking outside the officers' quarters was cramped, then the drivers thought nothing of pulling up on the manicured grass. Within a few weeks the camp's appearance was transformed; ruts where jeeps had overtaken by driving up on the verges, signs dented and posts knocked sideways. To the British Army personnel still on camp, the Yanks seemed to be obsessed with speed, breaking hard and jumping from jeeps before they had hardly stopped, yet often on the most trivial of errands. The aura seemed less rigid, the enlisted men louder and more outspoken. Some described the GIs as brash, even big-headed, but Freda and her daughter Jean, like many Tidworth residents became very fond of their US Allies and shared with them the 'best days' of their lives.

Freda and her daughter lived with Freda's parents at Carters Cottage as close to the camp as you might get and next to The Ram pub ... 'the only pub in Tidworth!' B Company soon found the pub and Sergeant Bill Pressley soon noticed the landlord's daughter Peggy. It was one of the first relationships between a B Company man and an English girl, yet Bill Pressley and Peggy would stand the test of time. Bill would gain the Distinguished Service Cross for his bravery and leadership, survive the war and take his English bride home to Pennsylvania.

Dalton, Allbritton and Austen regularly strolled down to the pub, usually around nine in the evening, but one mid November night they were late. The nights were drawing in, the Bourne River swollen from the autumn rain and the men could hear the water rushing beneath the footbridge which lay just a few yards from The Ram. There was no other noise save the joviality emanating from the pub. It was close to last orders, for the British licensing laws dictated that no alcohol could be served after 10.30p.m. on weekdays. The old men of the village, including Jean's grandfather, were already collecting up the glasses. Because of the shortage of glass, a two shilling deposit was charged on each pint glass; returnable at the end of the night providing it was brought back to the bar intact and with no chips. Many of the GIs either forgot about the deposit after a few pints, or couldn't be bothered to collect it. Either way, the elder statesmen of the village didn't complain and gained free drinks from Uncle Sam. It was after the tinkle of glasses had quietened that the three buddies heard a commotion on the other side of The Ram. Instead of going straight in, they walked under the horse chestnut tree and slid around to the back of the building. Amongst some empty beer barrels, a man was squirming and three or four GIs were 'kicking and punching the shit out of him'. As they got closer they could see more of the man, now on the ground, 'he was colored', a coloured American serviceman. As the blows landed, the GIs were shouting at him, for he had walked into The Ram and ordered a drink. A kick to his groin, followed by a boot to his head and with his face already bloody and teeth missing, Dalton, Allbritton and Austen waded in to 'break up the party'.

"OK, he's learnt his lesson," Allbritton said, "no need to kill him."

The 3rd Platoon men helped the guy up and as the attackers walked off, one of them turned and said, "If he comes in the pub again, we WILL kill him!"

The news going around the pub that night was good, B Company would soon be receiving a weekend pass and even Dalton celebrated with a 'warm flat pint of beer'. It wasn't that the folks of Tidworth didn't try to make the men feel at home, it was just that a weekend pass meant 'a whole different ball game' and almost to a man, 3rd Platoon would be heading for London. Bob Sales from 2nd Platoon had already tasted the life at Andover and Salisbury, catching the bus to travel there and he more than most, could feel the pull of the capital city. It wasn't the first time men from the camp had been unleashed on London, it just happened to be B Company's turn. Most felt they deserved the break, Captain Zappacosta had put them through it and they were ready 'to hit the city'.

Training on Salisbury Plain had proved difficult, not the equipment training but the fitness work. Covering twenty-five miles in a day with heavy packs and sleeping wet, on windy, rain-swept hill tops. Austen, Allbritton and Dalton slept in a two man pup tent - Dalton always in the middle, with boots covered in the white chalk-tinted mud and the wind buffeting the down grasslands outside. There was no getting up in the night. Not even the cover of roadside fences did they have, for the highways were without borders. Tank ruts easily turned an ankle in the poor light and November proved harsh with frequent deluges. Wet through, eating cold rations, making nature calls with pants dragging on the damp grass, crawling through the night to some imaginary target, elbows and knees scraped and muddy were aspects that had became routine and engrained in their memories. The river valleys offered some protection to the elements, the soil deeper and the vegetation thicker. But then that was too easy and so through the river and up onto an exposed hillside Zappacosta would lead them, to settle somewhere for the remaining dark winter hours.

Once American food provision caught up with the men and replaced the British corned beef, spam and soya sausages, their spirits raised by as much as the wasted food was reduced. If an army marched on its stomach, as the British often said, then the GIs didn't hold out much hope for the British Army. After several weeks of training, the GIs had 'bloated egos as well as stomachs', according to the local lads; considering themselves super fit as well as crack shots, just because they had spent a week on the firing range to gain their marksman badges.

It was the unfortunate local lads who had to compete with the GIs for the attention of the girls. The Americans presented stiff opposition. By comparison they had plenty of money, a smarter uniform, plenty of spare rations and plenty of spare confidence. Tedworth House was the main local venue for dances and to the annoyance of the English men, girls from the surrounding villages were transported in by the US Motor Pool. In addition, the Women's Auxiliary Air Force, the women of the Auxiliary Territorial Service and Land Army girls were also invited to partner the troops. Tedworth House was run by the US Red Cross with Eleanor Roosevelt in charge. Eleanor was the wife of Brigadier General Theodore (Teddy) Roosevelt Jr. Assistant Commander of the US 1st Infantry Division. She 'sure made the boys feel at home' and in addition to supplying coffee, hamburgers and hot chocolate also provided amenities such as a library, pianos, billiards, ping-pong, sitting rooms, a barber's and a tailor. Eleanor even turned the indoor tennis court into a theatre for performances and films where one thousand four hundred men were packed in per sitting. But the main attraction of the club was the weekly dance.

The rich founders of this grand manor house must have turned in their graves when their ancestral home was opened to the likes of the 3rd Platoon country boys. They had no appreciation of fine art, of the meaning of the stained glass windows or of the sculptures. The Three Graces, a copy of Canova's famous three figured statue adorned the stairs leading off the main saloon. The stained glass window at the end of the hall leading to the saloon depicted one of Aesop's Fables.

One night Smiler's hand, covered in soot from the saloon chimney, added a textural addition to the three graces. The white marble effect surface was interrupted by hand prints strategically placed on the three scantily clad girls. The statue was later moved 'out of harm's way'.

Dalton passed such things by, his keen eye tracing instead the fine lines and texture of the living, breathing young ladies who would congregate on the south side of the dance hall. Every dance they stood there, uniforms or homemade pretty dresses hugging their curves, with stocking lines pencilled onto their calves. Dalton would often take Paul Kennedy across with him, make the introductions and ask the prettiest to join him in one of the other rooms 'to get to know each other better'. Away from the loud music so he said for Dalton wasn't keen on dancing, unless it was close up and slow. Many of his buddies threw themselves into the music and soon everyone would be partnered up, either on the dance floor, somewhere in the house or in the grounds. Glenn Miller Music, 'In the mood', 'String of pearls' and other tunes played by the Benny Goodman Band would emanate through the estate creating a romantic backdrop for the young couples. The music, the elegance of the high ornate ceilings and ionic columns and the 'live for the moment' mentality, guaranteed that the youngsters got on.

Smiler however was one of the few who struggled to find a date. He was short and not altogether the best looking. He would have asked Jean for a dance for she would have danced with him, but she was almost six feet tall despite her tender age of fourteen. Secretly, Smiler liked Jean's mother, Freda. At thirty-three, she was 'damn good looking'. 'Are you coming to the dance?' he would ask her, visiting the Catholic Women's League Canteen more to see her than to eat. The canteen was situated next to St. Patrick's Church on the camp and Jean and Freda did voluntary work there. It was no more than a corrugated tin hut, the chimney and wooden L-shaped counter being the sturdiest parts of the place. 'No, I'm a married woman!' Freda would reply to Smiler, as she did to all such advances. Yet Freda's husband had gone missing fourteen years earlier, when Jean was no more than a shapeless form in Freda's womb. Missing and never found after he boarded a train back to camp.

Jean and Freda served the coffee, tea, sandwiches and buns to the GIs who came more for the female company and to be mothered by the older ladies. 'The Americans were wonderfully generous' and mother and daughter would return home each night with a bag of chocolate, cigarettes, gum and other presents that the GIs insisted on showering upon them. They found Smiler comical if not attractive and his practical jokes entertaining. Smiler had once blown up some French letters and passed them off as balloons to their neighbour. The neighbour cleaned at Tedworth House and having tied the 'balloons' to her handle bars, she cycled gaily back to her cottage through the camp. It was Jean's grandfather who educated the neighbour, Jean and Freda about the true identity of the 'balloons!'

Ignored by the girls at the dances, Smiler often ended up with Staff Sergeant John Holmes who went there more for the social side and to listen to the music. Then after an hour or so and following several refusals, Smiler would make his excuses and slip off to see one of the 'Piccadilly Commandos'. The girls were housed in the Round Tower on Furze Hill. Girls brought in from London to satisfy the men's non-dietary needs. They often hung around Ma's Café during the day and it was easy to organise something with one of them. Smiler always took a couple of French letters with him but they didn't end up being tied to handlebars.

At one of the weekly dances at Tedworth House, Dalton met a tall, pretty girl who was in the Auxiliary Technical Service and based on the Plain. She was 'a real doll' and Clayton kept telling him so, giving him a nudge from time to time as they stood around in the saloon. The dance floor was noisy and busy with guys teaching their English dates how to jitterbug. Dalton avoided it, dancing wasn't his best talent and in the saloon he could get to know his quarry, adoring her quaint accent as much as the rest of her.

It was a pleasurable encounter and Dalton looked forward to their next meeting, arranged mistakenly for the following weekend, the weekend of B Company's 48 hour pass. There was no choice about what he should do. Even though the girl made Dalton melt, melt like Momma's butter when the sun caught it through the kitchen window, he had to go with his buddies. The future didn't bear thinking about, so why commit to one woman, there were plenty around for the taking.

On the following Friday, Dalton walked up Station Road with his buddies heading for Tidworth train station and then to London. With Brylcreem on his hair, French letters in his pocket and a uniform especially cleaned, he was more than ready for the night life. Smiler was noticeably tired, but like the rest of the platoon, in high spirits. The milling, excited men cheered when the train arrived, standing as they were in the county of Hampshire, yet the ticket clerk sat in Wiltshire, a curiosity of the station. And when the train pulled away, the singing started and Smiler hung out of the carriage door window and waved at an imaginary woman saying, "Don't wait up sweetheart."

Chapter 16

Saturday at 4p.m.

London, December 1942.

The train carrying B Company left the Tidworth branch line and rejoined the main line at Ludgershall, picking up speed as though it too was eager to reach the nightlife of the capital. The clear night sky had left a hoar frost which still lingered where the sun's rays could not reach, behind hedgerows and north facing slopes. The crisp hard ground glistened under the blue sky and reflected the spirits of the men, untouched by the cold within the carriage. The sun seemed to rise, give up after barely climbing above the trees bordering the track and then fall to settle an early dusk on the countryside; bringing the city nightlife ever closer in the minds of the soldiers. With the interior of the carriages illuminated by dim blue light from the blackout regulation bulbs, faces were transformed to a ghostly blue white and matched the transformation of character that a weekend's freedom from camp had instigated.

Covent Garden, Leicester Square and Piccadilly Circus were places many of the men had heard about and most were determined to see all three. The night clubs with their bars, dance floors and big bands, the pubs, cinemas and theatres were a big attraction for overseas servicemen, they flocked there and so did the English girls. With the prospect of physical training, weapons training and another 25 mile hike in the week to follow, it was no wonder that the men were anxious to arrive. As the engine hauled the carriages round the last curve and under the 700 feet long Paddington Station roof, testosterone filled men crammed at the exit doors, determined to make every second count. Even before the train stopped, men burst from the carriages to invade the platform and spread into the main hall. There, almost thirty years earlier, a young James Eaglestone had watched recruits for the Great War arrive and finally the lucky ones trudge home, broken and dispirited.

James's opinion of Americans hadn't been changed by 'this new generation'. Whilst on fire watch duty, he had seen them leaving the pubs talking loud enough for the whole street to hear. Seen them heading for a hotel with a woman on their arm, some too drunk to know whether the girl was a Piccadilly Commando or some obsessed young thing, blinded by their over confidence and generosity.

'Over sexed, over paid and over here' he told Hetty, more often than she could remember.

Some would have added, 'overfed'.

The GI private was paid 3 pounds and 8 shillings a week compared to the British private's 14 shillings. There being 20 shillings to a pound, the GI earned five times as much and the British boys struggled to compete. Drinks flowed at the bar and purchases from the PX to shower nylons, chocolate, cigarettes and other luxury goods onto awe struck girls who had suffered three years of rationing. However what annoyed James most about the Yanks was the confidence which seemed to ooze from them like a solvent, engineered to dissolve British culture. Thank goodness Edith was married and Hetty engaged, for no daughter of his would date one.

Paddington Station, a rail terminus since 1838, provided little evidence that a war was on, save for two short rows of sandbags either side of the underground entrances. The first underground, built by the Metropolitan Railway Company, had run from here as early as 1863. Within the main hall of the station were wooden huts, kiosks so called; W.H. Smith being one, a refreshments kiosk another. Then there was the Salvation Army kiosk providing hot drinks and sandwiches, free to any serviceman in uniform. Arching over the B Company men and protecting the hall and platforms from the British weather, hung the great glass roof; the four wrought iron spans extending it to 350 feet in width, all intact despite the terminus being a prime Luftwaffe target.

The obvious choice for the GIs was to head for the underground platforms and take the Bakerloo line to Piccadilly Circus. But some of the guys just wanted to get a first glimpse of the city and headed straight for the main entrance, to then take a cab or a bus. As Dalton emerged from the station and with a back drop of newspaper sellers touting for business, Dalton could see gaping holes in the rows of houses down Praed Street and then down Eastbourne Terrace. It was here that many of the bombs destined for the lines and platforms had fallen; wiping out homes and whole families, perhaps several families in the one tenement.

Down Eastbourne there must have been at least fifteen houses demolished, maybe more, for the whole block closest to Praed Street seemed derelict. Down Praed Street itself and opposite the station there were as many as twenty demolished buildings and many seriously damaged; businesses with flats above, Premier Shoe Repair, Boots Chemist, Partridge and Co and the Express Dairy. Blocks of two, three, perhaps four buildings missing, in some cases a single brick wall remained, framing windows to the night sky. The blackened frontages and craters in the road unevenly refilled were a stark indication of London's location, just 85 miles from the French coast. Dalton looked around and thought it 'a hell of a lot safer back at Tidworth!'

The newspaper sellers continued their touting whilst the queue for the cabs edged forward and black cab after black cab gained more money from Uncle Sam than the ride deserved. "Newstansta, Newstansta," the sellers shouted; spat out as if suffering from a fit, like an indecipherable expletive, even as a customer stood before them.

There were three evening editions to choose from; the Evening News and the Evening Standard, both Conservative papers and the Star, a Labour/Liberal paper, and if the seller sold all three, he would shout 'Newstansta'. If the shout failed to draw in the 'punters' then the placard usually did, for it always bore an eye catching headline,

'Africa. Axis on the run' it said this night, and the papers were selling like hot cakes.

Following General Montgomery's success at El Alamein, the British were pushing the German and Italian Forces westward from Egypt and were half way across Libya. American and British troops under Eisenhower were pushing eastward along the same coast and had entered Tunisia; the 29th Division would clearly not be needed in Africa. The papers predicted that the final showdown would be somewhere between Tunis and the town of Tripoli in western Libya. Rommel, the renowned German Field Marshal, was said to be 'looking defeat in the face'. More importantly for the B Company boys, if the Germans lost Africa whilst still wasting manpower and machinery on the eastern front, Europe would be the Allies next target. Mussolini told Hitler so, but true to form, Hitler ignored the advice, believing that he could still take Russia.

During Hitler's first six months in Russia to December 1941, his forces had swept across the Steppes to within sight of Moscow and Stalingrad, yet one year later the front line had hardly changed. The autumn rains and early winter of '41 had stalled the advance and from there the decline had continued. Hitler was losing tens of thousands of troops, some simply frozen to death, endless supplies of equipment and aircraft to a Russian Army that was becoming stronger and stronger. The demise of the Third Reich had begun and the 29th would be kept waiting, for timing and preparation for the invasion of Fortress Europe was everything.

Paul Kennedy and Dalton were next in line for the taxi and jumped in with Smiler and Roy Perkins, another member of B Company.

"Where to Guvnor?" the taxi driver asked with an accent distinctly different to the Tidworth locals.

"Pick-cad-dilly Cirrcus sirrr," they sang almost to a man in their southern drawl.

"Old on to yer 'ats, I'll 'ave yer there in a jiffy," the driver assured the excited passengers, his Cockney East End accent coming out still more strongly and totally incomprehensible to them. And with that he pulled straight out into the London traffic and sped westward down Craven Road, the opposite direction to Piccadilly Circus.

"What did he say?" Smiler asked without response.

The number of vehicles on the road surprised the guys, so different to Tidworth and particularly to back home. Red double decker buses, black cabs, delivery lorries; one carrying the Selfridges livery, a Southern Railway parcel lorry, Royal Mail Morris commercial vans and only a few private cars, due to the petrol rationing. All the vehicles had dimmed headlights which illuminated just a few feet of road and with no street lighting it seemed that the cabbie was driving by a combination of memory and luck. Black grey shapes slipped by as the cab turned down one street, then another. Shops with dark display fronts and switched off advertising signs, banks and restaurants with their blackened windows and screened doors. So many people on the pavement, queuing for the bus home, others walking perilously across the line of traffic, some hailing a taxi. They seemed impervious to the cold night air and oblivious to the dangers. Dalton and Paul gripped the hand holds and Smiler sitting between them, looked panic stricken. Thick white lines had been painted along the kerbs and white horizontal stripes on lamp posts. Traffic islands were also white and most people seemed to be wearing or carrying something bright. Few blackout accidents now occurred compared to the beginning of the war when in the first four months, 4,000 people were killed. But to the new arrivals, the journey was precarious and Dalton decided that at night, he would either walk or take the underground.

Unlike the directional sign posts, street names had remained to prevent chaos developing round the city and in better light Dalton and his buddies might have seen that having cut through to the Bayswater Road, they were now driving past Marble Arch into Oxford Street. Marble Arch marked the north-eastern corner of the 340 acre Hyde Park. Once a royal hunting preserve, it had been opened to the public in the early sixteen hundreds and still a recreation area for the poor and rich alike. On its large lake, beyond the crowd at Speakers' Corner, skaters were enjoying the frozen Serpentine. A fog was forming as the air from the park mingled with that of the city and as the taxi entered Oxford Street, what little visibility there had been was lost. Slowing down, the driver edged his way between parked buses and the cast iron lamp posts intermittently placed down the middle of the street and which separated the two lines of traffic. Obscured by the mist, two ornate arms at the top of the posts curved over and downward, each holding a bulbous lamp. In peace time the lamps provided a beautiful display of light and shadow along the broad street with its classy department stores, banks and restaurants. But in these blacked out foggy conditions the posts were a hazard. Despite the horizontal white stripes around their bases, the taxi wandered too far over, clipped a kerb and bounced back towards a double decker parked at a bus stop. Dalton held his breath as the driver grappled with the steering to pass within inches of the bright red paint. The decision was unanimous; they would walk the rest of the way.

The people on the sidewalk were so friendly. Well-to-do ladies carrying their purchases smiled benevolently. Shop girls on their way home from work took shy glances at the fit, confident soldiers in their tight, smart uniforms. Dalton took to stopping the prettiest of them and asking the way to 'Pick-cad-dilly Cirrcus'. Then a few yards on, when another passed, asking her too.

A few blocks on from Selfridges department store lay the boarded up remains of the equally famous John Lewis store, a bomb site since September 1940. At Peter Robinson's at Oxford Circus they turned down Regent Street and approached Piccadilly with its large 'Dig for Victory' banner and a sandbagged and boarded Statue of Eros. Like many of the more famous London monuments, Eros was now unceremoniously tucked away to protect her from the bombing. Originally dedicated to Lord Shaftesbury for his work in providing affordable housing, the archer on the fountain represented the Angel of Christian Charity, not Eros the Pagan God of Love as most believed.

The American Red Cross club, Rainbow Corner in Piccadilly was situated on the corner of Shaftsbury Avenue and later the guys intended to return there to bed down, at no charge for the night. The club also ran dances and concerts and provided food exclusively for the Yanks and was the envy of the British serviceman. But on this weekend at least, Dalton and his buddies intended to savour London hospitality.

What struck the guys most was all the entertainment facilities. Down Shaftsbury Avenue alone there was the Lyric, Apollo, Globe, Queens and a bombed out Shaftsbury - all theatres. Whilst the London Pavilion Cinema stood on the corner between Shaftsbury and Piccadilly. On the Circus and down the Haymarket there were still more cinemas and theatres. No wonder the place was so crowded Dalton thought. But of bigger interest were the pubs and bars and the group of buddies strutted into one to order the first of the night. They had plenty of money, that was obvious and with anticipation to match.

After a couple of pubs and several partially drunk pints, it was just Dalton and Paul Kennedy who ended up together strolling down Coventry Street from Piccadilly towards Leicester Square. Some of their buddies were trailing behind whilst others had moved on a little quicker, all eventually headed for Covent Garden. They had tried the local Whitbread beer, Fullers of Fulham and Benskins of Watford; tried the pale ales, the stouts and the bitters and they all tasted like 'nat's piss'. Dalton's request for something ice cold was met with derision at one pub. A British Army boy standing at the bar had retorted;

"Fuck off back home and get your own cold drinks!"

It made Dalton recall something he had read in the 'Short Guide to Great Britain' published by the US War Department for troops going overseas. Something about not being 'misled by the British tendency to be soft spoken and polite, if they need to be, they can be plenty tough.'

The soldier 'sure looked tough', lean with a face that had seen hard times, military action or both, it was etched into the lines that had prematurely been carved into the young face. Veins bulged from his strong forearms and temples pulsed, seemingly intent on a confrontation.

"You come over here, throw your money around and think you're God's gift. You know fuck all!" he shouted getting closer to Dalton's face as he spoke, spittle landing on the smartly pressed, general issue uniform.

Dalton's physique more than matched the soldier's, but not his aggression and Dalton's soft face made him appear vulnerable by comparison.

"Sod off before I show you just how useless you lot are," the soldier shouted with a smirk, noting the nervous discomfort besetting the GIs. Dalton and Paul looked round at the throng of British servicemen standing holding their flat beer in Whitbread pint glasses and decided not to respond and merely slipped out quietly.

They stepped into the cold night air with relief, determined the incident wouldn't colour their night, but understanding now why there were so many military police around.

Entering Leicester Square, the two country boys were taken aback by the wealth of entertainment on offer: the Odeon Cinema, the Leicester Square Theatre, the Empire Theatre and Cinema; beneath the Empire in the basement lay the Ritz Cinema and next door to it, the Monseigneur News Cinema. The Monseigneur Cinemas showed hour-long news reels and were popular amongst women trying to catch a glimpse of a loved one serving overseas. The GIs had seen a Monseigneur on Piccadilly Circus and assumed the guy to be very rich. Crowds of people were milling on the sidewalks, which together with the cinemas and theatres surrounded a central green, where seemingly totally out of place, was an air raid shelter and trenches.

Next to the Monseigneur was the Queens Bar but the two decided they had had enough of pubs, they were as distinctly lacking in women and good beer as they were in hospitality.

It was Paul who spotted the grey outline of the Fortes Milk Bar standing like an oasis by the Ritz Cinema entrance. "Be able to get something cold in there," Paul suggested.

"What about the Black and White Milk bar?" Dalton said, looking back the way they had entered the square. The Fortes seemed quiet, whilst the Black and White lively.

"Saw a beautiful woman go in," Dalton said playfully, "might be able to get a date as well as a cold drink."

Without another look or word to each other, they raced over to see who could be first through the door. So preoccupied were they that they didn't notice an attractive young woman approach. Roy Perkins saw her. He had been catching up with his buddies, arriving in time to see the two pushing their way into the milk bar. "Whilst boys play, men pick fruit," he told himself.

Inside the milk bar a girl was serving on her own and was rushed off her feet. Dalton and Paul joined the queue, the place full with British and Commonwealth Servicemen. A few seconds later, the door opened and in walked Roy Perkins with an attractive accompaniment.

"Your milk shakes look almost as desirable as you," Dalton interjected as the girl behind the counter served two RAF boys, his broad face portraying a smile as irresistible as his confidence. The RAF boys were not impressed, but the girl was.

When it was Dalton's turn he ordered his favourite strawberry syrup and ice cream; whisked and served in a cold glass it tasted divine as it passed his lips. He ordered another and one for the girl. "What's your name?" Dalton asked.

"Maud," the girl replied.

"Pretty name, I'm Dalton, this is Paul." And after plenty of easy chat, Dalton had a firm date with Maud for the next day, Saturday at 4p.m. They would meet outside the bar when she finished her afternoon shift, on one condition; Maud was to bring 'a friend' for Paul.

When Dalton and Paul left the milk bar, it seemed as though half the milk bar emptied with them and walked in the same direction. Roy Perkins and his new girlfriend caught up with them, making three GIs, with perhaps eight RAF boys following. "This is Pat," Roy said, introducing his new girlfriend.

The buddies headed towards Charing Cross Road, passed the Leicester Square Underground Station and started down Long Acre in the direction of Covent Garden following Pat's directions. Pat Harrison knew the area well and took great delight in being the guide to this group of 'lively, confident, Yanks'. Pat had been going to see Maud but decided that better things were on offer. She would go back and see her friend later she promised but hadn't meant it. Maud knew the score.

Walking more quickly now, the cold night air turned the GIs' breath into vapour trails, the RAF boys still following. Closer and closer they approached, also heading so Dalton presumed, for Covent Garden. Another thirty yards on and the GIs decided the guys behind were getting too close for comfort, heard the word 'swank' and thought it time to look for a safe haven. The happy English girl, oblivious of their worries was holding tight onto Roy Perkins' arm and asking them where they came from in the States. It was difficult to focus on her questions with the British Servicemen so close behind and thought her presence might ignite the situation further. Another twenty yards on, they caught sight of Ted, Clayton, Austen, Allbritton and Smiler waiting outside the dance club for which they were all destined. Quickly they pulled Pat across the road to join the other B Company men and stood in readiness to await the reaction of the British Air Force boys.

But the 'boys in blue' walked on past, still on the other side of the street. Perhaps the sight of Ted had changed their minds or maybe the airmen were just out for a good time like the Yanks. When Dalton looked back, the last of his buddies was entering the club and not wanting to be alone on the street, quickly followed. The body heat embraced him after the cold night air and when he pushed through into the dance hall, Dalton thought he was in heaven, for the place was filled to the brim with English girls.

It was late when Dalton finally left the club with Roy Perkins, Pat Harrison and another local girl. The girls both lived in the Marylebone area and there was never any doubt that the GIs would escort them home. The blackout provided plenty of dark as well as derelict corners where a couple might not be seen or disturbed. "When do the air raids start?" the GIs asked looking up at the night sky as they exited the dance club. The girls found the question highly amusing.

"Love your accent," Pat replied as the other girl took hold of Dalton's arm still giggling. The ignorance of military events, past and present, was amusing and the naivety compelling.

"Don't get them much now," Pat explained, hoping the conversation wouldn't turn too serious. Fortunately it didn't, for Dalton started to mess and joke and the laughter spread across the narrow streets echoing off the London brick walls, telling those trying to sleep, if they needed telling, that the Yanks were in town.

Pat Harrison held onto Roy's arm as she had done all night and directed the four of them through dark side streets to reach the Marylebone Road. Dalton and Roy walked the two girls quickly now through the chilling night air, air that had once transmitted the rumble of bombs falling on the capital. Pat Harrison lived at Dudley House, a block of council flats on the corner of the Harrow and Edgware Road. But a couple of hundred yards before Dudley House, the four diverted up between Regent's Park and Marylebone Station, to get to St. John's Wood Road where Dalton's date lived, close to Lord's Cricket Ground. Neither Dalton nor Roy had heard of cricket, much to the amazement of the girls. The sport was apparently very popular in England, a national sport even. Pat's cousin actually played at Lord's, Pat told them with pride, but the significance was lost on the GIs.

After the last of the last of the goodnight kisses, the two buddies headed back to Piccadilly Circus, Rainbow Corner and a bed for the rest of the night.

It was like 'Little America' for everything inside from the food and posters to the personnel had been shipped out of the States just to make the GIs feel at home. There were two recreation rooms with pool, ping-pong and record playing facilities; two huge dining rooms providing American food, with meals at 25c and a basement snack bar offering amongst other things hamburgers, doughnuts, waffles and coca cola. A barber's shop enabled the boys to get the cuts they needed, showers to clean themselves up, letter writing facilities and even sightseeing information so they could make the most of their short visit to London. How jealous were the underpaid British boys when they learned of how much Uncle Sam cared for his troops?

Lying in bed, Dalton listened to the low hum of traffic still passing through the city. It was a clear night and would have been an ideal bombing opportunity. On such nights during the Blitz, the Thames had appeared like a sinuous, silver thread, reflecting what little light there was, to guide the attackers in. But those days were gone and difficult to understand for the new visitors. Dalton thought of the women he had met on this very eventful evening. And as he sobered he recalled the reception from some of the British servicemen and the bomb damage he had seen. "Thank God Church View is safe from all this," he said into the air of the dormitory, an air which carried the smell of stale English beer on intoxicated breath and intestinal releases of late night hamburgers.

Only when the London traffic seemed to finally slip away, did Dalton fall asleep. A sleep which brought dreams of home, the peaceful life disturbed by aircraft engine noise, the Dragon Swamp a noisy road and the plowing of a field disrupted by deep craters. Dalton woke often with thoughts always of Church View and wished that on Monday he would be hoeing a corn field instead of marching twenty-five miles across Salisbury Plain.

The Saturday started crisply, the sky clear, the cold night having turned into a beautiful clear blue day; just a thin layer of fog, being slowly burned away by a weak sun. Dalton rose late, ate well and passed the afternoon taking in new sights and mulling over plans for his last night away from camp. He thought about his date with Maud, wondered whether he should turn up for her or just have a good time at another club. To mingle and joke, to relish the touch of the dresses, the long hair and the smiles of those who like the GIs, didn't know what tomorrow might hold.

Dalton walked down Whitehall, saw Westminster Abbey, took a look at the Houses of Parliament whilst standing on Westminster Bridge, a bridge over the Thames. Actually touched the railings of Buckingham Palace and sat down on a bench in Green Park, the chill air moving him on quickly. So many servicemen around, many bright eyed and fresh faced like Dalton witnessing sights that only war could have enabled them to see. Then walking up Park Lane by the side of Hyde Park, Dalton made his decision; he decided to forget about his date with Maud.

Working the afternoon shift on Saturday, Maud would have no time later to find a date for Paul Kennedy, so leaving early and crossing town on the bus, she called in to see her best mate at Dudley house.

Pat Harrison was still in bed and Liz her mother, directed Maud towards Pat's bedroom.

"How's Mr. Harrison?" Maud asked Mrs. Harrison as they walked down the hallway.

"Fine luv, Tom's out working his barrow on Church Street today, bein a Saturday," then knocking loudly on Pat's door, Liz shouted, "You've got a visitor."

Pat was so full of her date with Roy Perkins that Maud found it difficult to explain why she had called by. Pat was in love, besotted even and looked vacantly past Maud at the very mention of an American soldier.

Eventually Maud was able to explain how she had come to have a date with a GI called Dalton and that if she didn't find a girl for his friend, then perhaps he would call the date off.

Hearing the name Dalton, Patsy sat up as though awakened from her hypnotism. "You mean the GI who chatted you up in the milk bar last night?" Pat enquired, recalling the long wait her and Roy had whilst Dalton 'said goodnight' to his girlfriend on St. John's Wood Road.

"I'll find someone," Pat promised without conviction, confident that Dalton wouldn't turn up and then continued to tell Maud all about Roy, from his chiselled chin down to his toned thighs.

As Dalton walked beside Hyde Park, he could have hopped over its low wall for in a drive to obtain iron and steel for the war effort, most of the Park's railings had been removed to be turned into war materials. Housewives had handed in pots and pans and the parks had lost their railings. Towards the end of Park Lane, Dalton wandered over to the Marble Arch, originally built as a gateway to Buckingham Palace. The arch was moved here in 1851, although by tradition, the Royals were still the only ones allowed through its otherwise closed gates. Opposite the Arch, at the north-eastern corner of Hyde Park, Dalton came across Speakers' Corner. Colourful, flamboyant orators and some much less so, stood on soap boxes, beer crates and whatever else they could find to then lecture and preach to passers-by. Groups gathered, dispersed and reformed as they idled past and spared some time to listen to the different people; messages spoken by deeply religious men and some impious, socialists, right wingers, others merely talking about sport.

Dalton moved between groups as the locals were doing and listened in on some of the messages. Since the right of free assembly in 1872, Speakers Corner had attracted a wealth of different speakers from the rich and famous to the tramps and insane. George Orwell and Karl Marx had spoken here, but there was no one famous on this winter's afternoon. A few hecklers became involved in the discussions but most just listened. Dalton moved on again and stopped before an orator who was talking of Jesus. The Baptist Preacher at Wares had often talked of the 'Son of God' and so catching some of the orator's words, Dalton decided to listen.

By 3p.m. Pat had run out of enthusiasm. Calling on a few friends down the street to find they were already spoken for, she had decided to call off the search. Sitting on the stairs waiting for Roy, she knew that if Dalton actually did turn up, Maud would be livid with her.

Pat's father Tom Harrison was in the parlour smiling to himself. The day's work on Church Street market had proffered a nice bit of extra cash. The 'Yankee' cigarettes had sold quickly and so too had the other merchandise, provided by a US Army 'bloke' in charge of stores at one of their bases. Unlike many, Tom didn't see the GIs as an 'army of occupation', more 'an army of opportunity'. His thoughts drifted to his brother-in-law, as they so often did when Tom was thinking about the Yanks. James Eaglestone had married Liz's sister Ethel about the same time as Tom had married Liz. James the old hardened Great War veteran he thought, was less than keen on the Yanks. Tom wasn't unhappy about them being overpaid and over supplied. Being over sexed he wasn't sure about, but would keep an eye on Pat just in case. As for being over here, well, as far as Tom was concerned, the GIs were just lads, out for a good time. 'Bring Roy home for tea one night' he had told Pat when she spoke of him.

The smile broadened as an idea popped into his head, it probably wouldn't get Pat out of Maud's bad books, but it was worth trying just to have a laugh on James Eaglestone.

Walking out to Patsy still sitting on the stairs, Tom said to his daughter, "Why don't yer go and ask that cousin of yours, needs a bit of excitement in 'er life."

Pat looked at him incredulously, "Don't be silly Dad, Hetty's engaged and you know that Uncle Jim forbids her to go out with anyone he doesn't know and he definitely won't let her go out with a Yank!" Pat thought her father so stupid sometimes.

Roy's knock at the door interrupted the exchange but before Pat could open it, Tom was there to welcome her new boyfriend. Made a real fuss, told him he should have bedded down on the couch instead of walking all the way back to Piccadilly last night. "Come in and 'av a cuppa tea," he said, almost pushing Roy towards the parlour.

"Dad, there's no time," Pat said.

"Ere," Tom said turning back to Pat, "take this and be a good girl and go roun' to yer cousin."

Tom pushed a few 'bob' into his daughter's hand with a wink. "Spend it on Roy, when you've made my good day even bet'er."

Pat rushed up Warwick Avenue, then along Shirland Road to reach Thorngate Road with the time closing on 3.30p.m. Skipping down the steps to the area, her aunt Ethel opened the door and Hetty joined them in the hallway. Pat explained the predicament.

"Sorry Patsy, I can't," Hetty said resolutely. "And anyway, Dad wouldn't let me," she added.

Ethel motioned Pat and Hetty into the front ground floor room and well away from James who was in the parlour.

"What 'arm can come of it?" Ethel said to Hetty as she closed the door behind her daughter.

"You haven't been out in ages and it's just to make up numbers, not a real date," Pat said.

Hetty was unconvinced and didn't respond, the mantelpiece clock ticked away the seconds and the bronze firemen stared coldly upon the scene.

"You're goin' out with family, not with the Yank," Pat added, her crossed fingers touching the money which her dad had given her to make his day.

"It'll do yer good to 'av some fun," Ethel said quietly.

"Yer always in, once won't 'urt," Pat corroborated as she glanced at the mantelpiece clock to see the time just slipping past the half hour.

"I'll tell yer dad you've gone out with Pat for a couple of hours," Ethel said, adjusting the position of the bronze firemen as if they had moved from her favoured spot. "Come on," Ethel said more softly and pulled her daughter out towards the stairs, "go and get ready."

With her navy blue winter suit to keep out the cold December air, Hetty came back down, her face lacking makeup and looking for reassurance. Pat grabbed Hetty's hand and with a big thank you to her aunt, pulled Hetty out of the front door into the area and up the steps onto Thorngate Road. As they rushed towards Marylands, Pat just hoped that her uncle Jim wouldn't look out and see his daughter leaving.

Reaching Shirland Road, Pat could not believe her luck and nor would Paul Kennedy she thought, for half the boys in Paddington wanted a date with Hetty. Pat considered that she had earned the two shillings her father had tempted her with and anyway Hetty was in for a good night. Pat knew better than most the difference between a night out with a GI and one with the 'cricket boys'.

Dalton had promised to meet Paul at 3.30p.m. back at Rainbow corner. It was a little after that before he approached the sandbagged empty platform of Eros, hidden, as was the true identity of the statue to most. Dalton had already decided how he was going to persuade Paul from meeting Maud and the mystery date; after all, he would say, the girl might be fat and ugly and both of them would be stuck with it. Why not have a good time at another club and make the choice themselves. As Dalton approached, Paul stood outside the Red Cross Club with the shadow of the buildings opposite almost at his feet, the sun's last radiance upon the young soldier.
"Thought you might have changed your mind," Paul said to his best buddy with a smile and a look of anticipation. Decision instantly reversed, Dalton slapped Paul on the back and said, "No way! Would I let you down? Let's head over."
Thus several minutes before 4p.m. on a Saturday in December, 1942, Dalton found himself outside the Black and White Milk Bar, on the corner of New Coventry Street and Leicester Square. Like 'cats on hot bricks' Dalton and Paul waited for Maud to finish her shift and for Paul's date to appear, having agreed that if the girl was built like a 'brick shit house' they would run for it.
A little after four, Dalton saw Roy and Pat walking towards him down Charing Cross Road, and there walking beside Pat was a young woman. Dalton watched her approach, watched every movement, for he could not take his eyes from her. She walked with no effort, so light of foot and full of energy was her stride. She was turning towards Pat, smiling, talking, laughing, probably embarrassed by the

circumstance of the meeting. The spring in her step and her animation caused her hair to move provocatively, dark hair which caressed her face and neck as it hung sensuously long to touch her shoulders. The blue suit jacket beneath defined her female form and Dalton followed its lines until it splayed out into a pleated skirt that came to just below the knee. When she came closer and was no more than a few yards away, Dalton was struck by her natural beauty, for with no makeup she radiated a glow from rosy cheeks that the chill air had painted, her skin white, emphasising her pink lips. As she came still closer and what seemed like inches from his pulsing frame, Maud walked out of the milk bar.

Pat started the introductions, "Hetty this is Paul and this is … " Dalton she was going to say but before Pat could say anything further, Dalton interrupted her;

"You're my date for the night," he said, still looking at Hetty, for he hadn't been able to pull his eyes away from her. Hetty didn't see Paul and Maud look at Dalton with utter disbelief, for she saw only deep, dark, mischievous eyes looking out from a handsome face that radiated a smile to send tingles down her spine.

Dalton took Hetty's hand and led the group away from the silence that had befallen it. Her hand was smooth, soft, small, loose, yet the fingers slightly curved, and the message the gesture carried made his heart race. His hand was firm, strong and she wondered how her fingers had become folded, lightly touching the roundness of his flesh.

Chapter 17

The Letter from Tidworth Barracks

Christmas 1942 to March 1943.

The weekend's freedom was over and the only train operating the Tidworth branch line on Sundays was the late afternoon 'GI Special', serviced by the front end of the Andover to Swindon train. The rear portion of which was left standing at Ludgershall until the engine returned from delivering the troops. Numerous complaints were made that the Swindon portion grew very cold whilst waiting, but the tired GIs would not hear of such concerns.

Dalton lay on his bunk that night, glad not to be in Tom Harrison's front room. After walking Hetty home he had spent Saturday night in an arm chair with Roy on the sofa. It was fine except that Roy kept trying to slip out and see Pat and when he wasn't trying to slip out, hummed 'White Christmas' over and over. The new Christmas release by Bing Crosby had embedded itself in everyone's brain, but Roy was smitten with it more than most.

Paul Kennedy climbed into his bunk above Dalton and like most, was determined to get some rest after the eventful weekend. Training was looming the next morning and the weather predicted to be cold and wet. It was going to be hard out on Salisbury Plain. Dalton however, lay on his side, knees tucked up under the thin blankets, thinking and sifting through the brief few hours shared with Hetty. Each element of memory analysed, from the instant he caught sight of her to the moment she turned the corner in Thorngate Road and returned to a life about which he knew so little.

He recounted every movement, the way she spoke, her laughter, the texture of her clothes, her touch and the sensations she had created within him.

Walking away from the others outside the milk bar, Dalton had asked Hetty if she would like a coffee.

Turning to look at him, a strand of hair had lain across her face, defining her cheek, contrasting with its rosy colour, dark upon fair and the fine ends made a line to the lips which responded. He had found it hard to absorb the words spoken, for his mind was focused on sight and sensation. Her smile seemed to confirm the response, despite being sure that tea had at some point been mentioned.

'That would be nice,' she replied with another fuller smile which sent Dalton's mind spinning out of control.

They crossed over the square, passing the Monseigneur and Empire to reach the Cafe Anglais.

'How do you like your coffee?' Dalton asked her, as they sat down together at one of the vacant tables.

'Tea,' she said grinning.

Roy and Pat, Paul Kennedy and Maud joined them, having finally caught up with the 'couple' and the unexpected turn of events. Dalton had made sure that only he could sit next to Hetty. When Maud sat by him and before Paul Kennedy had taken his seat, she leaned towards Dalton saying, 'You double crossing Yank!'

As Dalton recalled his date with Hetty, the soldiers settled into the large, chilly dormitory, tiredness from a weekend on the town causing it to quieten more rapidly than normal. The fire freshly made in the large brick fire place was just building, the warmth only slowly reaching the men. Paul Kennedy turned over, the rocking of the flimsy bunk petering out as pieces of straw fell from his mattress to settle on Dalton's blankets.

Looking down at his buddy, Paul could see Dalton staring into the orange glow of the fire as he relived events on Saturday night. Outside the Cafe Anglais they had finally agreed on a film to watch, Casablanca showing at the Odeon Cinema. The girls hadn't seen it. It starred Bogart and Bergman but Dalton couldn't remember much about the story, he still felt embarrassed over his decision to queue for the cheaper seats.

There were only British and Commonwealth troops with their girlfriends and locals in the queue. The more expensive seats were nothing to the American servicemen and many swanked past and went straight in with their girls.

When Dalton said they would queue, Hetty had looked at him strangely.

'See you inside buddy,' Roy Perkins had said to Dalton as he walked in with Pat and paid for the most expensive seats.

The queue shuffled forward and Dalton's chat came slow and stilted. The glances from the British Servicemen worried him for they reminded Dalton of his encounter in the pub. One of the British Army boys, a corporal, turned fully round, stood squarely on and looked directly at Dalton. Dalton tensed and anticipated a fight. Hetty quickly removed her hand from his. But instead of a punch, the corporal reached out to introduce himself.

'Who's your friend?' the corporal asked, shaking Dalton's hand and looking towards Hetty.

'This is Dalton, Dalton this is Stan,' Hetty said with obvious embarrassment.

Dalton suddenly became the centre of attention, for Stan Kirby and his mates took a real interest in him.

'Where you from mate?' and

'Where you based?' they asked.

Dalton became more relaxed but sensed that Hetty was far less so and he started to wish he had swaggered in with the others. They all seemed to know her and for some reason she didn't feel comfortable with him anymore.

Hetty's withdrawal still played on his mind and despite the cold he got up to walk out onto the veranda. A light snow was falling, fluttering past the red Dodsdown bricks and settling on the wrought iron railings. Deciding to take a nature call he descended the external stairs to the latrine block in the centre of the Candahar rectangle. It was whilst standing there in the dark, mist rising from his release that his brain finally started to work properly. She hadn't been embarrassed about being with a Yank, she was embarrassed because she already had a steady boyfriend, either that or she had a crush on the corporal.

Dalton walked in from the cold veranda and sat on the side of his bed, still turning over events, her words and gestures. Inside the cinema Hetty had allowed him to take her hand again. He had noticed every movement, each rise and fall of her chest and sensed her thigh close to his. Dalton held her hand for so long that both became hot, yet he worried about letting go, in case she withdrew it forever. Each move he made to get closer, a touch on her arm, to whisper in her ear or to place an arm around her bore no response, yet he felt sure she liked him for there was a glow in her smile and warmth in her eyes when she looked at him. She sure wasn't easy like the other girls, Dalton said to himself as snoring started to bounce around the internal surface of the barrack room.

On walking her home, his suggestion that they head for a hotel met with a predictable response. He was surprised at his own stupidity, the sentence was not even half spoken before he realised his error, but the damage was done. It was habit and a bad one and she had cut him down coldly for the mistake.

'If that's all you're after you can forget it,' she had said and walked away from him.

But she had trusted him to walk her across Regent's Park, allayed his fears when the air raid sirens sounded, 'Won't come to anything,' she reassured him and it didn't. And she had laughed at him at his shock of encountering a tramp braving such a cold night. He loved her laugh.

'Can I see you again?' he had asked her when they reached the bend in Thorngate Road. She would allow him to walk her no further.

'My father will be watching out for me, it's almost ten,' she explained.

'Can I see you again?' he asked for the second time.

'Maybe,' she replied and turned to walk to her door.

Dalton rushed to her, took her hand, she turned, he wanted to kiss her with a passion but motioned to place his lips upon her cheek. She didn't pull away. His lips had lingered, probably for too long and she stepped back, released his hand and said 'Goodnight Dalton,' almost as a friend would say. But it was her departing smile which spoke more than words, for it said to Dalton, 'I do want to see you again,' of that he was convinced.

The bunk suddenly moved violently as Paul rolled over to prop himself up on one elbow.

"You goin to sleep or sit up all night?" he asked.

Dalton looked up at his best buddy and said, "I'm gonna marry that girl."

Paul smiled at Dalton's serious face.

"Sure thing buddy but tomorrow's a big day and you need some sleep."

The snow turned to sleet and then rain in a dreary pattern of grey skies which opened only long enough to permit a few hours of weak sunshine over the whole month of December. Salisbury Plain was a challenge at the best of times and when the weather closed in, it was unforgiving.

As Major General Gerow, Commander of the 29th Infantry Division, watched the flakes hit the warm window of his quarters, melt and slide onto the wooden frame, he considered that even the weather was on his side. For the 29th was made up of National Guard units and consequently regarded less highly by the top brass. Gerow's personal mission was to prove them wrong and would use the weather to his advantage. 'The 29th would be as tough and battle ready as any unit in the US Army.'

Dalton hadn't written as soon as he had intended or promised, Gerow's training regime left little time and what with the mail calls, letters home and then the preparations to entertain local kids, everything seemed to conspire against Dalton's most important letter, his letter to Hetty. He had written and rewritten it several times until hopefully the balance was right. An eagerness to see her again which didn't hint of desperation, a sincere liking which didn't hint of love and an attraction driven by all the right reasons. Dalton knew one thing, there was no one else in the world he would rather be writing to. When he finished the letter his buddies for once were not party to its contents and he walked alone to the Garrison Post Office to place it in the hands of the British Royal Mail. Situated next to the Jellalabad entrance, the large red brick Post Office was civilian run, contained a shop and also acted as the local sorting office. Dalton paid tuppence ha'penny for the postage stamp, kissed the seal and prayed that the home for which it was destined, be kept safe.

The Christmas party the GIs held for the Saint Osmonds Orphanage was a 'real highlight' for everyone. The children from the Salisbury convent could hardly believe their eyes when they saw all the food. Huge hams with pineapple and as much ice cream, jelly and chocolate as they could eat. The guys knew that war and circumstance had conspired against their visitors and some of the GIs were reminded of their own poor backgrounds.

At the end of the party, when the guys played Vera Lynn's 'We'll Meet Again', some of the older children cried and more than a few of the men had tears in their eyes. Thoughts drifted back to the US and a Christmas at home, to families, families that they missed so much. Thus the empathy was enhanced and the children would never forget the wonderful time they had had or the generosity of the Americans, a link of friendship for a generation to come.

The first Tidworth Camp Christmas dinner staged early for the US media wasn't nearly as enjoyable as that on the day itself. But at least the papers were able to print the images the folks back home wanted to see.

It was their first Christmas away, yet it proved better than many had predicted. The food, fresh turkey with ice cream and tinned fruit to follow, the music, the mail call and the antics of buddies helped the day slip past without serious melancholy; though it was harder for the guys with wives and children back home. It seemed as though all of December's mail had been saved for the special day and the contact with loved ones raised spirits that army friendships couldn't.

When Dalton's letter to Hetty fell onto the hallway mat just before Christmas, it lay there alone for there was no other post. James Eaglestone often caught the first post around seven in the morning, but someone else usually picked up the second. James's work was now solely focused on repairing bomb damage and making bomb sites safe, either boarding them up or tearing them down. There were no resources available for new buildings, not the materials or manpower. Civic buildings and factories involved in the war effort were the first priority, then homes and finally other buildings. There was a severe shortage of housing, so if a roof could be patched up, a wall repaired or windows boarded, then a family need not be re- housed. Builders with the skills James had were like gold dust and worked long hours.

But then James always went to work on an egg, from the half dozen chickens in his small back garden and would not allow anyone else to boil it. Ethel didn't do it right and he claimed to have a one minute saucepan to cook it to perfection. As the egg boiled, James would whistle 'If You Were the Only Girl in the World' and anyone awake hearing it would be enticed to believe that everything was at rights again.

Ethel still left the house very early, off to clean and then serve the Red Cross. She always took a shopping basket with her, one with a separate concealed section in the bottom, for the things her family 'needed'. By early afternoon there was usually an opportunity for her to slip home, and it was Ethel who turned the key and stepped into the hallway to find Dalton's letter on the mat, for it had arrived in the second post.

She carried it through to the parlour, boiled a kettle and used the steam to expertly open the seal. After reading every word she stared thoughtfully into the past, resealed the letter and placed it safely out of sight.

The last Sunday before Christmas, Hetty's fiancé Paul Brooks, the cricket boys and RAF boys who could come, were treated to an extra special 'spread' for tea. Paul and Hetty sat side by side, the happily engaged couple, entertaining friends at Hetty's home. Paul's family came round later from Oakington, their house sufficiently repaired to be lived in again. The Christmas spirit had filtered into everyone and the decorations reflected the laughter in the room. The presents were few and unwrapped but the atmosphere was as it had always been, except not quite perhaps in Hetty's heart.

Her wedding cake had already been ordered, from Tregeser's on Clifton Road; the family connection with the bakers had lived on from the Great War. Hetty's Grandfather, Thomas Chapman and a man called Dennis McCarthy had protected the 'German run' Clifton Road premises from a mob. The bakers would therefore do their best to ensure Hetty and Paul had at least two tiers, iced and well presented, despite the rationing.

As the cricket boys played cards, talked about their work as Paul did about the fire service, Hetty's thoughts slipped back to her date with Dalton. She thought about the GI too much, even in Paul's presence and it worried her. It made her feel underhand, disloyal, shallow even and it was almost with relief that the letter Dalton promised hadn't arrived, for in truth she had been quite taken by him. He looked so good in his uniform, so handsome, so confident and very, very affectionate. No man had ever taken her by the hand and kissed her so soon after their meeting.

Although she had chastised him for suggesting they go to a hotel, secretly she was flattered. Dalton wanted her, desired her, Hetty had sensed it, and a tingle of excitement had run through her from the moment she saw him.

The New Year's Day of '43 came and went and the January and February proved far milder in England than the start of '42. Icy conditions were less frequent and with the strength of the Luftwaffe diminished, James's building work and night watches became easier. With the milder winter and the early arrival of snowdrops came more good news on the war front. In January the Germans surrendered in Stalingrad and Tripoli was taken in North Africa. On January 31st the RAF carried out their first daylight raid on

Berlin and by 6th March Rommel and Montgomery would face each other for their last battle in Africa.

During those weeks as Hetty sat with her father to monitor the progress of the allies, she had managed to fade the images and suppress the sensations that Dalton had created within her, sensations previously unexplored. The preparations for her marriage to Paul were now firmly and resolutely at the forefront of her mind. Never again would she go behind Paul's back. Meeting Stan Kirby in the cinema queue had been a great embarrassment. Hetty felt so guilty when she reflected on the encounter and chastised herself for the impulse to make up numbers.

As the tips of daffodils braved their heads above the soil in the parks where the Dig For Victory had left them untouched, Hetty's wedding dress was bought and the church booked and invitations posted. She would marry Paul Brooks in the June at St. Peter's Church on Elgin Avenue. Hetty looked absolutely beautiful in the bridal gown especially made for her by Daisy, a friend of Ethel's. When Hetty's brother Jimmy saw her trying it on for the first time, he exclaimed that his best pal would be the happiest man in Paddington.

"Paul's a lucky man," Hetty's sister told her whilst their mother fussed with the hem and kept adjusting the veil.

"Everything's fine Mum," Hetty said to Ethel who seemed preoccupied and whilst Ethel's preoccupation continued, James Eaglestone prepared for his Air Raid Patrol.

"I'll leave you girls to put everyfin away," Ethel said, seemingly satisfied at last with the way things were. "Make sure you hang the dress up as I've shown you," she added as she quickly slipped out of the door; leaving the girls to wonder why their mother hadn't done it herself - she normally always did.

Ethel closed the door purposefully tight behind her and crept down the hallway. Her husband was whistling softly to himself in the parlour and she knew that in a few minutes he would be gone. Up the stairs she climbed unnoticed and headed down the dark landing to enter her bedroom, lighting the gas lantern in the recess to provide the light she needed. From under the floor boards beneath the chest of drawers, she slowly withdrew four crinkled and discoloured letters. Not ordinary letters, for the surface of these were smoothed by the touch of caressing hands, the inked address fading and the foreign stamps losing their colour.

They were love letters, letters written in fine, sweeping fountain ink, that started with; 'To my Dear Ethel', written twenty-five years earlier by an Australian soldier whom Ethel had met whilst James was away fighting in France. They had fallen in love and when the soldier left for Australia he had promised to write. He never did, at least so Ethel believed and at first she was heartbroken. Then James returned, the months passed and slowly the disappointment lessened. After all, James was a good man and good men were hard to find. Then a few years later, when Ethel was cleaning her mother's home she found them; letters addressed to her which Lucy had hidden, yet strangely kept.

Thus there alone on the edge of her bed, with the dark of late winter settling again on a grey city, Ethel started to read his words, promising herself that this would be the last time.

'I love you, I love you and miss you ... I will find a way of bringing us together ... perhaps to settle in Australia' and in his last letter, pleaded, 'write to me for I long to hear from you and shall not rest until I do'.

The Australian soldier never did hear from Ethel and perhaps he never rested, but she kept the letters safe all the same. It was too late now, it was too late when she first read them, married with children she was and likely so was he. Yet still she gazed at his address, pondering over it, as she had done that first time, the writing now so familiar, the location another world away, but reachable if she had just put pen to paper.

When James came out of the parlour, Ethel carefully folded the thin worn sheets back into their envelopes and returned them to their hiding place beneath the floor. Then wiping away a tear, went down to cook James Eaglestone some supper, ready for when he came back from his watch.

James still did his shift as well as his wife's and daughter's. Fortunately for James, Edith was exempt, because of having a young daughter to care for whilst Thomas Duckett remained prisoner of war. James knew his patch well; who was away, who had lodgers, which people stayed in their homes during a raid and to which shelter the others went. When the bombs struck he was supposed to direct the emergency services according to priority, to those houses most likely to have casualties and where casualties might be found beneath the rubble.

Dressed in his blue uniform and tin hat, which he preferred to the recently issued beret, James called good night and left the house. As he closed the door, sealing his home against the escape of light, the wedding dress was hung in the wardrobe and before he had even reached the warden's post, Ethel called Hetty into the parlour, just the two of them to, "ave a chat."

Happy and smiling, the fitting having gone so well, Hetty stepped in, closed the door and sat at the kitchen table opposite her mother.

"You do love Paul don't you?" Ethel began abruptly.

"Course I do!" Hetty replied wondering where the question was leading to.

"It's just that this letter came for you," Ethel said, placing the letter from Dalton on the table between them.

"When did this arrive?" Hetty asked reaching out, pulling the letter close to look at the post mark and the name of the sender on the back of the envelope.

Ethel didn't reply and breaking the ensuing silence Hetty said, "You've read it haven't you?"

Ethel didn't need to answer.

"When did it arrive?" Hetty asked again, her voice rising.

"Doesn't matter when it arrived," Ethel said soothingly trying to calm her daughter's anxiety "just read what he's got to say."

"Mum, why didn't you give it to me before, it came in December didn't it?" Hetty almost sobbed as she deciphered the smudged post mark.

"What does it mat'er? You love Paul, so it makes no difference when it arrived," Ethel said, starting to lose patience and becoming uneasy with Hetty's questioning of her.

Hetty sat in silence and looked again at the sender's name and the address given as Tidworth Barracks. The British didn't write the sender's name on the envelope, it was a very American thing to do.

"So why give it to me now?" Hetty asked, wiping away her tears.

"Just ave, don't question me, I'm ya Mu'ver."

There was another pause as Ethel eyed her daughter.

"Well ya gonna open it, or keep lookin at 'is name?"

After several more seconds passed with no movement from Hetty, Ethel snatched the letter and made to throw it onto the few remaining embers in the parlour grate.

"No Mum!" Hetty screamed. Hetty was shocked by her own reaction and fell passive; her scream brought Jimmy into the room.

"Is everything alright?" he asked.

Hetty was sure he must have been listening for he entered so quickly and had that smug face she had seen so often. Ethel held the letter behind her back, but she knew her son better than anyone and told him to go into the front room, she would talk to him later. Jimmy closed the door grinning at his sister's discomfort, just deserts for going out with that Yank he thought. Stan Kirby had inadvertently told him by way of asking if Paul and Hetty had split up; Stan wanted so much to win her back. Silly Stan, Jimmy thought, he didn't have a chance. His sister wanted better than a corporal in the infantry. Paul Brooks had a lucrative career ahead of him and Hetty could look forward to a long marriage. Unlike with 'Infantryman Stan' who probably wouldn't survive the first month of an invasion on Europe. Jimmy laughed to himself as he recalled Stan's reaction to being called up for the army, 'must be a mistake' he'd said 'I applied for the air force'. Jimmy considered that the infantry were no more than cannon fodder, anyone with half a brain got into the RAF and unfortunately for Stan, he wasn't up to it.

"Mum, please give me the letter," Hetty said ever so quietly in case her brother was still listening at the door.

Ethel looked at her daughter, beautiful and bright with it, yet she could so easily be manipulated. Slowly Ethel brought her arm from behind her back and held the letter out for Hetty. "Don't think bad of me," Ethel said lovingly, "I did it for your sake." And she spoke with such sincerity that Hetty could not help but believe her. "It's alright Mum, I know," Hetty said as she slowly pulled the letter from her mother's hand.

Ethel watched as Hetty opened the envelope, pulled out the single page and read that which Dalton had written, written with such care and forethought. Hetty absorbed the sentiment as her mother had done. No brashness or arrogance, just a simple declaration of how much he had enjoyed their time together and a strong desire to see her again.

Below Dalton's name was a single kiss and it reminded Hetty of the kiss he placed on her cheek when they had said goodnight.

The feelings she had experienced in his company resurfaced. They surprised her for she had buried them so deep, but the trickle of memories turned to a flood and she blushed still more than the tears had already painted.

Hetty looked suddenly up at her mother. Dalton would be in London within two weeks and he had asked Hetty to meet him at 11a.m. on the Saturday, on the corner between Sutherland and Shirland Road. Not having had a reply he would assume her answer to be no and in some way she was grateful to her mother. Ethel had spared her the turmoil such a decision would have created ... but then there was still time to reply ... wasn't there? Two weeks? Long enough for a letter to reach Dalton ... if writing one was the right thing to do?

Hetty slowly got up from the table, walked past her brother in the hallway and shut her bedroom door to sit alone in the darkness. The gas lamp there was rarely used and for once she preferred it that way. Hetty sat motionless, elbows on knees, chin resting on palms with her fingers shielding her eyes from the penetration of the world beyond.

When her mother joined her, neither spoke for some time, then as though portraying the unknown to her daughter, Ethel said, "You do know Paul can't have children, don't you?"

"Of course I do Mum, why do you say such things now?" Hetty whispered through her fingers, her spirit drained.

"I just found out," Ethel said.

Hetty looked at her mother in the dim light from the hallway, unable to believe that she had known something her mother didn't.

With just the creaking of floorboards outside on the landing, the two women sat listening to nothing but their own thoughts. Finally Hetty crawled into bed, pulled the blankets up over her and fell into deep despair. Her mother thankfully left without another word and so Hetty's torture ceased, to be replaced by self torment, a torment which dripped into her like acid, eating away at her insides; she must make a decision, to put pen to paper or not and to decide what to write.

Chapter 18

Just a Friend

March 1943.

During January and February, General Gerow worked his 'National Guard' Infantry Division hard. They climbed the steepest slopes, camped on the most exposed hills and dug foxholes deep into the frozen high ground. The 29th were going to have to be better than the rest in order to be regarded as equals.

The company captains were just as determined as the more senior officers to meet expectations and a certain rivalry ensued between one company and another. Short and wiry Ettore Zappacosta, the Captain of B Company was determined to lead the best of the bunch. He was respected and hated all in the same breath as he led his men through cold winter streams, to finally bed them down on the open, windswept Salisbury Plain.

Six months training in England on top of the sixteen months in the US sure amounted to a lot of miles under their belts; marching, running and too often crawling through undergrowth. The 29th Division must be destined for something big the men thought, if this amount of preparation was required. Yet the plans for their destiny were only in their infancy, though starting to take shape none the less. On March 12th the Allied combined chiefs of staff appointed Lieutenant General Frederick Morgan of the British Army as the chief planner for a future invasion of north-west Europe.

The US and Britain had agreed from the outset that an invasion somewhere in France would take place. That the invasion would be followed by a ground campaign with the complete occupation of Germany its goal; the 'surest and swiftest course to Allied victory in Europe' according to General Marshall, President Roosevelt's senior military advisor. Marshall wanted an invasion in '43 but British General Sir Alan Brooke asserted that 'an invasion of Europe must not be rushed', German forces had to be stretched and thinned to a point where such a vast commitment of men and resources had a significant chance of success.

The Russians were doing a good job in absorbing German resources. At Stalingrad alone, when the Germans surrendered in January, they had lost 100,000 men, five hundred transport planes and six months worth of war production. A full German retreat from Russia seemed ever more likely and when it happened where would the Red Army stop? At their own border? Unlikely, after occupying Eastern Europe early in the war. They might eventually push into Germany. But why stop there? Russia had been an enemy before they were an ally. They could easily become an enemy again and Russian troops on the French coast did not bear thinking about.

It would therefore be prepare, watch and wait. The British considered spring of 1944 as the earliest an invasion could be mounted and the Americans were categorical that it should be no later.

The 29th would thus remain in England, their training intensified and more specialised, to eventually penetrate fortress Europe and perhaps even help save the continent from the Russians.

Few had any concept of world events and lesser ranks had no idea even of the plans besetting them and merely fulfilled the orders of the day. Each day following the next as surely as combat would one day follow the training. For his part, Captain Zappacosta regarded the 'Burp up exercises' as sacrosanct and used them more than most to promote his men's physical fitness. For the Expert Infantryman's Badge the men had to make a 100 yard sprint, followed quickly by 35 press ups and 10 chin ups. Then after crossing an obstacle course at a sprint, use a Colt .45, Garand M1 and a Browning automatic as accurately as possible. Soldiers who completed the routine in the required time and accuracy earned the badge and an extra five dollars in their monthly pay check. Zappacosta was adamant that all his company should pass. For their part the men were determined not to let each other down and with good soldiers like Staff Sergeant John Holmes supporting those who struggled, few failed.

Dalton and Paul Kennedy achieved their badges relatively easily as did Roy Perkins, Allbritton and Austin, but Ted, Clayton and Smiler had to work extra hard. Ted found it difficult to shoot straight, Clayton just wasn't as fit as the rest and Smiler always struggled with life despite his humour.

If Dalton had been fit on his first visit to London, he was even more hardy and muscular for his next. Many of the guys were equally more confident, but Dalton knew that measured humility was going to be needed if he was to win over a certain girl's heart. However, as the weeks passed, still with no reply from Hetty, Dalton became sure that her heart had already been won by another. Perhaps the man in her life was a serviceman from overseas, but from Hetty's embarrassment in the cinema queue, Dalton thought it more likely he was an Englishman, probably away in the armed services. He had suggested they meet on Shirland Road, the next corner up from Marylands, thinking it was a safe distance from Thorngate. For he had sensed Hetty's unease at him coming near her home and it all led to just one thing, Hetty was for sure dating someone.

When the letter finally did arrive from Hetty it was a real surprise, not least because within it lay a thread of hope. 'I can only meet you for a while', she said, 'for a chat'. "A chat," Dalton repeated to himself as he sat on the train heading for London. What did that mean?

Arriving late in London on Friday, Dalton spent the remainder of the night enjoying American style hospitality at Rainbow Corner. Waking early on Saturday he decided to walk to Shirland Road, take in a few sights along the way and think things through. Like what would he say to Hetty? And where would they go together? He wouldn't suggest a hotel that was for sure. And what would he do if she didn't turn up? Questions which passed through his head as he negotiated the Paddington streets, but what nagged him most and made his insides contort was wondering who held her, kissed her and were they in love?

With the last of the milk floats being drawn slowly back to the United Dairy on Elgin Avenue, Dalton arrived in Shirland Road. A brown, well groomed horse sluggishly passed him, its long milk round completed. Dalton looked at his watch - 9.45a.m. He was one hour and fifteen minutes early. "How could that have happened?" he asked himself and stared at it again to check the second hand was still moving.

"Sir, excuse me, do you have the time?" Dalton asked a man returning home with his newspaper, his dog in tow.

"A quarter to ten," the man replied, confirming that Dalton had somehow taken a direct route and hadn't actually seen any sights.

The milk cart with its few remaining milk bottles and mainly empty crates eased its way along in the flow of traffic, slowing everyone's pace and Dalton regained his breath from the anxiety of reaching their rendezvous spot.

Blinkered, Dalton stared towards the next corner, the one with Marylands, marked with the horse's droppings as it passed. Within seconds a man with rolled up shirt sleeves and flat cap upon his head came out with a shovel, scraped up the droppings and returned with them to fertilise his garden. Dalton didn't see him, he looked at his watch - 9.47a.m!

The milk cart passed into a blurred oblivion beyond the corner as Dalton thought again about Hetty's letter. She too had, 'enjoyed our evening together' she said and, 'Patsy and Roy were still dating'. But he knew that bit of news from Roy for he never stopped talking about his English girl. There was not even a hint in Hetty's letter that she was dating someone, so why couldn't she see him for longer than a 'while'. Not that Dalton or any of his buddies knew what the English meant by a 'while'.

As the time passed, Dalton's expectations heightened such that each person walking out from Marylands became a possibility of being Hetty and made his heart leap - even the postman heading back to the main sorting office on Lanhill Road, but only for that tiny fraction of a second it takes for realisation to dawn.

By 10.45a.m. Dalton had been fixed upon Marylands with such hope and concentration for so long that he was starting to imagine he saw her. His intensity was beginning to make him feel foolish and rising slightly from his fixation, noticed a woman looking at him as she passed. She had passed him almost an hour earlier and wondered what the stranger was still doing there. She crossed the road and Dalton's eyes for once became distracted from their focus. Older, middle aged, well set and strong like his own mother. Her arms seemingly stretched by the weight of her daily shopping expeditions. She was dressed for the occasion, being smart enough to be seen by neighbours. Long heavy overcoat belted at the waist and falling to just below the knee, heavy court shoes and a matching brown hat, round with a small rim at the front and sides but not at the back. Cumbersome and burdened she looked, whilst Dalton stood merely in his tight, thin uniform, attire more in keeping with summer than the late winter air.

The woman stopped outside her house, searched for a key and before entering, glanced back towards the foreigner, a Yank at that, still waiting on the corner. As the door closed, Dalton returned his gaze towards Maryland but there was still no sign of Hetty. Perhaps he should move down to the next corner he thought and once considered, his impulsiveness placed him there within seconds.

Down Marylands he could see the corner with Thorngate, only yards away. Beyond lay a long stretch of derelict houses, some demolished, others waiting to be; a street cleaner none the less cleaning the street, long brush in hand and three-wheeled cart at the ready to consume what he swept. Children played there, throwing balls against walls from inside which no one would complain. Young lads played within the bomb sites despite the warnings, calling to girls who would not come in. Lads taking risks just like back home on the Dragon Swamp, ignored by the girls but only partly so, for pretty smiles occasionally rewarded the mischief. As Dalton watched, a cloud drifted away from the sun to release its warmth, heating the bricks that were surprisingly smooth to his touch; there was a promise of summer now in the light.

About the same time as Dalton impulsively walked away from their rendezvous spot and headed towards Thorngate, Hetty made to get herself ready to go out. She had left it late to do so, starting casually, trying to convince herself that this was not an important encounter. Any clothes would do, she told herself, but kept mulling over what to wear. She'd been deciding for two days now and still hadn't made up her mind. She held up the new dress she had made, then an older one she always felt good in and looked into the long mirror on the back of the wardrobe door; her wedding dress hanging inside, just a few feet from her. She must tell Dalton of her plans, she thought, in fairness to him for she knew that beneath the GI soldiering bravado was a generous, sensitive man. His letter was lovely and her evening with him ... well ... one she would ... she would remember forever. She must finish their friendship properly, though Hetty couldn't understand her own logic for their friendship hadn't really started. There would have been no shortage of female company for Dalton during the weeks she hadn't replied. And he wasn't going to hang around for someone like her. He probably wouldn't even turn up, not just for a 'while' and 'a chat'. She suddenly felt stupid and wished she had been more positive in her letter, then seeing the white of her bridal gown defining the inside of her wardrobe, she felt relief. Hetty looked back at the dresses and skirts now lying on her bed, pondered a little more over the choice, then picked the prettiest skirt and blouse 'just in case'. She had just changed into them when something stopped her in her tracks.
The rap a tat tat on the street door was loud and unfamiliar and it made her breathing falter. She rushed downstairs and ran along the hallway with butterflies in her stomach, fearing someone else might reach the door first and rudely turn away the man she thought might be standing there.

She felt that her hair was a mess and her skirt bedraggled but there was no time. She flattened the second hand material against her hips in nervous response to a second knock. Then bending her slim body to keep her appearance hidden as much as possible, she slowly opened the door, peering round it to catch an early glimpse of the caller.

Dalton stood in the sunlight, his Brylcreemed hair and freshly pressed uniform making little difference to his confidence. He was nervous, as unsure as the young girl who answered the door. Catching sight of dark, lovely long strands of hair hanging away from her tilted head, Dalton knew instantly that it was Hetty and broke into a broad smile, relieved that it wasn't Mr. or Mrs. Eaglestone who answered.

"You look great!" Dalton told Hetty as the door opened fully and she stood there with bare feet and legs rising to a pleated skirt, her full blouse moving from deep breaths of anxiety.

There was a noise from the parlour, the scraping of a chair, a door opened and Mr. Eaglestone approached down the hallway.

"Wait for me, I'll come out," Hetty said nervously and quickly closed the street door.

"Who is it?" her father asked as the light from the mixed day was blocked from the passage.

"A friend Dad," Hetty said, grabbing her coat and shoes, "just a friend."

"Who?" James asked, but Hetty pretended not to hear as she slipped on her shoes in haste. "Who?" James asked again, in a tone which demanded a response. And Hetty respected her father too much not to give one.

"Dad, I'm just going for a walk, with a friend I met before Christmas, just a friend," she said again, placing her hand on her father's forearm and squeezing it as if to say, please don't worry.

Hetty slipped out before he could say anything more and knew that he would stand on the threshold, to watch her walk away with the American soldier.

Dalton too could feel Mr. Eaglestone's presence, the tall, large, upright frame in turn framed by the doorway. Dalton's own father would have made a scene there and then, in front of everybody, but not this man. He would wait for the right moment.

Curtains twitched in the house across the street. Mrs Wells had noticed the stranger, now walking away with Hetty Eaglestone. Mrs. Cave and Mrs. Green stood talking in front of number 31 and fell to silence as the two youngsters walked past. The ladies stared at the trim, V shaped back allowing their eyes to fall to the GI's snug fitting trousers. As their eyes lowered, gossip formed in their heads and the prospect of afternoon tea with neighbours or popping next door to borrow some sugar loomed large.

Hetty walked slightly ahead of Dalton and prayed he wouldn't take her hand. With her father still watching and Young Jimmy now glaring from an upstairs window, they passed the brick air raid shelter and crossed the road to cut the corner. As they walked towards Marylands the searching eyes were lost and of those who had watched, only Young Jimmy knew the identity of the man in American Army uniform.

Hetty led Dalton down Marylands, not towards Shirland but to the Harrow Road. There Dalton reached for Hetty's hand but without warning she moved away and then started to run. "Come on!" she called back, "let's catch the bus."

A number eighteen was about to leave its stop and Dalton shook himself into action and chased after her. Catching the accelerating bus Hetty hopped onto the platform and turned to watch as Dalton struggled with the increasing speed, then with a final leap he landed beside her and almost into her arms.

"You can sure run," he said panting.

Hetty was smiling at him. Dalton thought it a beautiful smile and he wanted to capture it and keep it forever.

"You might be able to march thirty something miles across Salisbury Plain," she said remembering his boasting that first night, "but you're not as quick as me," she teased.

"Okay, next time we start at the same time," Dalton said.

"Ladies first and I'll tell you when you can start running," Hetty retorted with the cheekiest of smiles and Dalton wasn't sure if his legs felt weak from the exertion or because of the warmth of her teasing.

The bus carried them away and as they sat side by side on a double seat which made their hips touch, Dalton's hand crept towards Hetty's. But before he could take hold of it, she moved hers to close the separation and gently folded her hand around his. As the reflection of the red bus passed window after shop window along the London streets, Dalton's spirit soared in Hetty's grasp and all thoughts of 'a chat' slipped from Hetty's mind.

The people at the bus stop just after Baker Street must have wondered what all the rush was about, for the GI and his English girl jumped off before the bus had even come to a halt and headed for Regent's Park, skirted it via Outer Circle and then entered by way of York Gardens. It was a world so different from that which they had just left. With its rose and spring flower beds tended by the older gardeners, the open green fields, the wide variety of trees and the large boating lake, it made for another life into which they had stepped. A wide patch of blue stretched across the city and after the dreary winter the spectacle was striking and suddenly the park benches appeared inviting and seemed to fill with people who had previously just been out for a stroll. With crocuses coming to life in the warmth and daffodils pushing upward to reach the light, Dalton and Hetty found an unoccupied bench and sat together, close together and as Dalton came still closer, Hetty slid further away until she ran out of bench and he caught up with her. But Hetty wasn't going to be seen kissing in public, someone might be watching. She sprung to her feet and said, "Come on let's walk over to the lake."

As she started along the path Dalton caught up with her but no longer wanted to hold her hand, he put his arm around her waist instead. A few seconds later he felt her arm pass around him and suddenly the world was complete, a truly wonderful place; all thoughts of home, training and his buddies switched off, for he only had space for Hetty. So preoccupied was he, that somehow he failed to notice two US Army Officers walking by. "SOLDIER!" the Major called, "take your arm from around that woman and salute."

Dalton was given a good dressing down and later reported to Zappacosta who placed him on kitchen duties for a week. The officers walked briskly on, leaving Dalton to return sheepishly to Hetty.

"Soldier, take your arm from around that woman and salute," she mimicked in an unconvincing American accent. She stood now before him, smiling, a gleam in her eye, her shapely body brimming with energy. Dalton felt dizzy, his heart raced, he knew he shouldn't but he couldn't resist. He reached forward to place both his arms around her thin waist and pulled her to him. She didn't resist, but delicately willowed towards his strong frame leaving her lips unguarded and they kissed, a long, long passionate kiss; they were in full view of everyone, but now … neither cared.

Chapter 19

Memories of Sunday Lunch

May 1943.

When the 116th Infantry Regiment started their six day march, a certain nostalgia lingered as Tidworth slipped behind - one last trudge across the plain, past Hare Warren, through Nine Mile River and over Brigmerston Field. As the early morning mist cleared so the landscape with which they had become so familiar could be seen falling away from them; the uniformity of the plough lines broken only by white clumps of chalk, whilst small coppices and white tinted tank tracks gave definition to the rolling grasslands. Then as the soldiers stepped onto a lane beside the lesser known River Avon, the chalky soil dropped from their boots and with it their last encounter with Salisbury Plain.

The move which the 116th commenced on 23rd May was part of Operation Bolero, the code name given to the build up of American troops in Britain; Bolero, the famous Ravel composition where fast music builds to a crescendo. Of the few original B Company soldiers who would survive the war, memories of Tidworth would last beyond the carnage. The red brick barracks, dances at Tedworth House, drinking at The Ram pub and the furloughs to London. The training on the Plain however would pale to insignificance in comparison to the hardships they were later to endure.

Like the rest of the 29th Division, the 116th Regiment was headed west towards Devonshire and although Brunel's Great Western Railway served the region well, someone had decided that it would be good for the men to walk. Carrying only a back pack, rifle, blanket and pup tent, the men's kit bags were transported by truck. And as they left Tidworth, fresh faced boys arrived from the US to fill the empty beds and so the build up intensified.

Three years earlier in the summer of 1940, when the Battle of Britain was raging, there were just 190,000 soldiers in the entire American Army, a smaller force than countries like Sweden or Switzerland. Yet by the cnd of 1942 there were 250,000 US troops in Britain alone and by May 1944, the number in Britain rose to 1.5 million. In the county of Wiltshire, with Tidworth, Bulford and other Camps, the British population only just out numbered the Americans by 2 to 1.

The big question mark for the British top brass was whether these hastily converted American civilians could match a German Army that had swept across Europe with such profound ease. One of Prime Minister Winston Churchill's highest generals described the Americans as 'mentally and physically soft and very green'. But General Marshall, Chief of Staff of the US Army thought otherwise.

Marshall, the highest ranking US soldier, was confident that with sufficient manpower and with the enormous industrial capacity of the North American continent behind them, the US Army could match anything and anyone. So confident were the American strategists that they still pushed for an early invasion. But the British remained cautious, an irksome characteristic as far as the Americans were concerned. But then they had to concede that the British had experienced more wars, campaigns and battles than the US Generals had eaten hot dinners.

Lieutenant General Omar Bradley had not even served overseas during the Great War. Prior to Pearl Harbour he hadn't commanded anything larger than a battalion of 800 men. Yet for the invasion Bradley would command the whole of the US First Army. The 29th Infantry Division with its fourteen thousand troops formed but a small fraction of his responsibilities.

In the late afternoon of their first day's walk towards Devon and about twenty miles from Tidworth, B Company crossed the River Wylye. The village of the same name lay just beyond the bridge, in the shallow river valley. The mill guarded the village approach just as Saint Mary's Church watched over the Bell Inn. And anyone standing on the grey stoned tower could have followed B Company's progression through the entire length of the village. As Dalton crossed the narrow road bridge beyond The Old Swan, a Great Western locomotive passed underneath. The steam billowed up on either side of him and the thunderous noise seemed to grab the bridge and shake it. Dalton watched as the train pulled up at the country station and half expected to be ordered to board it. Perhaps Zappacosta had been joking when he told them they would be walking the 150 miles. Dalton watched his captain optimistically and then the hope faded as the small, yet lean and hardy man led them up onto Wylye Down and into a large wood to bed down for the crisp May night.

Over the next three days the English countryside slipped past, changing with the onset of spring and as one county replaced another. From Wiltshire into Dorset and to houses with cement and lime rendered walls decorated with flint stones. The Dorset cottages were capped with characteristic clay tiles and their windows uncharacteristically draped with blackout curtains. As Devon approached, the hedgerows were gradually replaced by stone walls and the roofs with thatch. But unchanged were the road signs, for they had all been removed and unchanged were the children. In every county the children who watched the foreigners pass, laughed at the quiet tread of the general issue, soft, rubber soled army boots. So different to the crisp sharp step of the British Army issue hard boots.

"Are they real soldiers Mummy?" a little boy asked as the guys walked past in relaxed style, some smoking and most chatting. "They're American soldiers," the mother was heard to reply. And as the soldiers walked on, the children were left open eyed, clinging to an armful of treats.

Every step, every yard and then every mile took Dalton further from Hetty and as the distance increased so Dalton's thoughts lingered more and more on his last weekend furlough to London - his third and last from Tidworth. The weekend promised to be just as romantic as on his second furlough, when they had kissed for the first time in Regent's Park.

On the Saturday they walked hand in hand through Saint James's Park, the greenery promising to become lush and the lake alive with wildlife, camouflaging real events in the secret rooms and tunnels below. Hetty pretended to be Dalton's tour guide and teased him at his lack of knowledge. First to Buckingham Palace and laughed when he asked if she had met the Queen. Down the Mall to Whitehall with a view of Downing Street, where Dalton believed Hetty to be joking when she said Churchill lived in the little house numbered 10. To Westminster Abbey, then Westminster Bridge to gain a better view of the Houses of Parliament and of course Big Ben. Landmarks of which Dalton only had a scant knowledge and which still stood defiantly despite the bombing, though each carried its scars.

On Victoria Embankment they had stood for a while to watch the Thames glide past them, holding each other as though they might fall in should they let go. The kisses became more passionate and Hetty's reserved nature faltered ever more in Dalton's presence. Dalton told Hetty that the Thames was far narrower than he expected, even the Rappahannock River which formed the northern boundary of Middlesex County, must be at least ten times wider he told her.

'And I suppose you can swim it just as fast as you run', she teased, whereupon Dalton picked her up and pretended to throw her into the river.

Hetty's 'no, no, don't Dalton, everyone's watching' seemed to spur him on. Devilment overcame them both, she screamed and laughed and fell back almost reckless into his grasp. Pleasure ran with the excitement and pulsed at the touch of their bodies, tempting Dalton to ask Hetty to go to a hotel with him, but he somehow managed to suppress the urge. His restraint later reminded Dalton of something his Momma used to say, about leaving a beautiful flower unpicked in the field.

They walked back towards Paddington via streets which all looked alike to Dalton, bearing names which he could not recognise or remember; he was lost in Hetty's world. With

Hetty beside him, holding his hand everything else became insignificant and never properly in focus. She was to Dalton like newly formed ice on the Dragon Run, pure, intricate and fragile. Ice which could be carefully raised from the surface, to touch his lips, melt and refresh him. Reflecting on the day, Dalton could not remember being happier. But the Sunday contrasted in the extreme, the memory of which overcast everything and the dark cloud of events followed him all the way to Devon.

At the city of Exeter the men came closer to the sea than they had been since arriving at Greenock eight months earlier. Exeter had been seriously bomb damaged in May '42, losing 2,000 buildings. The damage on the High Street and adjoining roads was in evidence, leaving the Cathedral isolated, still standing in its full glory. It was a retaliatory raid for the RAF's bombing of Lubeck, where 234 Wellington and Stirling bombers had pulverised the Baltic port in the first major bombing success against a German city. Lubeck with 150,000 people had 45% of its buildings seriously damaged or destroyed and 15,000 of its residents made homeless. Unlike Exeter's Cathedral, Lubeck's burned to the ground.

Reaching the Exe Estuary, B Company crossed the bridge and gained a view down towards the English Channel where old leisure and fishing boats rocked at their moorings. The tide was on the ebb and soon boats would be left stranded, as Dalton had been that Sunday at the Eaglestone's. Their masts leaning towards the deeper stream, mud soaked keels and decking sitting uncomfortably.

Stepping onto the other side of the Exe River the men finally entered Devonshire and after bedding down near Great Haldon, were within a day's walk of Ivy Bridge Camp. As the last day's march began Dartmoor loomed ahead and with every step, the dark moor with its cap of grey nimbostratus cloud seemed to reflect Dalton's deepening mood. The valley of the Exe River had seemed by comparison relatively bright, but here the cloud was dense and clung to the high ground as if an extension of it.

Dalton watched the A38 slide underneath his feet just as the paving slabs of Thorngate had done as he approached the Eaglestone home that Sunday. Stomach knotted and mouth dry arriving at Hetty's invitation for Sunday lunch. 'Come in son,' Hetty's mother had said as she opened the street door.

Her show of affection surprised him and released some of his tension, but it was short lived.

Mr. Eaglestone stood further down the hallway with a posture bereft of warmth. Yet despite his antipathy, understood what it was to be a soldier far from home. He nodded at his unwelcome guest before entering the front room, shutting the door and switching on the wireless. James Eaglestone didn't intend to share the same table with a Yank. But allowing him into his house to eat his food and spend time with Hetty were concessions which were not lost on Dalton.

No it wasn't Mr. Eaglestone who crushed Dalton's spirit and drove him to leave the house, it was her brother.

Dalton remembered being no more than half way down the hallway when he was stopped by Young Jimmy. He stood in his way, expressionless at first, dangerous somehow but only for a split second before he thrust his arm forward to shake Dalton's hand.

'You must be Dalton,' Young Jimmy said knowing full well who he was and took Dalton's hand in a vice like grip. Dalton wasn't sure if the gesture portrayed immense welcome or immense dislike for no one had ever gripped his hand so tight. Cricket developed strong hands, the hard ball pounded and thrown at high speeds, but then Dalton's hands had worked horse drawn ploughs and he matched every pound of pressure that Young Jimmy could exert.

'Come through, come through,' Young Jimmy said, a little taken aback as he unclasped his hand from Dalton's.

He pointed towards the parlour, walking in front to 'lead the way'. Dalton noticed the tension in Jimmy's shoulders - fit, strong shoulders, those of a sportsman. Hetty was busy preparing lunch in the parlour. She smiled at Dalton as he entered behind her brother, but didn't move to kiss him. He sensed her anxiety and merely reached to lightly touch her hand, but the gesture didn't go unnoticed by anyone.

'Come out for a smoke in the smoke!' Jimmy joked as he directed Dalton towards the back garden, a yard by Dalton's experience and his reference didn't go down well.

Except for the chicken run, every square inch of the garden was covered with flower beds. Dalton looked at the roses with their young shoots, buds, some nearly in bloom and recognized the care with which they had been tended. The yard was probably no more than forty feet long and as wide as the house, maybe fifteen feet and each yard was separated from the next by a low wall. Beyond the back wall were more yards, some with air raid shelters and the backs of houses to which they belonged, houses bearing an Elgin Avenue address.

Young Jimmy eyed Dalton closely as he looked at the roses.

'Hetty likes red roses,' Dalton remarked.

'Does she?' Jimmy replied with a tone Dalton couldn't quite understand.

'The yards,' Jimmy said in a somewhat mocking copy of Dalton's referral 'are normally used to grow as much veg as possible. But my father grows roses!' he added with a sarcasm which surprised Dalton. There were aspects of his own father he disliked, flying off the handle for one, but spoke of it to no one and certainly never to a stranger.

'It's a pretty garden,' Dalton said trying to lighten the atmosphere.

Jimmy thought the comment weak and off the point.

'It means my mother has to work that much harder to feed us all,' he stated dogmatically. And Dalton now understood a little more about the family. 'But you wouldn't understand about food shortages of course,' Jimmy added with a penetrating glare, which Dalton ignored.

'Warm day, probably bring more buds to bloom,' Dalton said touching one of the climbing roses on the trellis which separated the rose beds from the concrete. His touch was not unlike James Eaglestone's and it seemed to annoy Jimmy.

'If it wasn't for people growing their own and the Women's Land Army the nation would starve,' he said in a manner bordering on irritation.

Dalton wanted to add 'and the supplies coming in from the States' but held his tongue.

As Dalton walked through the patchwork quilt of fields in Devon he saw women working the land and was reminded of the turn of events at the Eaglestone household.

After a few seconds of awkward silence Jimmy went on to talk about the county cricketers who had volunteered for the RAF and that 'Paul Brooks volunteered for the fire service, he's my best friend,' Jimmy added in a manner which suggested Dalton should know already.

Hetty had told Dalton about Jimmy's cricketing potential, but he couldn't remember any mention of Paul Brooks. He wondered why Jimmy was so determined to force the name upon him.

There were cricket pitches even in the smallest of villages across the southern counties and it seemed to Dalton that at every bend in the narrow roads something lay waiting to remind him of his conversation with Jimmy.

'Your daddy does building work and air raid patrol doesn't he?' Dalton asked, trying to keep the conversation on the war effort which by comparison now seemed a more comfortable topic.

'Paul and I went right through school together,' Jimmy continued ignoring the reference to his father and then proceeded to detail their progress to the giddy heights of the national sport. It meant little to Dalton but he tried to look interested and when Middlesex County Cricket Club was mentioned did his best to look impressed. Lords and the likes sure sounded high and mighty.

'It was through school and then cricket which brought Hetty and Paul together,' Jimmy reflected, looking more relaxed now, as if finally in control.

As Dalton remembered Jimmy's cleverly rehearsed line he kicked out at a large piece of granite that had been dislodged from the kerb side. It bruised his foot just like the words had bruised his heart and although his foot pained him for a few days, the agony in his heart lasted much longer.

'He only lives round the corner,' Jimmy added at almost a whisper as though divulging information which Dalton had long been waiting to hear.

Dalton was hanging on every word now and Jimmy knew it. As Dartmoor's hard intrusive hulk rose up above the column of men, Dalton recalled the words that dealt the final body blow and which pierced his heart. He tried to blank them from his mind but the sight of the harsh wind-swept moor chilled his soul just as Jimmy's next words had done.

'I expect you know that Paul and Hetty are getting married next month,' Jimmy said, almost squaring up to the man he hated.

Dalton was stunned. So Paul Brooks was Hetty's fiancé, "Hetty's fiancé," Dalton kept repeating to himself as his feet hit the Devon road. "Her fiancé, her fiancé," he said again and again more loudly and his close buddies started to wonder if the 150 mile walk was starting to send him mad. "To be her husband," he thudded and stomped and his footfall almost became as loud as that of the British.

Paul Brooks had been thrust into Dalton's life just as the hot magma had once been thrust into the earth's crust to now form the resilient moor. And likewise, Paul appeared as a bastion of stability rising above him, seemingly capable of weathering the challenges and standing proud in circumstance so long evolved.

Dalton remembered feeling very sick as he absorbed Jimmy's words and as his colour paled so he had detected a smile across Jimmy's face. Dalton's gut reaction was to walk out. He left the garden without another word and entered the parlour intending to 'make tracks' and quickly. Yet Hetty had stopped him, for her expression said so much and her silent, pensive stance softened his will. In Dalton's memory she looked like one of the spring flowers on the Devon roadside, delicate and easily broken should a man stray from his path.

Jimmy was standing now in the doorway, his athletic frame blocking out the spring sunshine, relaxed and happy. Dalton looked back at Hetty so fragile and unsure and simply smiled one of his broad smiles. He stayed where he was, Jimmy's eyes burning into his back, to feast himself upon her, yearning to take her in his arms. Despite her brother, Hetty radiated his smile back, flicked her hair and turned quickly to place the food on the table. The swirl of her skirt had barely caught up with the turn before she was off to get something else. Dalton watched her every move and tried to remind himself of the affection she had shown him and that he was there at Hetty's invitation, not Jimmy's.

The atmosphere in the parlour could have been cut with the knife that Ethel wielded to slice the meat. But despite his isolation and the problems his presence was obviously causing within the family, Dalton considered that the girl his eyes unflinchingly followed must have invited him home for a reason.

Yet when Dalton finally arrived at Ivy Bridge Camp on the 28th May, he was just as unaware of the reason for his invitation to Sunday lunch as Hetty was of the conversation in the garden.

Chapter 20

The Mantelpiece Clock

May/June 1943.

When Hetty closed the door on Dalton after the tense Sunday lunch, she returned to the parlour where all but her father sat. Her sister, brother and mother were talking in her absence and fell quiet when she entered. Jimmy held his pipe thoughtfully, whilst the woman folk let their cigarettes burn aimlessly, wondering how to start the conversation.

Hetty ran water into the thin, aluminium kettle and placed it on the gas to boil. A cup of tea for her father and anyone else who wanted one seemed like a good idea. She pushed the spoon deep into the tin of Brook Bond tea, reflecting the depth of her thoughts. They liked Mazawattee but after the company's New Cross factory was bombed they had changed to PG Tips. Hetty withdrew the tea spoon and shook the Sheffield steel until the brown leaves were just rising in a slight hump, adding one for each person and one for the brown, china tea pot. Tea - the staple drink of the nation, carried all the way from India, through war zones and evading the U Boats to maintain the British fighting spirit.

Hetty sensed each of her family looking at the other, questions ruminating in their heads, unsure of which to put first; whilst James's chickens, the Rhode Island Reds and the black and white Leg Horns, did the same over seeds outside in the 'yard'. Her father sensibly remained in the front room, avoidance of his family seemingly the best option.

Hetty wondered if she should have gone with Dalton to the station and returned when the dust had settled. But she was on self destruct after the terrible atmosphere during

Dalton's visit and had remained to await the outcome, her guilt demanding it.

"Well darlin, you've got us all wonderin," her sister said breaking the silence before taking a long awaited draw on what was left of her fag.

Hetty held her breath, but nothing followed. She walked out of the room and to the front door, opened it and looked up the street. Dalton was long gone, but she wished he wasn't. Hetty had wanted him to stay longer but he had to get back to Paddington in time for the GI special. Reflecting on the name for the Tidworth train brought a much needed smile to her face. Mind made up, she closed the black painted wood against the sunshine and strode resolutely back down the dark hallway into the parlour; the kettle about to boil, the whistle preparing to wake the dead.

"I love him," she announced into the smoke saturated air that hung above the gathering.

"Oh my gaud!" Edith exclaimed standing up and making for the door. "I'd better check on Gina," and left the room in a hurry.

"Look, Dalton's gone and he's not coming back," Jimmy said coldly to his sister.

"What do you mean not coming back?" Hetty demanded, wondering what her brother had said to him in the garden.

"Like he said, his division is moving to Devon. It doesn't take a genius to work out that there's going to be an invasion soon!"

"What's that got to do with it?" Hetty asked with eyes filling up.

Jimmy was glad of the opportunity to expand his point but his mother intervened.

"Do you love him more than Paul?" Ethel asked her daughter quietly.

"Oh for God's sake Mum!" Jimmy shouted scraping back his chair as though to leave, but changed his mind and remained a few feet from the table, seething and breathing heavy, his hands on the verge of shaking.

"Look, he's an infantryman, when the invasion starts he might last two weeks if he's lucky."

"No he's ..." but Jimmy wouldn't let Hetty finish.

"What future can he offer you?" he asked her forcefully, staring with such penetration, that Hetty could not look him in the eye.

And she couldn't answer his question either, for she could see no future. The British knew better than most that an infantryman's life was short lived.

"With Paul you have a future and a good income," Jimmy said pausing to take a deep breath, for air seemed to be evading him, his chest tight. "You've known Paul all your life," Jimmy continued, his sentences coming in sharp spurts, "he's my best friend, you're bloody well getting married, the wedding's in four weeks time, you can't cancel it now, we'll all look bloody stupid, not just you!" Jimmy finished with rising disbelief, his anger threatening to engulf him.

The kettle had started to boil, the whistle building to such a crescendo that it could no longer be ignored. Jimmy lunged towards the cooker and almost threw the offending item to one side, the racket from which was driving him to distraction.

Hetty could see his hands shaking; she had seen it before but never to develop so quickly. She was surprised at his reaction, expecting a tirade from her mother, not from Jimmy.

"You shouldn't have let him in Mum," Jimmy said after a pause, his voice quivering, slipping more out of control. "If he was half the man he should be ..." gesturing towards the front room, "he would have forbidden it."

Ethel looked at her son, searching for something within him she might never find, for her dotage had stopped it from developing. She wanted to prevent her son speaking but then when had she ever said enough was enough to him?

"If I'd known he was more than a passing fancy I would have thrown him out, made him wish he'd never set eyes on you," Jimmy said tensing his muscles subconsciously, which made his rolled up shirt sleeves push out.

With tears overflowing now, Hetty got up from the table. Her brother frightened her when he was like this, he needed a good cuppa and she needed space to think. Pouring the water into the tea pot she replaced the lid and sat the tea cosy over to let it brew. Then turning back towards her mother and brother, "I do love Paul, I love him very much," she said trying to calm the atmosphere and pausing to find her words ... "and Paul is a lovely man ..."

Jimmy looked up at Hetty standing between him and the mottled grey gas stove, still hot from the intense flame; she was coming round, finally seeing sense, he thought.

"I know I can make him very happy and he will always look after me, but ..."

"Fine then," Jimmy butted in "so forget this loser, he'll be dead or in bits by the summ ..."

His words drifted to nothing, perhaps because his mother was glaring at him in a way he had never seen, or likely because James Eaglestone had entered, wondering where his afternoon cuppa was.

"Sorry Dad, we've been talking," Hetty said trying to hide her blotched face and swelling eyes.

"No trouble," James said as he added milk to a cup, placed the tea strainer over and poured in the well brewed tea. The sugar added, he departed without a second glance at his family.

Hetty sat down searching for the words she wanted to say, pulling them from a place free of her family's shaping.

"I love Paul very much," Hetty said again, quietly continuing, tears again running down her cheeks, "but, but I don't love him the way I love Dalton. It's different, he's different, and I've never felt this way before, not ever, not about anyone." Her sentence petered out to a whisper, her upset overcoming her ability to speak.

A London sparrow alighted on the wall outside the open parlour door, looked in at the sorry scene before suddenly flying off as Jimmy jumped to his feet and stormed out. They could hear him stomping upstairs, hand slapping down on the dark wood banister as he went, they followed his foot fall as he walked into Hetty's bedroom and heard the wardrobe doors being thrown open. He grabbed Hetty's wedding dress and almost ripping the material from the hanger, flew back downstairs with it, his rage building uncontrollably.

With an image of his best friend, jilted at the altar, he thrust the white, pristine dress into Hetty's face.

"You've bought the bloody dress!" he shouted, crunching it up in his strong hands before throwing it onto the table. The dress fell limply over the table top, became dirty from the contents of the ash tray and then slid slowly and silently to the kitchen floor.

Hetty dropped her head and started to cry uncontrollably.

"Oh what have I done?" she murmured.

"The wedding cake is waiting for us to collect for God's sake!" Jimmy persisted with his arm outstretched and pointing with his finger as though at Tregeser's bakery.

"Oh Mum!" Hetty cried and put her hands over her ears.

Hetty's child-like plea seemed to tear Ethel from her restraint.

"Shut up ... SHUT UP!" Ethel shouted as Jimmy started to say something else. He appeared stunned, his mouth dropped open but no more words issued forth; she had dared say no to him. He stormed out like a petulant school boy but instead of leaving the house as the women expected, went into the front room. Had they looked in, it would have been a rare sight, father and son together, probably the first time for five years; the two of them in silence, the voice on the radio unheard, merely a background to their thoughts.

"Dalton loves me, he told me so," Hetty said through the sobbing, alone with her mother.

"I wanted to tell him I loved him but couldn't because of Paul. But I wanted to. And when I finish with Paul I will tell him, on the phone, in a letter, somehow I will tell him. I'll go to Devon with Pat and speak to him. I don't care, I just want him to know. I don't want to lose him Mum. I don't want to lose him," she said turning and crying into her mother's arms.

As Ethel cradled her daughter, it felt awkward, for she hadn't done so since Hetty was very, very small. But she thought less of the awkwardness and more of her daughter, childless as she would be with Paul and of the love letters she still kept. If things worked out, then she would make sure Hetty didn't settle in America. And if they didn't work out, then perhaps one of the cricket boys, Dick Martin or Eddie Routledge will come back from the RAF and win back Hetty's heart and live nearby. They could run errands for her and the grandchildren visit their Nan. And there was always Stan Kirby, Ethel said to herself, as an afterthought. "Come on ..." she encouraged her daughter, "let's clear up this mess and make a start on tea."

Ethel persuaded Hetty not to rush over to Paul and tell him quite yet. But to 'wait a while then maybe next week, when he calls by, take him in the front room, for a chat'.
Hetty wasn't sure if 'chat' was the right word. She knew Paul would be devastated, for how do you tell someone you don't want to marry them anymore, and what if he asks the reason? Always best to just tell the truth, her mother said.
As the days passed and with her daughter still of the same mind, Ethel went to the American embassy to check on Dalton Roy Slaughter. She didn't want her daughter getting involved with a married man. Word had soon got around about the Yanks; their bravado, claiming they were single, lived in Hollywood and owned a Chevrolet. No one knew Ethel had gone there and no one knew the outcome, save Ethel of course.
James Eaglestone had been well informed of developments in the parlour, yet said nothing. Army life had taught him not to piss into the wind and why break a wall down when you can go round it. Ethel had reassured him that nothing would come of the new friendship, Hetty was already coming round. She would soon realise that Paul Brooks was the right choice. Good that his wife had told Hetty to wait a while before rushing round to Oakington.
James was a busy man by day and by night and his daughter's whims and fancies were best left in Ethel's capable hands, for like him, his wife thought the world of Paul. Then there was the news from the war to keep abreast of, important developments, historic at that. And James

considered that any man worth the reference should have knowledge of things worldly. The month of May brought a wealth of good news, the complete surrender of German and Italian forces in North Africa and capture of troops on the scale of Stalingrad. The RAF had breached dams on the Ruhr with bouncing bombs causing extensive damage to one of Germany's most important industrial areas. Even the U boat war was beginning to be won. James knew the tide was turning in Russia and that Europe would surely follow, yet he was blatantly unaware of his wife's manoeuvrings.

"Have you been to see Mr. and Mrs. Brooks?" Hetty asked her mother when she came in from work one late May evening.

"No luv, why?" Ethel asked.

"Just that Mrs Brooks came round to see if you were in, said Paul would be calling by to see me for a chat tonight."

"Strange," Ethel replied and hurried away down the passage with her bits and pieces. She looked flustered mainly because she had been found out; the manager of the Red Cross shop had discovered the hidden compartment at the bottom of her shopping trolley, filled with items stolen from the shop and had given her the sack.

Paul arrived at nine, or thereabouts, for it was only just getting dark. He had always been polite to Hetty's parents and this night was no exception despite it all.

Ethel smiled and spoke back as though nothing was wrong. Hetty wondered how her mother could look and sound so relaxed, for Hetty could barely look Paul in the face.

A slim, handsome man with dark hair and sharp features, Paul was the catch of the neighbourhood. His skills in cricket were as much down to his intelligence as his co-ordination and it wasn't surprising that most of the girls wanted to date him. Yet Paul had wanted only Hetty. And he still wanted her; wanted her with such a passion that life would never be the same without her.

Paul's one and only sibling, an older brother with whom he was very close, had been in the Navy. Whilst serving, his brother had acquired gangrene and one by one, every limb had to be amputated. Left with just his torso, Paul's brother soon passed on and Paul became the focus of his parents' love and Hetty the focus of his.

Paul followed Hetty into the front room, followed her light step as he had so often done, since they were small. The rectangular oak dining table with its high backed chairs bringing back memories of Sunday evening teas with the other cricketers, the fire blazing, card games, the banter and vying for Hetty's attention. How proud he had been to win Hetty's heart over all the others. The black horse ornaments were still there, so too the bronze firemen looking expectant; hoses held at the ready, bracing themselves for the reaction. Between them, the mantelpiece clock ticked and the long black pointed hands pointed to something after nine.

Neither sat down and after an embarrassing pause, Hetty managed to look into Paul's dark eyes and knew it would be impossible to say what she had intended. Such a kind and gentle man, he didn't deserve to be hurt. She had always respected him. Paul showed the professionalism that her brother lacked and the commitment her brother would never have, not just to his sport but to everything, including the woman in his life. She felt terribly guilty at her meetings with Dalton, berating herself for being shallow and deceitful. Her brother would express it differently and she tried to push away the language which now seemed to fit her so well.

Hetty could only take Paul's hands in hers and as she did so was reminded that she had discovered something very beautiful with Dalton. That her love for Paul was different; he was to her like a precious friend and to marry him would be wrong. For she would always remember the way she had felt with Dalton and would long for that feeling for the rest of her life. Thus as she stood there with Paul looking into his dear face, Hetty tried to find the words she had prepared so well, yet could not find to speak. Paul ignored her struggle, he loved her too much to provoke that which was stirring within her. He withdrew his hands from hers and took his fiancée in his arms, holding her for longer than he had ever done before without speaking. Then with just the sound of the mantelpiece clock ticking away their final seconds together, he kissed Hetty delicately on the cheek and quietly left the house without a word to anyone.

Chapter 21

The Frantic Telephone Call

Ivy Bridge, Devon, June/July 1943.

After the torment of Jimmy's words in the garden, the six day march and leaving London further behind, Dalton tried to focus on home. Momma's cooking, Robbie and the trouble he was likely getting into and what Edward and Daddy would be doing; the plowing was over and the corn planted so they were probably thinning the crop right now. He recalled the last moments on the porch with Lucy and found it hard to believe that it was almost a year since he had last walked on Virginian soil.

Normally fun-loving and confident, Dalton was becoming melancholic, even unsure of himself. He considered that Hetty would not finish her long standing relationship for someone she had only known a few weeks. Yes he had told Hetty that he loved her, but there had been many such men in her life. She was engaged to be married. Married to the boy round the corner, her choice, the family's choice and Jimmy's best friend. Mr. Eaglestone's choice for sure and Dalton knew it. "Cricket, what kind of a sport was that?" he asked to no one in particular as he tried to settle into his new home by the side of the Exeter Road.

The 1st Battalion of the 116th Regiment was the only infantry unit stationed at Ivy Bridge. The 2nd Battalion was at Bridestowe and the 3rd Battalion in Plymouth; all within a few miles of each other and quickly reachable for the regiment's commander, Colonel Charles Draper Canham.

1st Battalion's camp lay beside the A38 on the right when heading into Ivy Bridge from Exeter, just 600 yards from the town - named after the old stone bridge across the River Erme, still covered in ivy and standing slightly upstream from the new one.

The A38, the Exeter Road, carried almost exclusively military vehicles. Few businesses were deemed important enough to receive fuel rations, not even the Blackler family newsagents on Fore Street. The first Nissen huts were no more than a few yards off the road behind the wire perimeter fence. Each hut was capable of housing twenty-four men, though companies were not yet at full strength. There were twelve bunks, six down each side and Dalton again shared with Paul Kennedy, Paul on the top bunk of course.

B and C Companies were in the first field by the road, then further up the slope beyond a hawthorn hedge were A and D Companies; each company eventually consisting of some 200 men. Beyond them, the fields sloped more steeply, being dissected by the main railway line before finally reaching the steep sided edge of Dartmoor. To the right of the camp, when looking north from their barracks, the eleven hundred feet high Western Beacon rose up and provided for a good two mile training run to and from its summit.

Nine year old Noel Blackler, the paper boy, knew the location of every company hut so well he could have delivered the papers blindfolded. Each evening he dragged his newspapers the 800 yards from the family shop on Fore Street to the camp, the bag almost as big as he was. Designed for an adult, Noel tied the straps up two or three times and still it only just missed scraping the ground. As Noel approached, the GIs could see his head, forearms and feet sticking out beyond the enormous bulging bag.

With up to twenty-four men in a hut, there were always several papers to be taken to each. The Daily Mirror being the most popular choice because of the comic strip where Jane found it difficult to keep her clothes on. Noel loved the Americans, for they loved children. Walking back from delivering the papers his pockets would be bulging with goodies. The GIs virtually adopted the friendly kids, who would stalk into the woods to watch them train, or hang around camp to talk, play games and be 'inspired by the positive, fun loving attitudes'. Invited into the mess to eat, into the cinema to watch films and the gym to see the keen guys work out, Noel almost became a member of 1st Battalion. The gym was always interesting for there was a black boxer who Noel thought to be Joe Lewis. 'Will you teach me to box Mr. Lewis?' Noel so often asked and 'Joe' always had an excuse as to why he couldn't.

The 1st Battalion together with the other smaller military units stationed in the area had almost doubled the population of the town and businesses were booming, not least the pubs. After Tidworth with just The Ram pub, Ivy Bridge was like an alcoholic oasis; the Sportsmans Inn, the Kings Arms, the London Hotel with its taproom and main bar, the Bridge Inn, White Horse, Duke of Cornwall, the Julian and even the Imperial. Eight pubs in all, excluding the ones outside of town. Just how much drink could the normally small population consume? Yet all eight were full as soon as the Yanks could escape from their camps in the evening and weekends.

The nearest pub to 1st Battalion, on the very eastern most edge of town was the Sportsmans Inn, run by Vera Luckham. Vera was a landlady with a head on her shoulders. Born into the trade, she was adept at picking the right clientele; it was the officers she encouraged and she looked after them well.

'The troublesome ones can go elsewhere,' she would say.

When the spirits ran out she would declare, 'no more spirits tonight gentlemen' but 'we still have plenty of beer', she would hastily add.

And when the beer ran out she made sure there were cards, dominoes, billiards and a roaring fire to keep the men from straying elsewhere. Likely the best entertainment when dry of alcohol was her father-in-law. The British ex-navy man would sit by the fire and play cribbage with the Americans whilst telling them how he had won the Great War single-handed.

Of all the customers who frequented the Sportsmans, it was Zappacosta, the B Company Captain who was loudest. Slapping his change onto the counter, calling for service and then conversing with a volume sufficient for everyone to hear; he could be heard not just in the public bar but also in the darts bar and perhaps even in the private room with its own small serving hatch.

The ranks learned to pass the Sportsmans by and go to the London Hotel or over the Erme River to the main part of the town where choice was not a problem. The first watering hole over the Erme was the Kings Arms, just down on the left hand side and it became very popular with the enlisted men.

With so many 'watering holes' as the Brits described them, there were few B Company men who didn't at sometime or other get to see the inside of the 'hutch'. The hutch lay opposite the guard room and jail, close to the Exeter Road camp entrance but tucked away behind the sentry box. The 'hutch' was where the military police stuck the drunks they rounded up in town. B Company man Drumheller knew it well and Dalton not at all.

The barracks were no match to those at Tidworth, with flimsy tin huts in place of double brick walls and tiled timber roofs. The rain sweeping in from the south-west hammered down on the corrugated metal roofs and during particularly heavy deluges created a thundering sound within. Some of the men couldn't stand the noise, but for Dalton it reminded him of home where just the cypress shingles and thin timber slats protected the family from the elements. Lying listening to the sound of God's replenishing rain Dalton could almost believe that his sisters and brothers were close by. With thoughts drifting back over the ocean, Dalton longed to fall asleep surrounded by Virginian country sounds. To listen to the frogs, the 'who, who are you' of the hoot owl and the whip-poor-will. And what he would have given to wake up to Momma's hot biscuits. Even the predictability of a day's plowing in the heat and humidity seemed like heaven compared to the endless training in England. The weather seemed forever damp and rarely anything other than chilly, but the worst part was the growing inevitability of combat. Colonel Canham, Commander of the 116th Regiment, let it be known that according to his estimation only one in three of his men would be going home.

Dalton looked around at his closer buddies in the Nissen hut and wondered which two of the six would more likely make it. He felt sure Clayton and Allbritton would. Clayton was an old head on young shoulders, he read almost as much as he smoked, his history was good but he also seemed to know everything about military weapons. Allbritton was equally sharp, able to weigh up situations and make a quick decision. Allbritton wasn't going to do something stupid as Dalton considered himself capable of doing. Too impulsive he thought, that was Dalton Roy Slaughter.

In Paul Kennedy, Dalton just saw a best buddy whom he loved like a brother and who had replaced Robbie as his closest friend and confidant. Paul would make it back, he had to.

Dalton wasn't sure about Austen's chances and of his five buddies it was Ted he worried most about. The big guy would present a large, slow moving target for a German sniper and somehow Dalton felt that Ted's childhood sweetheart wasn't going to get her man back. One thing Dalton knew for sure, Ted's daddy, who had cried on their departure from Blanding, would sure as hell cry tears for his son if he lost him. Quite simply, Dalton just wanted all six to make it, and being an 'optimistic Yank' he stuck with that notion.

Dalton had first observed death from the rail of the Queen Mary as men from the Curacoa drowned in the Atlantic, but in Devon, death came closer - on Dartmoor, at Slapton Sands and even in the Kings Arms. More GIs were killed in training between July 1943 and May 1944 than on Omaha Beach on D-Day. Some of the boys died by sheer unavoidable accident, many died from negligence and some were murdered.

The meeting between Prime Minister Churchill and President Roosevelt in Casablanca in the January of '43 set in motion the planning for D-Day and the greatest amphibious invasion in history. Lieutenant General Morgan of the British Army, the chief planner said of his task, 'I am to plan nothing less than the re-conquest of Europe'. The invasion planning for 'Operation Overlord' would eventually involve 3.5 million men, 1,100 warships, 4,000 landing craft, 1,600 other vessels and 15,000 aircraft and gliders. It had to succeed or Europe would be lost, there could be no second attempt. With memories of withdrawing 340,000 British and French troops from Dunkirk, of leaving thousands of New Zealanders, Australians and British troops behind in Greece and even further back to the stalemate of the Great War, the British held out for a spring '44 invasion. Thus the US 29th Infantry Division became known as 'England's Own' for they remained in England for twenty months. Dalton and his buddies became the best trained troops in the US Army, with three years from inception to the day they stepped onto Omaha Beach in Normandy.

Ivy Bridge camp lay on the southern edge of Dartmoor which replaced Salisbury Plain as their training ground. The men had never encountered a terrain like it. The 400 square miles of bleak, desolate upland, boasted only one main settlement, the foreboding Dartmoor Prison. Built to house French Captives from the Napoleonic Wars, it was now home to the most serious offenders. A good choice of location, for not only was it isolated but the harsh, barren moor would be difficult to escape. Despite being just 2,000 feet at its highest, Dartmoor was uncannily chilly, even in summer, compared to the surrounding coastal lowlands.

Through late spring and early summer of '43 as B Company trained on Dartmoor, Stalin's forces capitalised on their winter war of attrition and by July had pushed the Germans back to the borders of the Ukraine and Belarus, some 200 miles west of Moscow. A July engagement near Kharkov involving two million men and 6,000 tanks, forced the Germans into full retreat and although Hitler remained optimistic, his generals were conceding that Russia was lost.

With Russia's rapid advance, the Allies were anxious to open a second front and further stretch Germany's forces as a precursor to the Normandy Invasion. Thus on 10th July, British and American troops landed on the Italian island of Sicily, a stone's throw from the mainland. The invasion of Italy, 'the soft underbelly of the Axis' as described by Prime Minister Churchill, had commenced.

Whilst servicemen from both sides battled on the Russian and Italian fronts, B Company slogged up onto the moor to wait their turn, to survive or die as chance dictated. Wait as they must, to lead the most important invasion of the war, the largest in history and to experience their bloodiest of days. Yet for too many men amongst the swelling ranks of American servicemen in the UK, the savagery of training was as close as they would come to the grotesque and unforgiving savagery of the real thing.

Hetty's letter with the British Royal Mail stamps precisely positioned in the top right hand corner was placed into Dalton's hand as he stood outside his hut close to the Exeter Road. He was looking up at Western Beacon wondering if he had the energy to run up it again. Then as he realised from whom the letter had come, adrenaline filled him such that he might have reached the beacon even before the fastest of the company runners.

Dalton quickly walked past the PX and up beyond the barracks of A and C Companies to give himself some space. Whether he became angry, sad or even close to tears he wanted to keep it to himself. But the optimistic streak within him couldn't help but flush to the surface as he slipped his finger into the small unsealed gap, a seal which Hetty must herself have moistened. He could smell her scent, see her smile and the flick of her hair as he pushed back the flap to reach inside and reveal her thoughts, his eyes scanning, darting up and down, tracking the lines and curves to form the words she conveyed.

He sat himself upon an old railway sleeper, the appearance of the sun drying the damp grass, his legs weak, his breath shortening. Slowly he read each word, savouring them, ensuring their meaning sank deep into his memory. It was better than his wildest dreams, the most beautiful letter he would ever receive in his life. She loved him and would travel down to see him with Pat Harrison, the last weekend of July. "She loves me," he whispered, "she loves me," he said louder, "she loves ME!" he shouted ... but there was no one else in the field and Dalton told only Paul Kennedy the news, for as Dalton's momma said, 'you shouldn't go counting your chickens before they're hatched'. And he knew the pressure Hetty must now be under, from everyone, friends and family, but particularly family.

London.

Hetty's Uncle Len, Lucy Chapman's youngest son, hadn't been able to attend Hetty and Paul's wedding and so called by on the following Sunday to congratulate them. It proved embarrassing but Len Chapman wasn't alone in not knowing that the wedding had been cancelled. News normally spread quickly around the London streets where family and friends lived and died from one generation to the next. But there were always those to whom inexplicably, news didn't seem to reach. Len went home to tell his family about the turn of events and so helped to spread the next chapter of gossip, the reason for the cancellation. Hetty had met someone else, a GI, she had given up Paul Brooks for a GI! Had fallen in love with a Yank, love at first sight so it was said.

Paul had bought both the engagement and wedding rings at the same time and Hetty felt it only right she should return them, they were expensive and at least Paul could sell the rings, for how could either person keep such symbols of intent? But Hetty could not bring herself to hand the jewellery back to Paul personally,

"It would be like throwing them in his face," she told her sister.

Thus one evening when she felt sure Paul would be practising at Lords, Hetty walked round to Paul's home in Oakington Road and gave them to his mum.

Hetty also wanted to return the beautiful diamond studded brooch that Paul had bought her, but "Paul would like you to keep it," Mrs. Brooks insisted as she stood at the door to talk with her once future daughter-in-law.

Hetty looked down and fiddled with the glistening jewellery and didn't know how to respond. It was a lovely, forgiving gesture, typical of Paul, she thought.

"Paul's joined up," Mrs. Brooks said quietly as Hetty maintained her gaze on the brooch.

"Oh, I am sorry, so sorry," Hetty said, shocked and remorseful.

"Nothin' to do with you sweet'art, he's bin thinking of joining the RAF for a long time," Mrs. Brooks reassured her. What seemed like minutes passed as each stood silently at the threshold.

"I ..." Hetty paused, not sure how to express herself, "I hope he takes care," she said looking at Mrs. Brooks who knew exactly what Hetty was trying to say.

"He'll be fine, it's what he's always wanted to do, so don't you go worrying," Mrs. Brooks said and her compassion almost brought Hetty to tears.

But no matter what Mrs. Brooks said or didn't say, Hetty convinced herself that Paul had volunteered because of her and she felt 'terribly, terribly guilty.'

When she returned home to tell her parents, James Eaglestone could sense his daughter's turmoil.

"We know already sweetheart," James said "Paul came round to say goodbye, said it was something he had always wanted to do. Said he'd got bored of chasing after fires caused by the Luftwaffe and wanted to chase the planes instead, had a few scores to settle."

Hetty smiled despite herself, she could imagine Paul saying that, but wished she had been home when he came to say goodbye.

"He's a bright lad, he'll make pilot or air crew," James said, but it wasn't what Hetty wanted to hear. "He would have joined up whatever happened," James added and Hetty touched her father's hand for the love those few words conveyed. James let the touch go. He changed and left the house without a glance to anyone; his wife, daughters and grand-daughter could cope alone for a few hours. He might go for a pint, the Shirland perhaps or even a little further afield.

Ivy Bridge.

Dalton may have only told Paul Kennedy about Hetty's letter but his buddies sensed something was up, for Dalton seemed to have more energy than the whole of 3rd Platoon put together. On one of their long hikes, the company had been dumped from trucks on the north side of Dartmoor and walked thirty miles back across some of the highest points - Yes Tor, High Willhays and others. With forty pounds on their backs and muddy terrain it was hard going. Captain Zappacosta rested his men beneath Sharp Tor with three 'easy miles' to go. But Dalton didn't rest. He climbed towards the top and looked about him as if he might see Hetty's train approaching from across the Exe Estuary.

The solid granite of the tor upon which he stood had been weathered such that it had the appearance of being made up of blocks. Lying at the same angle as the slope, the blocks looked like they had been squeezed out of the top edge of the hill by some giant footfall and now slid one upon the other imperceptibly slowly towards the spot where the rest of the men now sat. Smiler watched Dalton scramble to the top of the weathered rock and wondered what the hell was wrong with him. With the black peaty dirt upon his general issue brown boots Dalton stepped on the hard feldspar crystals which were turning from brown to white, to eventually become the soft kaolin clay. Something seemingly so hard and permanent changed by circumstance. He could see the Tamar Estuary to the west but merely more hills to the east, the patches of ferns barely contrasting with the gorse.

"What's gotten into Country Boy?" Smiler asked Paul Kennedy and that was when Ted, Clayton, Allbritton,

Austen as well as Smiler learnt of Hetty's letter, of her declaration of love and her visit the next weekend.

Looking back down the slope towards his buddies Dalton could see grins spreading across their faces but merely absorbed the country air, the sound of the Erme River rushing over its boulder strewn bed, the colours and the smells.

"He's sick!" Smiler said as he watched Dalton and no one could disagree with the sentiment. By the time Dalton clambered back down, the rest of the platoon had heard the news and as he rejoined them, Smiler supported by a couple of other guys started to hum, 'Here comes the bride'.

With the singing petering out, Zappacosta signalled the off and Staff Sergeant John Holmes called his squad to order and joined the 150 or so other tired men to complete the hike. Keeping to the left of the ancient stone wall which separated the gorse and ferns from the pastureland sloping down to the river, Zappacosta finally led his men off the moor; past cairns and ancient settlements to Harford Moor Gate, to then follow the narrow track beside Harford Church. As Dalton floated past the pretty grey stone church he vowed to ask Hetty to marry him, the instant she stepped onto the station platform when she arrived on Friday evening.

London.

Ethel had escorted Pat Harrison and Hetty onto the platform at Paddington and as they boarded the south-west bound train, Ethel slipped a ten shilling note into her daughter's hand.

"Look after each other," she said and then stood back to watch the steam loco pull the long line of chocolate and cream carriages out of the station. Ethel waved goodbye, the hand of her daughter diminishing into the distance and wondered what would come of Hetty's visit. Many had left to travel west from Paddington, holiday makers and sea farers travelling to the other side of the world, soldiers and evacuees, but not Ethel. As she walked back past the buildings damaged when a parachute mine landed on Eastbourne Terrace to also damage the station's canopy over the cab road, Ethel decided to head straight home.

On May 13th Hetty had turned twenty-one years old and James Eaglestone told his daughter that had she not been of age then he would have forbidden her to travel to Devon, with or without her cousin. His words almost stopped Hetty from leaving but as the train left the confines of the city, there was no turning back, her course was set. Sitting as she preferred, to face the way the train was travelling, Hetty chatted away the hours with Pat. The green countryside passing unnoticed as the two 'young things' talked of their men, fashions, their men again and tide of events. It wasn't until Salisbury Plain that Hetty first noticed the scenery and then after passing Exeter, Hetty watched as the train climbed towards Dartmoor with Western Beacon looming large out of the right window.

Dalton had mentioned the moor in his letter and as Hetty looked up to see a heavy overcast sky, deepening in darkness as if to storm against the hills, the moor appeared ominous to her. Scary like its portrayal in the film she had seen, The Hound of the Baskervilles.

As the trees fell away to reveal a long high arching viaduct over the Erme River, the train slowed. Ivy Bridge station sat just on the other side of the viaduct perched as it was on the steep slopes dropping from Henlake Down into the valley. Only the tall chimney of Wiggins Paper Mill could be seen protruding up through the vegetation, all else was obscured as the girls craned their necks searching for what might be an army camp.

It was late evening when the engine screeched to a halt at the station and the two girls descended onto 'the lawn' as some railway workers still affectionately referred to the platform. There were soldiers, some boarding some meeting travellers and civilians mingling, cases and bags, coats and umbrellas adorning their frames, but no sight of Dalton and Roy Perkins. Yet they had promised to meet them. Looking at each other and shrugging as if to say oh well, they approached the porter to ask the way into the village.

"Down the zigzags onto Crescent Road and follow on round to Station Road," he said, "then it's straight down the hill into the village," he concluded with a beaming smile which revealed few teeth of yellowing hue.

At each turn of the zigzagging slopes the girls expected to see their boys hurrying towards them. But as they reached the last run of black painted railings and the railway lamp post around which dusk gathered, Hetty sensed that Dalton was not going to show up. Her impulse was to turn around and call it a big mistake.

Walking onto Station Road and turning right to descend the hill, the dark seemed to intensify, vegetation the only company and the sound of rushing water to their left, somewhere in the premature darkness. The Erme was in full flow, racing like Hetty's heart and churning like her mind, over the boulders in its path. Perhaps her friends and family were right about Dalton. Perhaps he couldn't be bothered to walk up and meet her. Jimmy had 'confided' in her, that he had heard that Dalton told all the girls he loved them. Was he with someone else now? Hetty had spent but a few hours with him, hardly knew him, not as she knew Paul Brooks. What had she done? About half way down Station Road the heavens opened and the deluge was to form the only welcome the girls had in Ivy Bridge. As Pat grabbed Hetty's arm beneath the umbrella she told Hetty not to be silly. "There must be a good reason for the boys not to meet us," she said and with that both fell silent as rain soaked into their thin coats.

Dalton was like his father, he made conversation with everyone, conversing with the men and chatting up even the older women he met in the village, just for fun. And it ran with a cheeky smile from his handsome young face. A trait seemingly obscure to the more self contained and reserved small islanders. In his first weeks at Ivy Bridge he had got to know and become good friends with Mr. Downing, the local postman. And on hearing of Hetty's planned visit, Mr. and Mrs. Downing had offered their spare room to the London girls. The rates were more affordable than the Kings Arms and anyway, Dalton didn't like the idea of Hetty stopping amongst the drunken sway of the lively watering hole that had become 1st Battalion's favoured venue. It was when Hetty and Pat finally found their way to the Downing home that they also found the reason as to why their men were not on the platform to meet them.

Colonel Canham, Commander of the 116th Regiment had viewed the predicted bad weather as an ideal opportunity to further toughen up his men. Given the number of fights developing in Ivy Bridge at weekends, he might also have considered that a weekend exercise would keep his men out of trouble. The weekend proved the forecasters right, rain clouds driven by a strong south-westerly blew in from the Atlantic and hung upon the moor to obscure its edges and hide the tor tops. Thus Dalton walked past the granite outcrops and through the bogs of hidden brooks on rain-swept Dartmoor, whilst Hetty sat but a few miles away drinking hot tea from china kept especially for guests. As she looked up at the hills, all her doubts about him evaporated and she worried only about Dalton's safety. Fearing not that he might be hurt by the accidental discharge of a weapon or misplaced grenade, but that he might be mauled by some wild moorland hound like that of the Baskervilles.

With nothing more than water droplets clinging to Dalton's face, the faint image of Captain Zappacosta kept disappearing into another Dartmoor 'pea souper'. Rain swept in and he struggled to focus on the path ahead, a path defined only by the passage of other soldiers. As the line diverted round gorse or extra deep mires, he was tempted to slip off and make a dash to see Hetty. Surely he wouldn't be missed in the fog. But then his knowledge of the moor was limited and even the locals would only trust a horse to get them home once the clouds dropped to engulf the unwary. Thus the slop, suck and squelch of each tread upon the soaked peaty soil was all that marked the passing of time. Time which stretched out as did the few miles of separation to seem so vast.

Hetty and Pat had to catch the 4.15p.m. train back to Paddington on the Sunday and would leave the Downing home sometime before that. B Company made it back to camp at around 3p.m. with instructions to clean up and report for parade at 4 o'clock. But Dalton ran in his filthy uniform, rifle still in hand to burst into the guard room to 'ask a favor'. To use the phone, it was important, it couldn't wait, he had to make an urgent call that minute or everything would be lost he said.

The guards eyed the mud cloaked private with amusement, they were used to 'bull shitters', got it all the time especially when men were confined to barracks. But Dalton's face was filled with such believable anguish that they handed him the phone and watched as he tried to connect to the home of Mr. and Mrs. Downing. Anyone might have slipped in or out of camp during Private Slaughter's phone call for the guards were completely distracted from their duties by the conversation which followed.

"Hetty? It's Dalton," the private said breathlessly.

Pause, as the girl on the other end said something.

"Only just back, I can't get to see you," the private explained.

Another pause.

"I love you!" the private declared.

Another pause.

"I want to spend the rest of my life with you! Don't cry darrlin," he added.

A longer pause.

"Darrrlin' will you marry me?" the private said in a southern drawl which stretched the words darlin' and marry into something the guards had only previously heard on a romantic movie.

There was another pause, a long anxious one, shared also by the guards, but then relief, they could breathe, the private had got the response he wanted. And after saying this, that and some other sweet nothings, he dropped the phone onto the receiver, ran out of the guard house into the beautiful British rain and whooped and hollered all the way back to his damp, tin hut.

From left to right –
Austen, ? Allbritton and Dalton,

outside their Nissen hut,
Ivy Bridge, Devon.

Chapter 22

St. Peter's Church

July to September 1943.

In July '43, General Charles Gerhardt replaced Major General Leonard Gerow as the 29th Division's Commander. To the B Company southern boys, Gerhardt dressed and acted in a way which portrayed his northern roots. But he immediately rose in their affections when he gave everyone three days leave. They were warned it would be the calm before the storm but Dalton didn't care. He climbed Station Road at almost a run and leapt up several steps at a time to reach the east bound platform of Ivy Bridge Station and the earliest London train.

It was the opportunity Dalton and Hetty needed to plan their wedding and for Dalton to ask Mr. Eaglestone for his daughter's hand in marriage. Hetty hadn't been able to face her father and it was Ethel who had broken the news.

As the southern English counties slipped past the train window, Dalton recalled his walk through them in the opposite direction. How things had changed since then. Yet Mr. Eaglestone still disliked him, though Dalton understood the reasons, so he thought. For compared to Paul Brooks whom everyone knew and liked, he was a complete stranger. Dalton had a respect, nurtured from very young, for older people and Mr. Eaglestone would not be an exception. He wasn't going to argue with the man. Mr. Eaglestone had raised a family through hard times and more than that, he had also been a soldier. Difficult, real difficult, if he wouldn't give his consent, Dalton kept telling himself as the steam loco carried him eastward and the miles fell behind, but not his worries.

Several long hours later Dalton arrived in front of the black gloss painted front door at 43, Thorngate, his touch on the woodwork more familiar, his knock recognisable. Hair

Brylcreemed to perfection and uniform cleaned and smartly pressed for the occasion, he was intent on making a good impression. As the door opened Dalton knew the moment had come and just hoped that simple good manners and honesty would win the day.

When he entered the hallway, Dalton was relieved that Young Jimmy's 'welcoming' handshake was missing.

"Jimmy told me to say hello and that he's sorry he can't be 'ere to see you," Ethel explained of her son, causing Hetty to look at her mother. "Jimmy's joined the RAF," Ethel added proudly.

Later, Hetty told him that Jimmy had been selected as wireless operator and placed in a Lancaster Bomber Squadron. Everyone was sworn to secrecy, for Jimmy had told his mother he was part of the ground staff; which to Ethel sounded almost as safe as working for the ground staff of Middlesex County Cricket Club. Edith and Hetty were taking it in turns to unpick his wings when he came home and sew them back on when he left. And Jimmy often got leave, which Dalton considered unfortunate.

No sooner had the brief conversation with Ethel finished than Dalton found he was alone in the downstairs front room with Mr. Eaglestone, though quite how he got there so quickly, he couldn't afterwards recall. There was a faint memory of being ushered there by two tense women, with a third looking on holding a child. But he was more nervous than they were and had somehow arrived where he now stood, alone with the man of the house for the first time.

As he looked across at Mr. Eaglestone standing by the fire place, Dalton realised just how imposing he actually was; tall and upright, with hair that was thinning but combed back neatly to present a youthful appearance. A proud, fit man so he seemed to Dalton. There was no greeting handshake, just a nod and "Take a seat," he invited, in a way which said - let's get down to business.

Dalton wasn't sure whether to sit at one of the many dining room chairs, on the settee or an easy chair. At home they always sat under the poplar tree, or on cooler days, at the long kitchen table. And the table and benches his daddy had made suddenly seemed so much more comfortable than they really were.

When Mr. Eaglestone sat down in an easy chair, Dalton decided to do the same; there was no disapproval so perhaps he had made a good start. But his discomfort returned immediately, because James simply looked at him and waited for him to speak.

"Real nice home you've got here Sir," Dalton said in a stilted Virginian accent, an accent which had always grated on James.

"Thank you," James politely answered.

Dalton looked around at the many ornaments, some in a glass cabinet, collections from a lifetime of marriage. On the mantelpiece, two bronze firemen stood like sentries to the clock between them, their hoses held at the ready. A piano stood in the chimney recess, nearest to the front bay window, its lid down and Dalton hoped he would one day hear it played. The Walden family had donated a piano to Wares Church just before he was drafted and it sure sounded good. To have such things in their home showed they had worked hard he thought, and had money to spare for things other than essentials.

James waited for the GI to ask him the question he had come to ask. Uncanny, James thought, how this twist of events had come about. An American, a country boy at that, sitting uneasily on the edge of his easy chair, in his front room, about to ask for his daughter's hand in marriage! The second request in a year, and of Paul Brooks and the less serious requests before him, this was the least desirable son-in-law of the lot. Strange thing war, James thought as he recalled men he had served with. Lives and destinies changed by the whim of a dictator. Two hundred miles from home had seemed a long way in the Great War, yet this young man was four thousand. Shouldn't be too hard on him, a lot was going to happen before this one was over. You didn't have to be one of Churchill's generals to know why there were so many Yanks in the country. If Dalton survived the war he would not only be very lucky, but a changed man. No, best not be too hard on him.

"Would you like a cuppa?" James asked of his unwelcome guest.

"Yes, thank you Sir," Dalton replied politely, knowing that he would have to force the hot, brown liquid down his throat without a grimace. 'The latchstring is always out' his momma and daddy always said to those marrying into the family, but here they offered you a cup of tea.

"A man I used to work with on the building site hated our tea, said you drink it cold and with ice, is that right?" James asked.

"Yes, I mean no sir, your tea is fine ... but we do drink it cold, with sugar and lemon juice added, when Momma can get hold of one ... tastes real good with lemon."

Hetty brought in the teas and James watched Dalton as he tried to drink it with relish.

"Sir," Dalton said hesitantly, putting the cup not quite central in its saucer. "I love Hetty," he blurted "and I know I'll love her all my life!" he added.

James smiled at the naivety.

"I ..." but James cut him off, James Eaglestone was 'as straight as a die' in the way he conducted himself, he didn't say one thing to a man's face and different behind his back.

"Look lad," he began, "you don't need my consent to marry Hetty. As I've told her, she's twenty-one now."

"I know sir," Dalton said submissively, worried about upsetting him further, "but, your consent is real important to ..."

"Hetty's twenty-one, she doesn't need my consent," James repeated, interrupting Dalton again.

There was an awkward spell of silence.

Dalton didn't know if he should say anymore but his look must have betrayed his thoughts.

"I shall be there to give my daughter away," James said reassuringly. "And I've told Hetty that I'll pay for the wedding."

"Thank you sir," Dalton said and decided not to offer to help with the costs. Holding his tongue, he looked into Mr. Eaglestone's stern face. Behind those hard defining lines hid compassion and Dalton could sense the love and concern for his daughter. Neither man could predict the future and what it might hold; but being young and being Dalton, he was optimistic that everything would work out just fine.

"Everything will be alright Mr. Eaglestone," Dalton said and regretted it almost immediately. How often had Dalton told his momma that? 'It will be alright Momma', when he and Robbie had gotten into trouble and it made his momma angry. But this time he knew for sure things would be alright, never before had he experienced such a driving desire for anything or anyone, it just had to be right, whatever.

In the days following his 72 hour leave Dalton wrote to his momma to tell her of his intentions. Of course she already knew about Hetty. He had mentioned her in every letter. Fleda's reply wasn't the supportive endorsement he had expected and it upset him more than the reception he was getting from just about everyone, except Hetty's mother.

You shouldn't get married, his momma told him, 'two countries too far apart' ... 'for the sake' of the families it would be better not to. It wasn't just his momma who thought this way but 'Daddy too' and 'the whole family are disappointed' she told him.

The wedding was set for the 4th September, at St. Peter's Church on the corner of Chippenham Road and Elgin Avenue. The same church Hetty and Paul Brooks were to be married at. The vicar, Reverend Keith Hamilton, was a little taken aback by the cancellation of one marriage and the arrangement of another a couple of months later, for the same woman, with a different man.

'The youth of today!' he said to Mr. Crabbe the church organist when booking him for the event. But then strange things were happening with the war. People were meeting one week and marrying the next so it seemed to him.

Edith had suggested Hetty get married in a registry office like she did, "Save the money as well as the embarrassment," she said, but Hetty wouldn't hear of it.

"Dad has agreed to pay for everything," Hetty told her sister. "And I've always wanted to get married at Saint Peter's, Dad knows that."

"Dad knows a lot of things," Edith retorted.

"Why can't you wear the wedding dress you've already bought," she went on, "not as if anyone's seen it?" She asked, correctly predicting her sister's response.

The reception was planned to be at the Eaglestone home and the food provided by the family.

"We'll all muck in," Ethel promised. "And I'll make sure we've plenty of food to make it a proper do," she added, to which Edith just raised her eyebrows.

Sometime in August, Ethel took Hetty aside and insisted she and Dalton spend their honeymoon at home. For "What will people think if you book into a hotel with a GI!" Ethel said to her daughter.

When Hetty told Dalton of the honeymoon arrangement he just shrugged, considering that he had already upset the family enough. He was marrying Hetty and that was all that mattered.

But when Ethel announced that 'Young Jimmy' would be best man, Dalton struggled to keep his mouth shut, especially with Jimmy smiling across his mother's shoulder at him. Hetty was expecting it and had asked Dalton to promise not 'to cause a scene'. It was hard but he kept his promise. And probably best, for Ethel was still the only one supporting the marriage.

The next day, the Saturday, Hetty and Dalton planned to go shopping for the engagement ring and try to buy the wedding rings at the same time, for they would otherwise not get another chance. Dalton's next furlough would be the wedding weekend, extended to 5 days, by courtesy of Uncle Sam. Hopefully his closest buddies would be able to come; there would be no one else there for him.

The youngsters were excited at the prospect of shopping together and as they made to leave, Ethel got her hat and coat to join them.

"We thought we might go on our own Mum," Hetty said tentatively.

"What and get fleeced, no fear, load of thieves. Don't you worry, I know just the place," and without another word, led the way onto the street.

As Dalton followed his future mother-in-law, her build reminded him of his momma's short, thick set frame and a strong constitution to match but in different ways. Dalton reached for Hetty's hand, who despite her mother's presence, allowed him to take it and as she did so, Dalton gave thanks for the good woman who had come into his life. Ethel led them down a well worn path which ran from Thorngate Road to Edgware Road and Boshers Pawn shop. "I put a lot of business their way," Ethel said when Hetty realised where they were headed. "We'll get a barg'in," she assured them.

The jewellery laden, well made up shop assistant was approaching her fifties and was just eating a pie from the market when they entered. Ethel would normally have described her as mutton dressed up as lamb, but not today. Hetty started to look at the wide choice of rings under the glass counter. They sold new as well as unredeemed jewellery, lots of unredeemed jewellery and as soon as she might settle on one, her mother suggested another, always a new one.

"How about this one?" Dalton said sometime later, pointing to a narrow band wedding ring, which he considered looked delicate and pretty to match her small hands. He didn't realise it was an unredeemed pledge, "Second hand," Ethel cut in. But Hetty loved it, loved it because Dalton had chosen it. And she quickly found one to match, for him, a new one as it happened, 9ct, whilst hers was 22ct. "It will wear well with all that you're going to be doing," she explained, caressing him with her smile.

Ethel sighed and looked at the made-up assistant as if to say, these youngsters and then proceeded to insist she gave a good discount. And if she didn't "I'll see the guv'nor on Mond'y!" Ethel warned.

Whilst Ethel haggled over the price of the wedding rings, Dalton and Hetty found a lovely new engagement ring. It consisted of a resplendent raised central diamond with two smaller ones on either side, held in delicately woven clasps.

"It's too much money," Hetty gasped when she saw the price.

"Do you like it?" Dalton persisted, as Ethel continued her bartering.

"It's beautiful but I don't need something so expensive, I've got you," she said squeezing his arm.

"Ma'am," Dalton called to the assistant, who stopped and looked as if she had forgotten the two were still there.

Ethel stopped and looked also, wondering what had been going on whilst distracted.

"I'll take this Ma'am," Dalton said passing her the diamond ring.

Ethel craned her neck to see it. "What's it like?" Ethel asked still trying to catch a glimpse of the jewellery as the assistant placed it in a little, soft padded, wooden box.

"It's lovely Mum, you'll like ..."

"How much is it?" Ethel asked, cutting off Hetty's sentence.

Hetty was going to tell her but Dalton stepped in, "It's alright Mrs. Eaglestone," he said and proceeded to count out the pound notes with which he was now becoming familiar.

Ethel watched as the notes piled up on the counter before Dalton finally shoved the pile towards the happy assistant.

"I'll wear it for the rest of my life," Hetty promised Dalton in a whisper, and she did, until needs must.

Whilst Captain Zappacosta worked Dalton and the rest of B Company hard in the warmer summer climes of south-west England, wedding planning was in full swing in Paddington. A car would collect the two bridesmaids, Pat Harrison and Hetty's best friend Maud, although perhaps not quite her best friend after stealing Dalton from her. It would also collect Ethel, Edith and her daughter Georgina. The church was just around the corner but even that was too far for a bride and maids to walk with elegance. The car would then return to pick up Hetty and her father, whilst Jimmy would take good care of the rings and Dalton, he promised.

Another wedding dress was bought and Tregeser's bakery on Clifton Road baked another cake, a single tier this time rather than the previous two. A large round tier with white icing upon which were placed little silver shoes and horseshoes. The edge of the cake was decorated with small flags, the Stars and Stripes alternating with Union Jacks.

Saturday the 4th September 1943 started sunny with just a few clouds in a blue, late summer sky. Dalton arrived early with just two of his closest buddies and left them outside the Eaglestone home, to walk over to the church with some of the other guests. Dalton meanwhile joined his 'best man' at the Shirland Pub, for Jimmy had suggested the groom have one last drink as a single man, for good luck he had said. And Hetty thought it a nice idea, pleased that her brother was trying to be friendly.

By midday when the first guests started to arrive outside St. Peter's, it had become a little overcast but still promising to stay dry.

"Another drink?" Jimmy asked Dalton, "to calm the nerves," he added. But Dalton wasn't sure.

"Don't worry, I'll make sure we get there on time," he said as he ordered two more warm, flat British pints of bitter.

"He's getting married this afternoon," he said to the barman, pointing to Dalton with a grin, "doesn't even know where the church is!" he joked.

Handing the pint to Dalton, Jimmy said, "Tell the barman which church you're getting married at." Dalton looked blankly back, the barman and Jimmy both grinning at him, "It's Saint Saviour's," Jimmy said laughing.

"Saint Saviour's," Dalton repeated with a broad smile and feeling a little foolish.

As always, the unpredictable English weather was a good talking point for the guests outside the church, especially for those without gossip or better things to remark upon. As the ladies in wide brimmed hats and below the knee length suits met so they cast away their partners. The men adrift in their Sunday best, dust and moth balls removed, clustered for safety near railings that had survived the haul for metal. Servicemen stood proudly in their uniforms and of the guests, three stood out, Austen and Allbritton and Kitty Harrison's little boy. He was dressed in a sailor's uniform and might hold it against his mother for the rest of his life.

Despite its situation in the heart of Paddington, surrounded by tenements and war damage, St. Peter's grey stonework rose up from the streets as a symbol of longevity and steadfastness. The large, grand church had thus far avoided the Luftwaffe and with its Church Hall and Vicarage continued to serve the community as it had done since the 1880s. But war had not returned the English to a God fearing nation and some might have said that St. Peter's was already long past its heyday. Congregations in the four hundred capacity church were down to perhaps no more than fifty.

The accumulating wedding guests continued to loiter on the pavement as though entering the grounds without the safety of numbers might allow God to better identify erstwhile worshippers. Like most of the residents of Paddington, the Chapmans, Eaglestones and Harrisons attended only Christenings, weddings and funerals, mainly for the obligatory London knees up or bun fight afterwards, as in the case of the latter.

Dalton arrived at about twelve forty-five with Jimmy. "Nearly went to Saint Saviour's!" Jimmy joked to the guests still outside in the intermittent sunshine, thumbing towards Dalton.

Their arrival was followed by Hetty's mother, sister, niece and two bridesmaids in the hire car. Pat and Maud looked lovely in their turquoise blue, full length dresses and immediately started to flit in and out of the guests as people, more often the men, beckoned the young ladies over. Maud was friendly with Dalton but hadn't completely forgiven him for his actions outside the Black and White Milk Bar.

Finally, in sufficiently safe numbers, the guests ventured through the vestibule into the large nave and to the welcoming smile of Reverend Keith Hamilton. Keith lived in the vicarage with his mother and had a 'hell of a laugh' according to Tom Harrison, although how he knew was a mystery. All the Harrisons were there, Tom and Liz Harrison had brought their six kids; Kitty, Eileen, Billie, Dickie, Tommy and Pat of course was bridesmaid. Tom Harrison had been looking forward to the wedding, for he couldn't wait to see James Eaglestone give his youngest and prettiest daughter away to a man that was 'over paid, oversexed and over here!' The market stall tradesman had hoped that Roy Perkins might propose to his Patsy, but things seemed to be cooling between the couple as indicated by Roy's absence from the wedding.

As more guests arrived, there were hushed whispers from the long wooden pews as people turned to acknowledge friends. And in the background Mr. Crabbe, the rather bald but very energetic organist softly played the vast variety of grey pipes that constituted the grand organ. Whilst Mr. Crabbe teased air into his resonating columns, the choir boys fidgeted in the Chancery, turning the oak beams into goal posts and the tired army flags into emblems of favourite football teams, breaking the monotony of yet another war time wedding.

The forty or so guests made little impression on the large nave with its side aisles and pews extending beyond the arches, and Dalton's side of the church looked even more deserted. As the bridal car left Thorngate Road, the final trickle of Hetty's friends and family thoughtfully sat to the right and restored some balance. But not in a lifetime could they have replaced Dalton's family. He just hoped they were thinking of him.

A little late as tradition would dictate, at just after 1p.m. the bridal car turned into Chippenham Road from Elgin Avenue to pull up outside the main church entrance. Pat and Maud made frantic last minute adjustments to Hetty's attire as she stepped out onto the pavement and James Eaglestone checked his appearance in the reflection of the car window. A few seconds later, the Church Warden standing at the back of the church waved to Reverend Hamilton. The Reverend nodded to Mr. Crabbe and as the bride and her father with bridesmaids in tow stepped through the arched doorway so the 'Bridal March' started to reverberate around the grey stone arches and rendered walls. The congregation immediately stood to welcome the bride and Dalton instinctively turned completely round to watch Hetty as she made her way down the aisle.

With Wagner's music from Lohengrin flowing out onto the city's streets, Dalton stood with eyes filled with tears, to watch his bride approach. It was against British tradition but Dalton didn't know and would not have cared, for he wanted to capture every second and keep the memory of this moment for the rest of his life. As their eyes met, Dalton smiled and Hetty wanted to run to him and kiss him, for he looked so handsome in his uniform and she felt so loved by him.

Her virgin white wedding dress hung long to the floor, its plain, square high neck with long sleeves accentuating Hetty's lines. The farthing sized buttons which ran from the wrist to the elbow on each sleeve and again from the neck to the small of her narrow back were covered with the same material as the dress. With a sash round her waist and a tiara crowning her long hair she looked beautiful. The veil which also fell to her silver shoes finished the effect and for Dalton, the woman coming towards him was the most beautiful and precious thing in the world.

Standing at the Chancery steps with the stained glass window framing the Reverend Hamilton, Hetty and Dalton stood together; the children of two distant countries to be united in a marriage swift in the making, though most predicted would not be long in the savouring.

The Reverend welcomed the congregation and with memories of a different groom, who was supposed to have been standing there with Hetty, told them they had come to share the couple's joy and celebrate their love. And progressed towards the part which always caused tension so the Reverend noticed, though no one could ever explain to him why;

"First I am required to ask anyone present who knows a reason why these persons may not lawfully marry, to declare it now."

Thankfully, there was silence in the church save for the traffic on the Chippenham and Aunt Nine trying to muffle a cough.

Turning to Dalton the Reverend asked,

"Dalton, will you take Hetty to be your wife?

Will you love her, comfort her, honour and protect her,

and forsaking all others,

be faithful to her as long as you both shall live?"

"I will," Dalton replied.

And after repeating the same with Hetty turned to the congregation and asked them.

"Will you support and uphold them in their marriage now and in the years to come?"

"We will," most responded and some who did, actually meant it.

Standing before the minister, and looking at each other, Dalton began to say his vow,

"I, Dalton Roy Slaughter take you Hetty Elizabeth Eaglestone,

to be my wife," at which Hetty couldn't help but cry,

"to have and to hold," he repeated after the reverend

"from this day forward,

for better, for worse, for richer, for poorer

in sickness and in health

to love and to cherish,

till death do us part ..."

tears were now running down Hetty's face whilst two or three ladies in the congregation, Ethel included sniffled and blew into handkerchiefs.

Hetty composed herself to recite her vow after which Jimmy was supposed to have stepped forward with the rings but had to be prompted to do so by the reverend. Still he didn't move but fished around in his pockets, seconds passing whilst he remained centre of attention, before finally

passing them into the Reverend's safe hands. Dalton placed the second hand gold ring onto the fourth finger of Hetty's left hand and commenced his recital,
"I give you this ring,
as a sign of our marriage ...
all that I am I give to you
and all that I have I share with you ..."

and Dalton meant it absolutely.
And with both rings exchanged, the Reverend turned to the congregation;
"In the presence of God ... Hetty and Dalton have made their vows to each other ... declared their marriage in the joining of hands and by the giving and receiving of rings ...

I therefore proclaim that they are husband and wife."

It seemed a long time to some, but after The Blessing, the registration and endless prayers, Mendelssohn's 'Wedding March' blasted out of the organ pipes to wake them, and with it playing in the background, Dalton and Hetty stepped out into the bright afternoon light to be showered with confetti. Kitty Harrison's little sailor boy gave Hetty a silver horseshoe tied with ribbon, whilst smiles beamed from faces, some out of relief that it was all over. Pictures were taken by the official photographer, as tradition would have it, building in numbers and in number of guests around the happy couple. The picture with the bridesmaids, best man and one set of parents had Jimmy strangely alone at the back, with just his head and a slight bit of his shoulder on view, leaning sideways to look over Dalton's shoulder. It also contained Austen, Allbritton and another GI called Gentry to represent Dalton's side, though quite why Gentry came and how he got into the picture no one knew, not even Dalton. Then eventually after five photographs were taken, the wedding car drove Dalton and Hetty back to Thorngate Road to start their new life together. Quite what that life might hold neither knew or cared, for on this day

Hetty and Dalton were at the height of happiness and deeply, deeply in love.

The reception at number 43 was a good London affair, the men got merrier as the evening progressed, whilst the women recalled more romantic days long past, before they had children and when they loved their husbands; when life seemed rosy and their vows easy to abide by. Eventually someone opened the Old Joanna and encouraged Ethel to 'hit the ivories' and play everyone's favourite, Vera Lynn's 'We'll Meet Again'. Too many beers had been drunk, weak or not for anyone to notice that Ethel could only play the chorus and all joined in with "We'll meet again don't know where, don't know when but I know we'll meet a – gain some sun - ny day."

The words 'I'll not forget you sweetheart' were omitted but may well have run through the minds of at least two men that night, Paul Brooks and Stan Kirby. Paul was flying missions over Italy, RAF aircrew, Bomber Squadron, with nothing but a thin fuselage to protect him. Whilst army boy Stan Kirby went out and got uncharacteristically very drunk and lost his stripes.

From left to right –
Austen, Allbritton, Gentry, Pat Harrison, Jimmy, Dalton, Hetty, Maud, Ethel, James, Edith.

Dalton and Hetty marry
4th September 1943.

St. Peters Church, Elgin Avenue,
Paddington.

Chapter 23

The Stranger She Married

Ivy Bridge, September 1943 to March 1944.

Dalton returned alone to Ivy Bridge and the stricter regime dictated by General Gerhardt. If a man was late back from leave he was fined 30 dollars and confined to camp for 30 days. Dalton and his buddies were no longer allowed to eat or smoke on marches, if caught their next leave was cancelled. Some men risked it but not Dalton, he saw Hetty little enough as it was. Uniforms had to be immaculate and whilst helmets were on, chin straps had to be done up. At last, a bit of discipline, so Vera Luckham's father-in-law said when he overheard the officers talking in the Sportsmans Inn. The Great War British navy man was adamant that discipline wasn't what it used to be.

Chanting their new slogan 'Twenty-nine Let's Go' on exercises, the 29th were typical of troops who had not yet seen action. But as live ammunition became more frequently used, casualties mounted and educated the uninitiated. Some spoke of casualties when General Gerhardt dropped grenades from his Piper Club Spotting plane whilst observing manoeuvres. Maybe it was just rumour but fortunately the 'Northern Dandy', as some called him, never came near B Company whilst they were on the moor.

The autumn of '43 crept into winter with Dalton and Hetty only managing to see each other for the occasional weekend. Hetty travelling down to Ivy Bridge by train and staying at the Kings Arms, whilst Dalton tried to get to London when he could, stopping at the Eaglestone home and sleeping with Hetty in her small bedroom. Despite the often unruly behaviour in the pub so popular with 1st Battalion enlisted men, Hetty and Dalton preferred it. For Ethel seemed to maintain a constant nightly vigil on the landing outside Hetty's room. And the bed springs which stretched across the metal base frame seemed the noisiest in the house, perhaps the whole street.

Their weekends together passed too quickly and the intervening weeks too slowly for Hetty. The intense training kept Dalton busy and the knowledge that Hetty was his wife gave him all the comfort he needed. She would wait for him and be faithful he knew with absolute surety.

But Hetty missed and needed the company of her husband, for she was still alone with her choice and never completely at ease in any social circle. Few asked of him, not like the wives of men in the British armed forces and it was as if Dalton didn't exist. Life was the same but not the same.

'How's Mr Overpaid?' Jimmy might ask, smiling as if it was a little friendly joke, leaving out the 'over sexed and over here' part if their parents were around. Yet he was always happy to borrow a 'few bob' from her, money which now came courtesy of Uncle Sam as well as from the Black and White Milk Bar.

'Pay yer back' he always said but never did and Hetty never asked. How could she? Jimmy was her brother. And 'family are family' as their mother always said.

With the winter nights stretching to sixteen hours, the weather closed in and the training on Dartmoor became harsh. The high winds on the granite upland seemed to drive the rain and snow through the tents. Placed on sodden ground, the small shelter would then be occupied by three dripping wet men, Austen, Allbritton and Dalton usually being together, to endure a night where moisture from their bodies replaced any that might dry. With the flapping of hastily erected canvas, the wind howling through fissures in the granite tors and the complaining of men, few slept. When the snow came, it was freezing on the tors and dropped by three degrees in the frost hollows. The mires and brooks which snaked their way through the scrub and bracken became encrusted and boots broke through the ice to enter the muddy bog beneath.

The barracks with their corrugated tin roofs at least kept the men dry, but the two windows in the wooden end walls allowed just a few candles of light to enter from the grey winter hue. At night the inside was lit by a single electric bulb and the glow of the stove. With no shortage of coke, the cylindrical, blackened metal stove formed an oasis of comfort. It was situated in the middle of the hut with its flue running to the roof and radiated heat towards even the coldest corners. Dalton was 'selected' to keep it well stoked; 'Country' as they were starting to call him, 'is good with fires', they said. He had so often worked with his momma to keep the kitchen stove burning that he understood their needs and the security they offered.

The men would stand by it to warm themselves before stepping outside, for it was a certainty that a south-westerly would be blowing from the direction of Plymouth. The wind seemed to be guided by the moor to press against their hut door. They would struggle against it to get out and then be chilled by its consistency as they crossed the field - perhaps to the latrines, the mess hall or to the camp store.

Christmas '43 passed in more sombre mood than their first at Tidworth. Entertaining local kids was a highlight but they missed home with a greater passion and the full mail bag was more desperately awaited. With loving letters, containing snippets of local papers and pictures of family, men often re-read the same lines many times. For the married men, their sons and daughters were now fifteen months older. Babies and toddlers had turned into little boys and girls, happy in play and gradually forgetting the days when they had a father. The pain showed as the Christmas music played and young men hid their faces behind whatever they read.

Of all the guys, those who had married English girls or who were seriously dating one coped best. And in Dalton's case, thoughts of Church View no longer wrenched so hard on his heart.

Buddies tried to cheer each other by saying they might be home in the New Year. But it was shallow rhetoric; all knew that there was still a long road ahead. Clayton received a fruit cake in the Christmas mail bag which had deteriorated to little more than crumbs. But he ate every piece and right he did for it was the last his momma would bake for him.

Whilst 1st Battalion made the best of a second Christmas away from home, 3,000 residents to the south of Ivy Bridge left their homes by order of the War Office. Under the 1939 Defence Regulations and Compensation Act, 30,000 acres of land, eight villages, 180 farms and many other dwellings had to be completely evacuated by 20th December. The aim was to create a training ground, typical of the topography to be encountered by US troops in Normandy. Slapton Sands would be the invasion beach and the land behind, the terrain of Normandy that must be overrun and secured. Within six weeks of the residents being told, Slapton, Torcross, Stokenham, Chillington, Sherford, East Allington, Blackawton and Strete became ghost villages and all land between vacated. Farmers moved or sold cattle and though people were able to take possessions, much was left behind. Allan Soper and his family in East Allington moved not just their home but also lathes, drilling machines and the other equipment which formed part of their farm machinery repair business. Like others, they had to find new accommodation, business premises and build new custom.

Whilst the War Department prepared the ground for the final phase of training, the 116th endured the last of the delights of Dartmoor. Regimental manoeuvres took place on Hanger Down; a flat topped stretch of moor once deemed a good landing spot for German paratroopers. Telegraph poles, planted to thwart glider landings, were removed to allow tanks, trucks and other vehicles along with mock buildings to be used in the fray. Regimental manoeuvres were a prelude to divisional manoeuvres which took place near Okehampton on the northern side of the moor.

Dalton had thought himself really fit after training for eighteen months in the US. He realised at Tidworth that he wasn't and now considered Tidworth to have been a 'walk in the park'. Yet each week Captain Zappacosta still took his men on their three mile fitness route. With Ted, Clayton and Smiler, Dalton's hut never ranked very highly but that didn't stop the fitter ones trying to outrun the others. Drumheller, the tough guy of B Company made a bet at the New Year party that he would beat everyone back to camp from 'Country's hut' in the first run of '44. They were all 'about as fast as my grand daddy', he told everyone. The bet worried Dalton simply because Drumheller worried him. 'Mean' and 'easily got into a fight' and not the sort he felt comfortable with.

On the day of the run they exited the camp as usual onto the Exeter Road. Dalton's buddies were all together by the time they reached the Erme River, some 800 yards away, with Drumheller only several yards in front. But as they turned up Station Road to steadily climb the valley and despite their determination to stay together, Ted and Clayton fell behind. Smiler, surprisingly, hung on with the leading bunch.

With the stream to their right, its trees and bushes marking the edge of town, the gradient became steeper, breathing heavier and despite the cold winter air, sweat started to pour off them. Smiler hung on until about half way to the viaduct when he yelped and dramatically crashed out in the dirt. Flat on his face and desperate for breath, "Beat the son of a bitch," he managed to gasp; a brave gesture, coming from Smiler the others thought. By the time they reached the viaduct, a mile from camp only half of Dalton's hut were in touch with Drumheller.

At the brick arches the men veered off right, passing under them to take Lover's Walk; a path bordering the picturesque river, often littered with 'white balloons' as Noel Blackler, the battalion's paper boy described them. Balloons which seemed to become more plentiful on pay days and the arrival of professional ladies.

Here, the gushing stream with its rapids and pools was a playground for the local kids. The sluice pool for the Wiggins Tepe paper mill was their favoured swimming spot. Weather permitting and at weekends, the GIs would join them to play and while away the hours. It was also a good spot for the kids to stand and watch the GIs, cheering the men they knew and making cheeky comments to the slower runners.

After the sluice pool the men passed the old reservoir before taking a sharp left onto Hunter's Path; a very steep climb back to Station Road and the hardest part of the run. Hunter's Path sorted the men from the boys and legs started to burn. Despite cajoling each other, Dalton and Paul Kennedy fell some twenty yards behind Austen and Allbritton, with Drumheller now well ahead. Staff Sergeant John Holmes dropped back when half way up, to rally the others on the steep incline and ensure everyone at least jogged it. "You can do it," he told his men as they ran on.

Once back on Station Road it was all downhill, 700 yards to the viaduct and thence to the village. At the viaduct the kids rejoined them, to run beside the soldiers as they always did, the GIs turning the air blue with their comments. Drumheller looked complacent as he bantered with a couple of them and Paul Kennedy motioned to Dalton that this might be their chance. Finding a reserve, fuelled by the thought of beating the hard guy, they used the slope to pick up speed rather than cruise as they usually did. They caught up on Austen and Allbritton, and at the bridge overtook Drumheller, passing him to turn onto the Exeter Road. With 800 yards to go, Drumheller wasn't going to be beat, cussing, he left the kids and sprinted.

When Austen and Allbritton arrived, Drumheller, Paul and Dalton were holding onto the camp gates gasping for breath. Drumheller claimed to have won, but the expression on Dalton's face and his pointing at Paul Kennedy, fortunately unseen by Drumheller, told them otherwise.

Smiler and Ted were amongst the last back, but the difference being that Ted could have kept going for several more miles, likely carrying Smiler if he really had to.

Ted always did better in the 'Battle Order' training; for wearing full kit and carrying their rifle, the men needed strength and stamina more than speed. Ascending the valley on the paper mill side, they crossed the Erme on a rope bridge, just above the Wiggins Tepe sluice pool. To then climb a thirty feet high gantry at the edge of the old reservoir and descend into flat bottomed boats via cargo nets. Although not aware of it, this was the first step in their preparation for an amphibious assault onto Omaha. Reaching the other side of the reservoir, the men had to run up the steep, muddy slopes of Henlake Down, bayonet a dummy and continue till they were on the moor, several hundred feet above where they started.

The problem for the company captains of having exceptionally fit men to command, was dealing with their overflowing energy during free time. Fights and insubordination were commonplace, particularly after a few drinks. One evening two spitfires were having a training 'dog fight' above the camp when one of the planes failed to come out of a spin and crashed just under the lip of Western Beacon. Without permission from the officers or organisation from the NCOs, several excited men grabbed shovels, ran to the top of the beacon and without pausing for breath, shovelled soil onto the burning plane in an attempt to douse the flames. Fortunately the fuel and ammunition failed to go off.

Fights between different units sometimes started over nothing more than a piercing look. If the New Zealanders or some of the 250 coloureds based at Stowford House called into town, things became heated and the military police 'sure got busy'.

Through January and February new men like Harold Baumgarten joined the 1st Battalion from the US and on the 10th February fifty joined B Company, taking it up to full battle strength with 200 men. With the increased tension of combat looming and the arrival of new men, discipline became more difficult. Friendship groups built up over three years were unsettled and with relatively little army training, the new men were mistrusted. Those from common backgrounds were often accepted more quickly, as in the case of B Company man Charles Conner who ended up sharing Dalton's hut. But even Charlie had to prove himself.

One of the worst confrontations occurred at The Kings Arms. The guys were holding a party there when some New

Zealanders tried to gatecrash it. During the fray, a few coloured American servicemen slipped in and started buying drinks and asking the girls to dance. As the coloureds were beaten up and thrown outside, the white GIs encountered 'a whole load more' on the high street. A running battle of some two hundred men developed with sticks, knives and stones being used as weapons. Injuries became serious as urgent messages were sent to camps for the military police and officers to come and quell the riot; many soldiers were arrested and some hospitalised.

When Hetty arrived to stay at the Kings Arms the next weekend she was surprised to hear what had happened. She had become friendly with the daughter of the landlord who was dating a coloured American serviceman. The daughter explained how difficult it was to associate with one and had been very upset by events on Fore Street.

At the beginning of the war the British accepted coloured servicemen like any other. Girls dated them, pubs served them, cabbies picked them up in order in the queue and picture houses, like buses and trains, allowed them to sit anywhere. But many of the GIs viewed coloureds very differently and encouraged their British allies to do the same. Back in the States, coloureds lived in coloured only areas, went to coloured only schools and sat in the back of the bus in seats allocated to coloureds and couldn't ride if those were full, even if 'white' seats were available.

To come from segregation to integration was a culture shock as much for the coloured as for the white GI. But there were few coloureds who didn't love the British culture, drizzle or no drizzle.

Hetty had arrived early on the Friday afternoon and after her chat with the landlord's daughter, was anxious to find out if Dalton had been involved with the fighting. To think of her husband being hurt was bad enough but to be so hateful of people just because of their colour worried her.

Pat would have said of course he wasn't involved, but Hetty was travelling alone now that Pat and Roy Perkins had split up and missed her reassurances.

After his release from camp, Dalton rushed down to the Kings Arms, longing to see his girl. Alone in the rented room, together at last, Dalton reached out for Hetty but she moved away, brushing off his attentions.

"What's the matter?" he asked, surprised at her coolness, hurting a little from the rejection.

"Nothing I just want to talk," she replied, "there's things I want to know about ..." She was going to add 'you' but omitted it.

There was also something she wanted to tell Dalton, but the time wasn't right, not now.

"What happened here last weekend?" she asked, sitting on the bed beside him.

Dalton couldn't tell her.

"It was mainly A Company men at the party," Dalton said, "I was at the White Horse." He could sense her anxiety. "It happens a lot," he added, "trouble between whites and coloreds."

And he mistakenly started to recall an incident which he and Charlie Connor witnessed some weeks earlier.

They were there with a whole load of other B Company guys, he told her, drinking at the White Horse. Most were doing their usual, drinking up the supply of beer and spirits and absorbing the atmosphere to help them through the cold night ahead. The pub was crowded and the owners making a fortune as small change was discarded and spirits added to the weak bitter to give it some bite.

The pub was just quietening for the BBC wireless news when the door opened and a coloured US serviceman stepped inside.

Hetty looked at her husband with anticipation.

Dalton and Charlie were near the bar and were not the first to see him. It was the silence that rippled from where the coloured soldier stood that brought their attention to the brave but 'foolish nigger' as one GI called him. The ripple of silence reached the bar about the same time as a wooden chair rose up out of the crowd and came down on the man's head. There was then complete silence as the soldier hit the hard floor with a thud, a silence which lasted but a few more seconds before the lifeless body signalled a quick exit. As the locals were left to stand and gape at the dead soldier, one of the last GIs to leave threw the guy's hat onto the fire. Hetty was shocked at the story. Though she had seen Yanks complain in cinemas when staff allowed coloureds to sit where they liked, she hadn't realised the hatred some seemingly happy-go-lucky GIs felt towards their own countrymen. Hetty looked at the man beside her, the stranger she had married and realised she knew very little about him or his background. She definitely didn't want to live and bring up a family where there were such terrible feelings between its own people.

Hetty asked Dalton if he knew who killed the 'poor soldier?' He didn't and explained that Scotland Yard had come down from London to investigate. There had been an identity parade of B Company, but the landlord and another local were unable to identify anyone. When questioned, none of the GIs could help. As for Dalton, he had seen the arms which raised the chair but had no idea as to the identity of the soldier.

"Would you have said if you knew?" Hetty asked tentatively. Dalton looked into Hetty's face and finally realised what all the coolness was about. But he dare not answer her, for he didn't want to lie. Hetty was a culture apart, both from the US and army life. He honestly didn't know who had killed the GI, perhaps Charlie knew. But if Charlie or anyone else had said, then sure as hell a stray bullet would have been the man's reward. For the violence was mutual. A white GI 'had his throat cut by a nigger' in Plymstock not long before the incident in the White Horse. So Dalton merely sat in silence, not sure what to say.

Hetty inched herself away from him and started to feel panicky, hot, wondering what on earth she had done. Stupid to have married someone she hardly knew. Jimmy was right, everyone was right, she should have listened to them.

It seemed a long time before Dalton spoke and when he did he didn't answer her question but talked of life back home.

Of 'gray bearded Uncle Dick Tucker, the old colored guy' who likely still visited the Slaughter home place, riding there as he had always done, on his horse. Dalton's momma would make coffee and then Daddy and Uncle Tucker would sit in the kitchen to drink, chat and pass the time of day.

"Many whites won't have a colored set foot in their homes," Dalton explained and then realised for the first time the distinction between his parents' attitude and that of others. And then he recalled to Hetty a time when he was aged about ten. It was a hot, humid Sunday afternoon in Church View and Dalton was walking with his momma along the dirt road in the direction of the Dragon Run Store. They walked slowly keeping to the shade and in their baskets carried food that Fleda could spare from the fruits of her labour. They were taking the food to a coloured family, where the husband had been so badly injured at work that he 'hadn't earned a dime for several months'.

On nearing the run-down house, his momma had turned to Dalton and said, 'no good just a prayin' for the hungry, you also gotta go feed them'.

Although Dalton had never consciously formulated an opinion about how coloureds should be treated, he now realised he had one, but express it he couldn't. He just knew for sure that he respected everyman equally and that given the chance, he would in time prove himself to Hetty.

In the silence that followed, with Hetty still looking at him strangely, Dalton remembered an oration at Speaker's Corner. He couldn't recall the words exactly, more the sentiment, for it was one of those long speeches which eventually drove listeners away, but essentially the message ran; 'miracles are not achieved in a stroke of time, but achieved by many small gestures by many people over many years'.

As the memory slipped through his conscious thought, Dalton decided he would make his gestures if God gave him the time and whilst Dalton looked sad and wallowed in his thoughts so Hetty moved back closer to him, her worries ebbing away.

"I've something to tell you," she said looking more intent at her husband than she had ever done before.

Dalton turned and braced himself.

"I'm pregnant," she said with a face so serious and then after gauging Dalton's reaction, replaced it with a smile so beautiful.

Dalton could have eaten her there and then and in the night hours which followed, amidst the laughter and the loving, almost did.

Chapter 24

You Had Best Go Home

March/April 1944.

On the 18th March '44, 1st Battalion left Ivy Bridge on the 0835 train. After hugging Dartmoor, the steam loco pulsed south-east towards the Teign Estuary and followed its wide, calm waters to the sea. Keeping to within a few feet of the English Channel, the men were pulled past Teignmouth, Dawlish and the red sandstone cliffs to then follow the Exe Estuary into Exeter. After the cathedral city, instead of continuing eastward towards London, the train branched north-west along the Taw valley to circumvent Dartmoor and follow the meandering river. With steep wooded slopes and all but a narrow country road to share the valley floor, the twin tracks weaved northward. Just after Umberleigh station the train crossed the river. The Taw was twenty yards wide and full with the rains of winter, grey rushing water, as grey as the stone pillars upon which the girders of the train bridge rested. Not now the glint of summer upon the surge but the hint of rapids where fishermen stand among the reeds and watch the trains rattle across the hundred year old bridge. Then on towards Barnstable ran road, train and river together, passing few souls upon the way and finally some six hours after leaving Ivy Bridge, yet only fifty-five miles from it as the crow flies, Dalton entered Braunton Assault Training Centre.

The tents were situated around Croyde Hall, just yards from the north Devon beaches which face out towards the Atlantic. Croyde Beach together with Woolacombe Beach to the north and Saunton Sands to the south all formed part of the training centre. Dalton had spent 21 days here in October '43 and this second visit was less welcoming than the first. With cots to sleep on, a small stove for heating and oil lamps for lighting, the men soon longed for their hut with its coke stove by the side of the Exeter Road. Through the two visits and their total of thirty-one days at the centre, B Company was taught about amphibious and land based assaults. Starting with squad assaults involving a twelve man team under a staff sergeant, they were moved onto platoon, company and finally regimental amphibious assaults. They learned how to attack pill boxes constructed for the purpose on Baggy Point, how to best take control of beach emplacements, negotiate barbed wire entanglements, beach obstacles and entrenchments and to recognise and deal with booby traps.

Lectures were followed by practice and practice by more practice, with training on the use of a variety of weapons; from machine guns to bazookas, flamethrowers and Bangalore torpedoes.

The introduction to the LCVP (Higgins landing craft) provided the platoon with some amusement for it gave Smiler an opportunity to come into his own. He had struggled with the physical training on the cargo netted obstacle course, but verbally there were no obstacles for Smiler. The concrete model of a Higgins boat situated at Crow Point was, 'our new secret weapon', he declared, much to everyone's amusement. The centre used it to teach men how to embark, disembark and to space out and balance in choppy seas. Dalton embarked and disembarked more times than he could remember and each time Smiler found something new to say. 'Do these really float?' he once asked with such a straight face that even Staff Sergeant John Holmes had to laugh with his men. When they moved on to the real thing and then eventually to land in one, Smiler compared the Higgins boat to a bath tub, except that in a bath tub there's, 'warmer water', he quipped. For even in a light swell, a strong breeze would send freezing spray over the side to soak the men. The journey from the embarkation area at Crow Point to Saunton Sands wasn't so bad, but during the eight miles to Woolacombe the cold North Atlantic seemed to reach in and chill a man to the bone. The only advantage of being soaked to the skin was that when they waded ashore the water that had previously felt as if it had just arrived from the Arctic, felt no colder than their already sodden frames.

The Higgins boats were supplied from Appledore and Instow, just across the Taw Estuary. But once the 1st Battalion had been assigned the most strongly defended section of the most strongly defended beach, Dog Green sector on Omaha, it was decided that they should use the British LCA (Landing craft assault). The US Rangers had used LCAs in training in Scotland and preferred them for the more specialist missions for which they were generally deployed. It was perhaps through their adoption of the LCA that led to the decision that 1st Battalion should utilise them also.

Thus during 1st Battalion's second trip to Braunton, LCAs were supplied from the British Landing Craft Centre at Instow and the men trained almost exclusively in them. The LCA was different in many ways to the Higgins boat. The design of the Higgins was governed more by production costs and ease of manufacture than military expediency. It was useful in calm non-combat situations, but it offered little protection to the men or crew in rough weather or in battle. Completely open, soldiers had to stand up in transit and when the wide, front ramp dropped onto the beach everyone was exposed to enemy fire. The LCA however had armour protection and a narrow exit ramp, only wide enough for one man and his equipment to disembark at a time. Thus the remaining soldiers were not nearly as exposed. And instead of a rush of men providing haphazard covering fire, cover was provided by the mounted machine gun. In an LCA, the men sat down and three foot wide decks on either side partially covered them, providing some protection from the elements. On a long rough sea crossing, waves washing over the craft and the incessant spray not only wearied the men but its accumulation could eventually destabilise the Higgins. Standing up and being thrown around in a heavy swell also drained a soldier's energy and the swaying human cargo created greater instability to an already unstable boat. Thus the LCA was ideal for Dog Green and the two and a half hour sea journey from the mother ship to the beach on D-Day; a journey made after no sleep in what turned out to be a very rough English Channel.

It was at Braunton that the officers finally dispensed with the twenty plus mile hikes, and moved on to the shorter speed marches of some five to eight miles carrying weapons and kit. This was a simulation of their expectations in Normandy where the 1st Battalion would hopefully be pushing the enemy forever back from the land they had occupied almost exactly four years earlier. On the 21st March, Dalton and his buddies were taken on an eight mile speed hike to practise firing assault weapons. The next day they practised again and Dalton, together with Austen and Allbritton, had the pleasure of forming a machine gun team; carrying their equipment with them and periodically setting up as though under fire. The three were more than a little tired at the end of the day and Dalton savoured his best night's sleep at Braunton, despite a storm which flattened some of the tents. During the following three days they made several beach assaults. Then on the 27th and 28th March they practised beach landings with assault weapons and tackled beach defences under live fire, mortars and artillery. It was an intense experience which changed the soldiers from basic infantrymen to assault teams, versatile in weapon craft and confident on the sea.

Finally on the 30th March, again by virtue of the Great Western Railway, with its 9,000 miles of track and 1,500 stations at the complete disposal of the military, 1st Battalion arrived back at Ivy Bridge.

The training at Braunton had made every man realise the seriousness of their cause and injuries in training had opened eyes that hadn't yet been opened. The build up for an invasion had clearly begun in earnest and hopes that the war might be over before the 29th Division was needed were dashed.

Just twenty-four hours after arriving back at Ivy Bridge and as habits fine-tuned over a period of ten months started to be re established, 1st Battalion was again told to prepare for departure. Not a departure as to Braunton but a complete exodus. Huts had to be emptied of everything except the stove and bunks. All the ingenious improvisations that the men had utilised to make their barracks more homely had to be removed. The wire-weaved drying racks, the wooden boxes and packing cases adapted as chairs, tables, clothes cupboards and book shelves. Everything had to go, either burnt or buried. Even spare military equipment was buried. Only the bare essentials were to be transported, because at their next destination, all they needed would be provided.

This was it, the invasion must be imminent.

Yet April dragged on and two weeks later 1st Battalion were still providing for a lively trade in Ivy Bridge. But when Hetty finally arrived on Friday 14th April, she had to walk to the Kings Arms on her own. The town was quiet and the normal hum of activity replaced by local trade and debates as to when the invasion might occur; everyone it seemed had an opinion on the destiny of the 1st Battalion.

By the Saturday afternoon, Hetty still hadn't heard from Dalton. The landlord told her that the GIs were confined to barracks and would soon be leaving, but when he couldn't say. It was mid afternoon when Hetty decided to walk up the Exeter Road to try and catch a glimpse of her husband. Dalton had once taken her onto camp as his guest. She had eaten in the mess and been given a quick tour of the PX, gym and the cinema so she knew that his barrack lay close to the road. As Hetty approached the camp, a soldier edged into view and started running towards her. She didn't recognise him at first, for his head had been shaved and his face was ghostly white and full of anxiety. But as he came nearer she realised it was Dalton. Private First Class Slaughter had slipped out of camp desperate to say goodbye and was running to make every second count. At five months pregnant Hetty hardly showed her bump and Dalton almost forgot about her condition as he pulled her close to feel just a slight pressure of her developing tummy against his groin. Hetty ran her fingers through his short hair and as they kissed, Dalton cupped her face in his hand as he had so often done before.

"I think this is it," Dalton exclaimed breathlessly. "We're moving out tomorrow," he added looking with such intensity at Hetty that it upset her.

"I'll be waiting for you sweetheart," then after a pause "we'll both be waiting for you," she added patting her tummy as her eyes filled with emotion. She had nothing to give Dalton to remember her by save the photo he wanted, but took three small, very old silver coins from the pocket of her purse. "I've had these since I was little, they'll bring you good luck," she said pressing them into Dalton's hand.

The sound of a military jeep suddenly bounced off the walls of the Sportsmans Inn as it made its way across the Erme River Bridge. It interrupted Dalton's thoughts. A military jeep meant only one thing, an officer was heading their way. "I shouldn't be out," he whispered. "I think this is the big man coming," Dalton said looking across Hetty's shoulder at the fast approaching jeep.

Forgetting everything they had intended to say and with complete abandonment as on their first embrace in Regents Park, Dalton and Hetty kissed like it might be their last and held each other as if they might never hold each other again.

With the jeep just yards away, Dalton buried his head into Hetty's neck and covered his face with her soft sensuous hair and waited. He wanted to absorb her fragrance and the touch of her soft skin in the seconds of intimacy he had left. Sensations that could keep a soldier strong in battle, or after a wounding, provide the will to live. Then as the jeep stopped beside them, he brushed his hand over her firm, rounding tummy, a father's last caress of his child, yet unborn, to bring it up to his eyes to wipe them.

"Soldier, back to camp!" Colonel Canham barked. And as Dalton started to walk away from Hetty, "at the double!" he shouted.

Dalton ran up the road without looking back and as he disappeared from Hetty's view, Colonel Canham turned to her and said slightly less authoritatively, "You had best go home Ma'am."

That evening the Company Chaplain visited Hetty at the tranquil Kings Arms and told her that she may as well head back to London; Dalton would not be allowed out of camp again.

Chapter 25

Tragedy in Training

April/May 1944.

On the Sunday morning of the 16th April, 1st Battalion marched out of Ivy Bridge Camp to cross the Erme River for the last time. As the soldiers turned to walk up the valley they knew so well, residents stood to watch and wave the soldiers goodbye. The lively, confident young men would be missed and the town transformed back to how it was a year earlier, or at least almost so.

Climbing the steep hill, the soldiers finally wheeled left to reach the station and the train that would carry them on the next phase of their journey. Clouds were building over the moor behind them as a fresh wind again blew up the valley from Plymouth, yet still they would miss this place. Dalton stood on the platform and looked down onto the town, an uncontrollable desire gripping him to see his Hetty for she was only a few hundred yards away.

When the train was delayed and everyone was told to stand easy, Dalton saw his chance and impulsively slipped away. Keeping away from the roads, he made a dash for the Kings Arms, confident that if Lieutenant Donaldson discovered him missing, he would be alright about it, provided he made it back for the train.

"Your boots are muddy Slaughter," Donaldson said when some time later Dalton edged back amongst the men on the platform. As Donaldson moved on down past other soldiers, he looked back and winked.

Travelling east, the men were slowly pulled across the viaduct and by the time the engine had picked up speed, even the chimney of the paper mill could no longer be seen. Then with the rhythm of the locomotive established, the soldiers focused their thoughts on what lay ahead. By 4p.m. they had reached Blandford Camp in Dorset, their home until being moved to their marshalling area, just prior to the invasion.

At Blandford the soldiers received specialised equipment and Robert Torrence, the B Company supplies man, waxed his jeep and trailer to protect them from the effects of salt water. The countdown had begun. In late April and early May there would be two, full scale, final dry runs onto Slapton Sands. One for the Utah invasion force and one for the Omaha force. For the final dry runs, the top brass wanted units to be stationed in the same location as they would be just prior to D-Day, hence 1st Battalion's early departure from Ivy Bridge.

1st Battalion had participated in several smaller scale exercises onto Slapton. On 12th February they had trucked down to Brixham, boarded an LST and early on the 14th, crawled down cargo netting into LCVPs (Higgins landing craft) just off shore from Torquay. These then carried the men several miles back westward to make a beach assault as part of Operation Duck 2. On the 8th March they boarded the USS APA 33 at Weymouth. On the 11th they transferred again into LCVPs to make another assault onto the beach in the early morning hours. Completing the push inland on the 12th they then walked the 20 miles back to Ivy Bridge from near Cousins Cross. Thus together with a previous exercise, Duck 1 in January, 1st Battalion knew Slapton well.

But the final dry runs would be a world apart from these previous exercises. The final dry run for the Utah Beach invasion force was called Exercise Tiger and took place before Exercise Fabius, the final dry run for Omaha. Both Tiger and Fabius came as close to the real thing as could be managed without drawing too much attention from the enemy. With troops and equipment leaving from the same ports upon the same ships as they would do on D-Day, other facets were scheduled into a programme which although complicated, was infinitely less daunting than the real thing.

Generals Bradley and Eisenhower were concerned at the inexperience of their troops, for only one of the eleven divisions had seen combat, the 1st Division in Africa. They therefore decided that live ammunition would be used extensively in the final dry runs as a way of countering this perceived inadequacy. But the ranks were not officially told of the decision and not all officers were informed as to the full extent to which live fire would be used. The troops had much to learn, but then so did the generals. Not least about the likely losses of 1st Battalion's full frontal assault on Dog Green, Omaha. Perhaps live ammo would help everyone become better educated.

In readiness for Exercise Fabius, B Company was trucked out of Blandford Camp at 0800hrs on the 24th April to travel the fifteen miles to the marshalling area. The same marshalling area they would use for D-Day, designated D-1, D for the county of Dorset and 1 indicating the village of Dewlish, just twelve miles from their port of embarkation, Weymouth. The whole of the 116th Regiment was encamped there, all three battalions under Colonel Canham.

During their six day wait at Dewlish, Exercise Tiger took place on Slapton and it was a catastrophe. Despite extensive efforts to keep it a secret, word got round of something major going wrong; from those involved in the cleanup operation out at sea and on the beach, the ambulance drivers and hospital workers, and those who saw the bodies washing up in the harbours and beaches and the diggers burying the dead.

The enlisted men at Dewlish were confined to camp and the camp supposedly sealed. But security wasn't as it would be before the invasion and many men slipped out. And there were those who came and went every day, the engineers and servicing guys, caterers and delivery people to pass on the Chinese whispers - the worst sort of communication, especially for those about to carry out an identical exercise. Then there were the more senior officers who had to be told and the lesser ones who didn't, but got to hear anyway; never in detail, just the implications.

The men involved in Exercise Tiger hit Slapton Sands just after day break on 28th April. Almost immediately, the live naval fire and the live fire from the defenders' machine guns and artillery caused fear and confusion amongst the disembarking troops; with some platoons even pushing into the white taped-off area before the naval bombardment ceased. Men were dumbstruck at the casualties about them and most believed that they had actually landed in France. But casualty rates reduced as defenders became aware they were hitting GIs and some semblance of procedure was restored amongst the invading troops. Finally the beach was secured and a push inland initiated.

But the worst aspect of Tiger as word would have it, involved its LSTs (Landing Ship Tanks); these followed in after the infantry. An LST was an ocean going vessel of about five thousand tons. It had a flat bottom, was slow and difficult to manoeuvre but capable of landing several hundred men, lorries and tanks. The 4th Division's convoy of eight LSTs, each travelling some 400 yards behind the other, crossed Lyme Bay in the early hours of 28th April.

The coastal waters between the ports of departure and Slapton had become very busy in the preceding months with practice runs purely for naval vessels and then smaller scale exercises with troops and equipment, such as Duck 1 and Duck 2.

The enemy were aware of the increase in coastal traffic, though unaware of the purpose and had several times slipped through defensive cordons to achieve successful hits on transports, though fortunately not thus far when men were being carried. But on the night of the 28th, nine E Boats stumbled across 4th Division's convoy of eight LSTs. An E Boat was a well armed, manoeuvrable vessel, 100 feet in length and very fast, capable of up to 40 knots. The E Boats had slipped out of Cherbourg the night before and avoided defensive screens in the channel to happen upon the slow LSTs with just the moonlight as a backdrop.

With torpedoes, 20mm and 40mm guns, the E Boats were versatile hunter killers, but in the dark, could only guess at the defensive potential of the convoy. They were not to know that it had been left virtually unprotected and that some 4,000 men were at their mercy.

Around 2a.m. an E Boat strafed the lead LST (LST 515) and in the confusion, the second LST also strafed LST 515. The LST at the rear of the convoy was then hit by torpedoes and sank with all its men and equipment. Two more LSTs were subsequently hit by torpedoes within seconds of each other. One rolled over and sank within six minutes, whilst the other crawled back to port. For some reason the attack was then called off but the death toll reached 946 soldiers and sailors before survivors were hauled out of the freezing water many hours later.

The disaster was a great shock for all divisions. It defined the reality of their circumstance and highlighted the vulnerability of the invasion force. Removing the bodies from the water, beaches and harbours was of major importance not just for morale but to prevent any indication that the disaster had happened at all; for the Germans might realise its significance and the proximity to Normandy might also have indicated that an invasion was planned for that part of the coast.

In particular, recovery vessels searched for the bodies of a handful of missing officers who knew the time and place of D-Day. Had one been hauled from the water by an E Boat, then under interrogation, everything might be revealed. Eventually all such officers were accounted for. Survivors were treated under strict security. The fit were isolated and those hospitalised forbidden to speak of the incident. The able-bodied were later separated and placed into different units.

But despite the care with which the terrible events of Exercise Tiger were handled, an air of gloom lay over the senior officers with the prospect of even more casualties during Exercise Fabius, scheduled six days after Tiger.

On 30th April B Company trucked out of Dewlish to Weymouth, where a little before midnight they walked onto the deck of the Empire Javelin to join the rest of the 1st Battalion. They remained on board for four days whilst the hundreds of vessels manoeuvred and slowly made their way back along the coast towards Slapton.

In the early morning of 4th May, the convoy stopped several miles off shore and A Company, followed by B, C and D transferred into LCAs. (The more protective Landing Craft Assault). The naval bombardment commenced and airborne units dropped into the evacuated area behind Slapton, whilst tanks made for the beach. The ride in for 1st Battalion was uneventful except for some live naval shells falling short amongst the landing crafts and the men of B Company eventually hit Slapton at 0750hrs.

There, on the sand that had already cost the lives of too many GIs, the 202 enlisted men and eight officers of B Company negotiated the live fire from the mock defenders. The defence was less intense and better placed and beach casualties for the force as a whole were far fewer than for Tiger. However the disorganisation and confusion was still worryingly prevalent. How for example might units landing in the wrong place on Utah or Omaha, move laterally along the beach to strike their allocated target, as they had done on Slapton? Whole companies would surely be cut to pieces?

Bradley could now estimate with a little more accuracy, his likely losses; they would be substantial. He might need many more men than anticipated to throw at the German defences, particularly the Vierville Draw.

Of the eight officers, only 2nd Lieutenant Tunstall would not be leading Dalton and his buddies on D-Day. Captain Zappacosta, 1st Lieutenants Williams, Donaldson and Winkler, Second Lieutenants Taylor, Pingenot and Frisby would all be there to face the Vierville Draw, shoulder to shoulder with the men. 2nd Lieutenant Varadian would replace Tunstall on the 22nd May, two weeks before the invasion. However, only three of these eight officers would remain in command at the end of D-Day.

Twelve days after leaving Blandford Camp all men and officers of B Company safely returned there to sit and 'wait it out', to wait for their next departure, this time to the Normandy Coast and the well-trained, well- armed German forces.

Chapter 26

On The Brink of Destiny

May 1944.

Driving down the few miles from Blandford Camp on the 15th May, B Company approached the village of Dewlish from the direction of Milborne St. Andrew. With the last right hand bend in the narrow lane negotiated, the trucks descended Park Hill and provided the men with a view of the tents that sprawled across the marshalling area. At 3p.m. the sun was still high in a clear sky and the lush, green valley reflected the onset of summer as opposed to shedding the cloak of winter as it had been in April. The unusually warm spell was expected to last for some days and the D-Day planners hoped it might extend into June.

The cottage gardens now displayed the fruit of spring labour, with developing vegetable patches and early roses behind the flint stone walls. The smoke from wood burning stoves wove patches against the blue sky as housewives cooked food for hungry families and Devils Brook slipped quietly through the scene on its way towards Puddletown.

The lane down which they descended had been cut into the 75 million year old chalk hill and to their left, on the valley side, stood the Ross family cottage. The young soldiers were anxious to check it hadn't been hit by a stray enemy aircraft, because Francis Ross owned a cider press and brewed cider for the more discerning farm folk. And with a little persuasion and a bounty of gifts, Francis might also refresh a thirsty GI.

The trucks reached the valley floor, crossed the stone bridge over Devils Brook and climbed the incline on the other side to pass the twelfth century church and relatively younger tower. The wide wheel based trucks barely grazed past the walls of the flint stone cottages as they turned down Dorchester Lane to finally approach the camp. The check point at the end of the village and adjacent to the camp was the first indication that things this time would be as different as the weather.

D-1 lay just a few yards south of Dewlish Village in the grounds of Dewlish House. The Purbeck stone fronted, three hundred year old house was a magnificent building by Dalton's standards and once stood in equally magnificent grounds. But instead of trimmed hedges and immaculate lawns, the grounds were now occupied by row upon row of tents. The grass between covered by duck boards running in all directions to provide slatted walkways a few inches above the drying mud.

The grounds and thus the encampment lay east west between Dorchester Lane and Devils Brook and from Fishers Lane in the south to the hedgerow and the check point in the north. The entire perimeter was completely surrounded by barbed wire, two rolls lying side by side, with a third mounted on the other two in a triangle rising to over seven feet. It appeared to Dalton that it had become a prison camp and his observation was an accurate one. For the men were strictly confined to camp until departure. The perimeter was patrolled by British armed guards and in the days that followed rarely acknowledged the presence of the Yanks.

This was not another exercise Fabius but the real thing. And it was in the marshalling area that the ranks finally learned of their destiny. Security therefore had to be tight and the guards had orders to shoot anyone who tried to escape; the officers didn't want someone 'shouting their mouth off after a farewell drink'. Nor perhaps did they want anyone going AWOL, driven by the prospect of a bloody beach landing.

Dalton and his close buddies were directed to one of the identical eight man tents in the lower field where it rose to meet Fishers Lane on the southern boundary. They were up wind of the two incinerators which consumed all combustible waste and close to a latrine and mess tent so they considered themselves well placed. With Paul Kennedy and the rest of the platoon near him and the whole of the regiment within shouting distance, it was difficult to feel lonely. Equally, it was impossible to find personal space and the country boy thought more about home than he had done since marrying Hetty. The soldiers were now on an unstoppable tide, carrying them where it willed; to dash them upon rocks or to place them gently upon a shingle bank. In three weeks time each man's destiny would be revealed.

The whole of the 116th Regiment were again crammed into the grounds of Dewlish House and in its hay day, the Luftwaffe might have been able to wipe out all three battalions and 2,400 men in one well directed raid. But now the main danger was nerves.

The day the men were to be briefed on their mission, the atmosphere became electric. Finally they would know where they would be landing and the purpose of all that training. As men gathered in their boat teams, they learned not just of which beach, but the actual section, its defences and the team's objectives. As the more senior officers had known for months, 1st Battalion was to land on the very heavily defended Dog Green sector of Omaha Beach in Normandy. Only Charlie sector was further west, beyond which the cliffs stretched towards the Cotentin Peninsular and eventually the Atlantic.

Dalton would not be landing with the rest of his platoon. Together with Paul Kennedy, Ted, Clayton, Smiler, Staff Sergeant John Holmes and a couple of other guys, Dalton would beach with part of the heavy weapons platoon under 2nd Lieutenant Pingenot. They would be organised exactly as practiced during Exercise Fabius - eight riflemen under John Holmes supporting the weapons guys. Their LCA would again be to the far right and the western most of the six B Company LCAs. The rest of 3rd Platoon, including Austen and Allbritton would land with their own platoon's lieutenant, 2nd Lieutenant Frisby in another LCA.

The aerial photo of Dog Green portrayed a formidable reception. 2nd Lieutenant Pingenot highlighted his boat team's landing zone and pointed to the concrete machine gun, mortar and artillery emplacements. Like the others, they had been buzzing with excitement when they had huddled round to learn of their first combat mission, but as the extent of the defences sank in, they became deathly quiet.

During the briefings, every lieutenant with every boat team stressed the positive; the USAF would 'bomb the beach to hell' and the naval guns would finish off what was left. There would be plenty of bomb craters for shelter, the defenders were mostly those coerced from occupied countries and would be pleased to see their liberators and unlikely to put up a strong fight. The six B Company boat teams, (the 32 men in each LCA) were to neutralise any remaining emplacements, flush out the enemy from the French Village of Vierville and push on through the countryside of Normandy and by night fall, be at least several miles inland.

Pingenot pointed out the Vierville Draw, a gently sloping exit from the beach which led up to the village of Vierville. Like the beach landing zone, it was infested with enemy emplacements which optimistically would also be pounded to oblivion by the time the infantry arrived.

Of Dalton's buddies, Clayton was later to remark that even if all the emplacements were 'bombed to hell', the surrounding cliffs provided good vantage points for the enemy. Men exiting their craft and slowly crossing the sandy beach with their 60lb packs would be very exposed, even to small arms fire, let alone machine guns or any surviving mortar or artillery crews.

As the days passed and June approached, some men became very jittery. With the unprecedented security, feigning sick or sustaining an injury was the only way to escape the invasion. And whilst some still hoped the invasion would be unnecessary, others dreamt up reasons why they might avoid it and bolster their life expectancy. Richard Hatton, whom Dalton had known since signing up and who had met a girl from Looe in Cornwall, shot himself in the foot. And just before the off, Marchello or Marshmallow as the guys preferred to call him, suddenly became very sick and missed the beach welcome. It wasn't the first time Marshmallow had gotten sick real quick, but likely the most crucial.

Most men remained positive portraying a brave face for their buddies despite being knotted up inside, but smiles were transient and anxiety soon replaced them.

It was only the enlisted men of the infantry who were holed up; the officers, guards, engineers and servicing guys were again free to patronise the local pubs. The fourth building into the village from the camp was the Royal Oak, the only pub in Dewlish. It stood tantalisingly close to the northern boundary of the camp such that the thirsty enlisted men could see its sign and hear the tinkle of pint glasses. Without their help it still ran dry within three days of a fresh delivery of ale. The Hall and Woodhouse Brewery wagon from Blandford was usually spotted long before any other vehicle and was a sight which further tormented those who couldn't indulge.

On 1st Battalion's first visit to Dewlish for Fabius at Slapton, many of the B Company boys had slipped out for a quick pint, if not at the Royal Oak then to the Rivers Arms in the nearby village of Cheselbourne. It was no more than 1,500 yards to The Rivers Arms, by way of a well trodden path that ran across the fields and delivered the soldiers right to the back of the pub. The big challenge for B Company, in these their last days in England, was to get a soldier over 'the wire' to drink a final pint in their honour. Private First Class William Drumheller was the man to do it - and Drummer liked the idea. With his promotion from Private having been delayed because of all the fighting and trouble he had previously got into, Drumheller considered a pint worth an immediate demotion or even 'a bullet in my ass' the tough cookie joked. Thus in the gathering dusk one evening, men lifted the wire with duck boards and Drumheller crawled underneath into temporary freedom. With the Royal Oak and Rivers Arms likely crawling with officers, Drumheller crossed Devils Brook and the adjoining field to visit the Ross family on the Milborne St. Andrew Lane. Drummer wasn't discovered and returned unnoticed except for the cheers from the guys who had shared the secret. The pint was his last; Drummer was killed on the beach a few days later.

Along Dorchester Lane several posts had been planted close to the barbed wire fence with notices warning locals against 'loitering' and 'talking to the soldiers'. But that didn't stop the local lads from lingering long enough to pick up the cigarettes that the GIs would throw over the wire for them. Down the other side of the road to the wire fence, US trucks and jeeps were parked bumper to bumper right up into the village and provided a bit of cover for the lads.

With the space outside the Royal Oak often occupied by army motor bikes, the landlord, Mr William Bailey, would have to ensure that space was reserved for his grandson's pram. His daughter Elvie liked to park the pram outside for little John Burgess to get some air, so good for babies. On wheeling him in, the pram would be three times heavier, not from the fresh air, but loaded with treats from the passing GIs; gum, chocolate, cigarettes and even tins of fruit.

The first of the row of three cottages by the pub was used to billet guards for the two check points, the first point at the start of the camp and the second at the southern end of the camp, where Fishers Lane joined Dorchester Lane. Each check point was manned by three soldiers and with nothing better to do, Dalton and Paul watched Ginger, one of the more recognisable guards, check the local lads - lads Ginger now knew so well, yet despite checking them every morning and night, did so again the next day with equal authority. One of them, fifteen year old Ed Parsons, would cycle to Dewlish Lodge on Fishers Lane every weekday morning to catch the double decker bus to Weymouth College. With all the military traffic, the bus driver would often have to slip the bus into a convoy of trucks or tanks to travel the twelve miles to the coast; directed not by the British bobby, but the American military police.

After twenty-six B Company promotions from Private to Private First Class just before departure from Blandford, further promotions were made at Dewlish to account for predicted casualties and the reorganisation into boat teams.

On 16th May, Sergeant Womack was promoted to Staff Sergeant and Corporals Brennan, Churchill, Ferrell, Kucera and Malmberg were promoted to Sergeants. Four of these six served at their new rank only until the 6th June; Womack, Kucera and Malmberg died on the beach and Joseph Churchill died of his wounds the next day.

At 8.30p.m. on the 16th May, just a few hours after the six guys were promoted, Pfc Walker Parrish returned to duty after spending eleven days in hospital. Forty- eight hours later he was critically injured.

On the morning of the 18th May, whilst Dalton was on guard duty, Staff Sergeant Palmieri and a group of B Company men including Walker Parrish were standing in a circle passing a live rifle grenade around. Charlie Conner the Virginian who had joined the company at Ivy Bridge and shared Dalton's hut, stepped back from the group as did several other men. Why mess with live ammo when you didn't have to, so Charlie thought, remembering his basic training.

When Palmieri jokingly flung the rifle grenade across to Parrish, Parrish was caught unawares and dropped it. As the grenade fell to the ground the surrounding men fell with it into disbelief. For on hitting the duck board it exploded. Parrish took the brunt of the shrapnel and most of the men in the circle were injured, some severely. One guy had shrapnel enter his eyes and another was hit in the throat. Several men had shrapnel enter their groin whilst most of the men were splattered in the legs and torso. Ironically, Palmieri was least hurt. Charlie ran for help and flagged a Red Cross truck to the area. It took several frantic minutes for Charlie to notice he too had been hit. Despite being well back from the group he had taken several small pieces of shrapnel in the hip and his trousers were full of blood. Altogether twenty-one men were injured and transferred either to the 228th Station Hospital or to the 50th Field Hospital. When Dalton saw Walker Parrish's boots brought back from the range, the prospects didn't look good for the guy; five days later, on May 23rd, Parrish died. In his morning report of that day, Zappacosta simply wrote,

'Parrish, Walker L Pfc Absent sick at 50th Field Hosp to deceased 0355hrs'.

Many of the injured men didn't make the invasion. However despite his condition, Charlie Conner was back on duty on the 28th May and landed on the beach 6th June with his wounds still taped up.

On the 20th May, to replenish B Company's depleted boat teams, soldiers were transferred from other companies: seven from Headquarters Company, four from A including Harold Baumgarten and three from D. It was like Russian roulette, move to B Company and survive or die, whereas before, a different fate might have awaited. Eight of the fourteen men transferred died on the beach and two were severely wounded. Harold Baumgarten, who had only just joined the battalion three months earlier, was now having to change his unit again and would have even less time to get to know the guys.

After the final kit preparations when uniforms were water proofed and gas proofed, the last days of May were spent grinding down the hours. Many men just sank into their own thoughts or wrote letters home. Others released the tension by playing baseball, firing off their weapons at the range or playing cards with a bunch of rowdy buddies. Some of the men got fatalistic and became lackadaisical with their bets, whilst the more optimistic were happy to relieve them of their pay. Everyone was issued with French Francs and Smiler wondered how many it would take to hire the equivalent of a Piccadilly Commando. Clayton explained to Smiler that he might have to wait until they liberated Paris. "Paris?" Smiler inquired, "Who's she?"

On the 31st May, with strong indication that B Company would depart the next day, Dalton went back to his tent to write his last letter to Hetty. Austen, Allbritton and Clayton decided to watch a film in the large 'cinema tent' and Dalton considered it a good time to concentrate with them out the way. As he lay on his cot, Ted and Paul Kennedy crawled in to sit on their beds and write home as well. Quiet and in solemn mood the three buddies wrote to their loved ones and perhaps said things that in peace time would never have issued from a twenty year old's hand. But with the uncertainty of tomorrow they told their parents they loved them, girls that they would marry them when they came home and asked questions about things that normally would have seemed inconsequential. Ted wrote not only to the parents he worshipped but also to his childhood sweetheart, her picture many suspected being secretly tucked away in his breast pocket with that of his parents. A year earlier, the men had been encouraged to take out a $10,000 life policy. It cost only $6 a month and was deducted straight from their pay packets. Ted's platoon buddies were split 50/50 as to who they thought Ted had made his out to.

Dalton had changed his beneficiary to Hetty so that she might be able to support herself and their child. Dalton was convinced that in a few months time he would be father to a son. And in keeping with Virginian tradition, he intended to name him Dalton. As Paul Kennedy finished writing, he leant over and said, "Tell Hetty, if anything happens to you, I'll look after her."

Dalton smiled and pushed Paul's head away, "I'm coming back," he said.

Dalton slipped his letter to Lieutenant Donaldson who would ensure it was promptly posted; Donaldson had joined B Company at Ivy Bridge and soon earned the respect of the ranks. He understood his men and knew Dalton well, "Don't try going AWOL tonight," he told Dalton as he took the letter.

"No sir," Dalton replied with a big grin. Donaldson wasn't the only lieutenant to have caught Dalton slipping off to see Hetty. One weekend at Ivy Bridge he had gone through the bushes at the back of camp. Returning by way of the back gate, 1st Lieutenant Williams caught him. Dalton told Williams that Sergeant Maddox had given him permission. But the excuse didn't wash and the following day, Dalton received extra duties on a march over Dartmoor. As the officers left camp for a last drink, men could watch their progress towards the Royal Oak along Dorchester Lane. Donaldson was the first back to join his men; he had posted more than one letter and hopefully some of his own, for he was killed by machine gun fire within seconds of disembarking onto Omaha Beach.

In the late evening light as Dalton strolled to nowhere in particular, two guys stood at the wire on Fishers Lane telling a local couple that they had been issued with French money. "We probably won't be here tomorrow evening," they added, to which the lady responded "Oh dear ... well, good luck and ... take care." And whilst the breach of security went unnoticed except by Dalton, the rest of the men prepared themselves in their own individual way for what lay ahead.

Chapter 27

Weymouth and the Well Known, Best Kept Secret

June 1944.

On the 1st June, after seventeen days at Dewlish, B Company finally left the marshalling area and headed for Weymouth. Exiting the barbed wire encampment, the trucks crossed Fishers Lane and headed down the mile long Coach Lane towards Dewlish Lodge. As they rounded the brow of the first incline, still within the grounds of Dewlish House, the men lost sight of the tents. Behind them, May blossom, torn from the bordering hedgerows by the wide vehicles was strewn across the lane, to pale and shrivel like forgotten confetti. With the fading of the engine noise, the hawthorns were left to regain shape and colour, and soon, would show no trace that these men had ever passed this way.

At Dewlish Lodge the trucks passed out through the elaborate gates of the grounds, said to be from the Summer Palace in Peking. Designed for horse drawn coaches not the vehicles of the US Army, the large stone spheres crowning the pillars had again been knocked to the floor. During their short stay, the transport guys had likely dislodged and replaced them more times than anyone would like to admit.

A sharp turn of the wheel after clearing the historic gates left the trucks facing west on the A354. Then directed by American military police the convoy headed towards Weymouth via Dorchester. Waiting for them in Portland Harbour was the Empire Javelin, ready to take them across the channel.

To some, the accident with the rifle grenade was a bad omen and without the friends they had known for so long 'things just didn't seem right'. Yet when departure from Dewlish had finally been announced, bravado dictated a longing to get on with the job. Entering Dorchester,

Drumheller pointed to a pub and said, "Next week, I'll be drinking a beer in Paris."

Dalton sat by Paul Kennedy and Clayton, each with their own thoughts. Clayton observed his surroundings as he had done so often from train windows, the back of trucks and whilst on marches. He had looked out upon much that had interested him; twelfth century churches, tenth century castles and five thousand year old standing stones. "I'll come back after the war," he remarked as they passed through the old Roman town of Dorchester. "Look up a bit of history," he said to no one in particular.

Clayton often spoke of things few could conceive. He intended to teach High School after the war, 'a crazy idea' so most of his buddies thought. But there in the back of the truck as he inhaled the relaxing smoke of yet another Lucky Stripe, Clayton decided he would bring his daddy back with him; to spend some time together, for it was Clayton's daddy who had nurtured his interest in the past. Clayton was sure laid back except when it came to education and as Clayton often quoted his father, 'England's history makes ours look like yesterday's news'. But Clayton would not come back and he would never know that in the field just beyond the northern edge of Dewlish Camp lay the site of an ancient British village, Dewlish, being Celtic for Dark Stream. Nor that under the soil near Fishers Lane, within yards of his now empty tent, lay the remains of a fifty room Roman Villa, with mosaics and under-floor heating.

In one of the accompanying jeeps sat the Chaplain, destined to land on Omaha a little after the men. He would be needed and God's work must be done. A few days earlier he had visited the company's GI Brides to tell them that their husbands would not be receiving any more leave. The wives read between the lines and he was glad of it, for he couldn't thus be accused of breaching security. Hetty Slaughter worried him most for she was pregnant. The pretty thing hardly showed her condition and he recalled how nervous and vulnerable she had looked. It was one thing to be a widow, quite another to be one with a child, for his experience dictated that such women faced years of loneliness. He had subtly warned them to be careful and yet now questioned his judgement; perhaps he should have been more direct. But then the youngsters of today didn't seem to consider the conscquences of their actions. How often soldiers wanted to leave a legacy and wives to retain it, such was the influence of war and the brevity of an infantryman's lot. At least Hetty wasn't going to America to have her baby as Dalton's mother had requested. Ethel Eaglestone had put paid to that, 'look a right state walking down the gang plank like that', she had said to her daughter. Not very subtle, but effective, the Chaplain reflected. The Eaglestones had only ever met one of Dalton's family and otherwise knew little about them. Robbie, Dalton's youngest brother, had visited just once whilst stationed near Banbury; he had arrived late after a few drinks and left quickly after breakfast and the family hadn't been impressed. It was probably a good thing that Hetty would stay in England, the Chaplain considered. And with those thoughts, he looked back at his men knowing all his prayers could not be answered and women like Hetty would have to find their own way down the path they had chosen.

At Dorchester the road to Weymouth port became clogged with military traffic. The B Company trucks crawled along, stopped, and then crawled again and it appeared as if the invasion might have to be delayed because of the jam. Bob Sales of 2nd Platoon hung out the side of his truck and looked skyward. How could all this movement be missed he wondered and searched for a German reconnaissance plane that surely would fly over any minute. He looked towards Dalton's truck and 3rd Platoon crawling along in front and nodded to the men he had known for so long. Three years was a long time. They had come so far and experienced so much and to Bob they felt 'like brothers'.

Bob Sales had joined the company in '41 at the age of sixteen, having lied about his age; nineteen now and still one of the youngest.

Bob stared on past 3rd Platoon at the long column of vehicles and again was unable to conceive how this vast contingent and the armada of waiting ships would not be detected. All the residents of Dorset County seemed to know the invasion was about to unfold, so why didn't the enemy? People lined the route; young girls waved with big beautiful smiles, Great War veterans watched with tears in their eyes and mothers held up children for the soldiers to kiss; a last encounter with tenderness, the love of a child for good luck. For the child upheld and the children of that child, these soldiers would lay down their lives for their freedom. "God protect you," Dalton heard an old woman call out from the crowd. And there were some He did.

In France, Belgium, Norway and the other occupied European countries which bordered the sea ways from the UK, the waiting enemy knew that an invasion was imminent. But they didn't know where or exactly when. Over the past several months, the British intelligence services had gone to enormous lengths to convince the Germans that the invasion would occur anywhere other than Normandy. The deception had been extensive and highly sophisticated and any slip up, even at this late stage, might cost countless lives and even cause the invasion to fail.

They had created two fictitious armies 'assigned' to Scotland, which consisted of no more than sixty people in Edinburgh castle. These specialized intelligence personnel sent endless radio messages characteristic of Armies with armoured, infantry and airborne divisions. Communications about supplies, promotions, unit movements and so on for the benefit of the eavesdropping enemy, to convince them that a large force was stationed in Scotland. Half a million German troops and two Panzer armies were thus maintained in Norway, in the belief that the build up was in preparation for an invasion there; an invasion which potentially could push through Sweden and then Denmark to enter Germany from the north. How different the odds if these enemy forces were relocated behind the Normandy beaches, rather than being tied down by sixty intelligence staff.

The biggest deception however was in persuading the Germans that the invasion might take place at Pas de

Calais. Pas de Calais presented the shortest distance from England and had port facilities crucial in supporting an invading force. It thus seemed the obvious choice to many German officers, who were conscquently more receptive to the deceit. Hundreds of plywood and cloth landing craft were floated on rivers and estuaries in the south-east. Fake barracks were built and fake tanks and other vehicles were placed in fields and lanes. Miles of tank and other vehicle tracks were created by dragging suitable objects behind lorries and again radio traffic was made to indicate the presence of large armies in the area. German aerial reconnaissance and radio eavesdropping therefore indicated that there was a large build up of armies just across the water from Calais. Their secret agents reported the same. Yet all German spies had been captured and those still 'operating' were acting as double agents, delivering only that which facilitated the deception. As a consequence, many German infantry divisions and armoured units were tied down behind Calais by no more than dummy equipment and intelligence personnel sending endless fictitious messages.

The real trick for the British intelligence services however, would be to convince the Germans that even after the Normandy Invasion had commenced, Calais remained the real target. In this way a foothold might be achieved before reserve units were sent towards the Normandy beaches and before the spare capacity at Calais could be moved the two hundred miles down the coast.

The plans of MI5 and MI6 were ingenious but helped by the fact that many German officers believed it too difficult for the allies to secure suitable port facilities in Normandy. These same officers considered that any invasion in Normandy would be a feint. The invasion would require ten divisions to be landed during the first five days and one division per day thereafter. Ten thousand tons of supplies would have to be landed on the first day and two weeks later, eighteen thousand tons a day would be required to keep the invading force fed, watered, armed and advancing. The Germans knew the statistics well, they had invaded many times. They knew that only so much could be landed by vulnerable landing craft and if a port wasn't achieved in the first two or three days the invasion would stall and fail. In Normandy, it would be virtually impossible to secure a port in the first few days. The invasion would not take place in Normandy, the Germans concluded.

The greatest guarded secret of all in the invasion planning was the fact that the allies were taking ports with them. These massive, yet secret engineering projects would result in quays, causeways and storm protection units being floated across the channel to establish a port on Omaha beach and a port at Arromanches, one of the two British invasion beaches. It was this that made the invasion of Normandy viable - a most vital secret within a wealth of secrets.

Halfway between Dorchester and Weymouth and with just three miles of friendly soil left to cover, the convoy of B Company trucks reached their highest point on the chalk downs, the Ridgeway. There they gained a panoramic view of Weymouth Bay and of Portland Harbour. The protected waters were packed with ships: cruisers, destroyers, battle ships and troop ships, most of them at anchor, a few manoeuvring. Smaller vessels such as mine sweepers and LSTs (landing ship tanks) plied this way and that, and still smaller boats scuttled around avoiding all the others.

Private Robert Gentry sat opposite Dalton on the truck. He had shadowed Dalton for some time following the wedding, even visiting him at the Kings Arms when Hetty was down for the weekend. With precious little time together they had to ask him to leave and not visit again. From what Gentry had said to her, Hetty knew he wanted to step into Dalton's shoes if anything happened. But sitting there, looking at Dalton in the truck, Gentry didn't have much longer to dwell on his intentions nor Dalton to worry about them.

Descending slowly into Weymouth, with military equipment and men converging on the port, the convoy's movement became even more of a snail's pace. The reception for the soldiers was as jubilant as that in Dorchester and try as they might, most men found it difficult to behold the enormity of the responsibility which had befallen them. Then being no more than helmets within a seething mass, B Company joined the others on the esplanade, to slowly make their way to the hards - the concrete wharfs for loading. Many of the beach defences, simply metal scaffolding poles driven into the sand, braced and capped with barbed wire, had been removed. Crews had since practised landing their amphibious vehicles there: the jeeps, tanks and trucks with raised exhausts and air inlets. The landing craft tanks, gunboats and rocket launchers plied amongst the armada and the USS Texas loomed large above them. Weymouth Bay contained more ships than even on a pre-war navy day, when the home fleet would visit and the beach would be packed with holiday makers. Again, Bob Sales looked skyward searching for the German reconnaissance plane that must surely come soon, at low altitude to miss the Radar station at Ringstead. And though the line of barrage balloons waited to ensnare it, thankfully they waited in vain.

With their gaiters rising above their brown boots, the B Company men shuffled behind the general issue before them and slowly made their way to the landing craft being used to ferry the soldiers over to their troop ships. The Empire Javelin, anchored in Portland Harbour, had sent out eight LCAs and each would have to make three or four trips to get all 800 1st Battalion men across. The wind picked up as the columns moved forward and the good weather of May having ebbed away with the month, was now gone. The Bofors guns and the steel ropes of barrage balloons cut the stiff breeze and framed the buildings along the esplanade as grey cloud rushed eastward above them. Descending the concrete steps of Weymouth quay, Dalton and his buddies stepped away from the safety of England. By 5p.m. they were on the Empire Javelin - next stop, Omaha.

Chapter 28

Enough Harm

Paddington, April/May 1944.

"We don't wanna go talking about yer condition 'til we 'ave to," Ethel said to her daughter when Hetty suggested that people must be noticing her growing tummy.

Edith looked at her mother knowingly; she was planning ahead, in case of bad news, of that she was convinced.

"Hetty is too obedient for her own good," Edith told Pat Harrison later when Pat came to see them. "Easily manipulated, that's Hetty, and easily taken advantage of, particularly by that brother of ours." Pat nodded in agreement; she had seen the way Jimmy spoke to her.

"The money she's lent him and not got back," Edith continued, shaking her head. "But then if Dalton was a real man he wouldn't put up with it, my Tom wouldn't."

"Maybe she ain't told Dalton," Pat suggested, knowing Hetty almost as well as Edith.

"Yeah, maybe," Edith replied as she continued to knit a cardigan for her daughter. Serves 'em right then, Edith thought. "Shame though she can't go talking about the baby," she said to Pat, returning to Hetty's condition. "Telling everybody and talking about it was the fun bit ..." Edith recalled, "easy then, didn't 'ave to feed or change 'er."

Pat laughed and thought of the dreams she once had of a life with Roy.

"Lucky Hetty," she said to Edith who looked up questioningly. "Or maybe not," she added, for the thought struck her that Roy and Dalton might be heading into combat at any moment. The whole country seemed to know an invasion was imminent and Pat was convinced of it. "Just need to go down the night clubs," she told Edith. "First all the army and navy boys disappear, then last week the air force," Pat said with an element of frustration.

"Blooming boring," she added as Edith organised her wool for the change in colour.

"Not as boring as looking after a bleeding kid all day, every day," Edith said. But then Pat would learn as Hetty was about to.

The 300,000 United States Air Force personnel were based almost entirely in East Anglia, north-east of London. The airfields covered these counties at little more than ten miles apart and London night life during May declined to almost pre-war days. If the Germans wanted an indication as to when the invasion might commence, they should have posted a spy at one of the dance clubs.

Word in the pub was that Jerry would throw everything 'at em' as soon as they stepped on the beach. The old soldiers who debated tactics around the tables of the Shirland thought they knew exactly what Jerry would do. Stamp out the invasion on the beaches or create a stalemate and walk back to Germany and try again in another twenty years. If Italy was any indication, then there was going to be another blood bath. Germany might be under threat from the Russians in the east and the Allies to the south, but it was still capable of offering formidable resistance. Even whilst James Eaglestone sat with his old army friends in the Shirland, slowly drinking a pint or two and debating Jerry's options, Rommel was strengthening his beach defences along the French coast ready for the inevitable.

Italy.

Paul Brooks thought of Hetty as his Lancaster Bomber taxied down the captured Italian runway near Brindisi. The squadron had been moved from North Africa as the ground troops advanced, but now the advance had halted at the Gustav Line.

Despite what Hetty had done to him, Paul still loved her. He would always love her, of that he was convinced and no one could replace her. He knew he shouldn't have, but the last time he left home to be stationed overseas, he secretly stowed away a photo of Hetty and every time he looked at it, his feelings of loss became more intense. As the fuselage shook under the weight of its payload and rose into the blue Mediterranean sky, Paul hoped that the rings he still kept might yet be called upon. War played strangely on young minds and he knew better than most not to make assumptions; nothing was certain.

The squadron had flown this path many times, for the ground troops had not moved in six months. The route was familiar and the reception from the German defences predictable. The long white beaches bordering the Adriatic slipped away as the aircraft gained height; the rugged mountains replacing the still green vegetation, the grass preparing to be scorched by the heat of summer.

First produced in early 1942, the Lancaster was the most versatile of British heavy bombers. Able to carry 14,000 lbs of bombs to a range of 1,200 miles, the formidable aircraft carried pilot, flight engineer, navigator, wireless operator, two gunners and a bomb aimer. Under fighter attack, all were gunners or their replacements except the pilot and whilst bombing, all rallied to the cause. Of the three gun turrets, one amid ships, one in the nose and one in the extreme tail, it was the tail gunner who 'copped it the most'. Despite having four .303 Browning machine guns in a hydraulically operated turret, the tail gunner's vital, yet isolated position, made him prime bait for enemy fighters. Charlie Stern, Hetty's old school friend was a tail gunner and 'he didn't last long'. But of Paul's destiny Hetty took longer to find out.

The visibility was perfect as the Bomber Squadron approached the deep river valleys of the Gustav Line and the seven man crew prepared for the role each would have to play. Paul hoped that the Luftwaffe would be occupied elsewhere this day, they had downed too many crews and the shrapnel from anti- aircraft guns seemed preferable to the 20mm and 7.9mm bullets that the German fighters unleashed.

After the July '43 landings on Sicily, Allied troops finally hit the Italian mainland in September at Reggio di Calabria, Taranto and Salerno. But the 'soft under belly of the Axis' proved anything but soft. Hitler poured men and equipment into the country and used the topography of the Apennine Mountains to maximum advantage. The many large rivers and steep sided valleys running east and west to both coasts proved treacherous and as winter approached, Allied progress slowed to a halt. In November, British, American, New Zealand and French forces were facing the Gustav Line which ran along the Sangro and Garigliano Rivers and included Monte Cassino. But by May '44 they had still not completely broken it and Rome, half way up the country, was still in German hands.

With the payload released, Paul's bomber followed a wide sweep away from the defences and headed for home. As they turned south with the sun bearing directly into the cockpit, a Messerschmitt swooped upon it, strafing it with its 7.9mm machine gun, synchronised to fire through the single propeller. Nonchalantly the steel shells bore holes into the thin fuselage of the Lancaster, creating jagged edges which in the slip stream were as flimsy as autumn leaves in a passing gale. Zipping through the interior they hit only strengthening braces and equipment before bursting out the other side. But then a second and final burst was released from some distance, perhaps meant for another aircraft. Stray bullets crossed the air space to be slowed down by the huge distance; some penetrated the fuselage and one the fabric of Paul's seat. With its last remaining energy the 7.9mm bullet entered Paul's spine to lodge there, between the vertebrae, imbedded in the spinal cord.

As the plane limped home, the crew did what they could for Paul, and back at the airfield so did the medical staff. The decision to fly him back to England was taken with much debate, but if there was any chance of saving him, then send him they must. To remove the bullet might kill him and not to would definitely do so and if he was spared, then paralysis was a certainty from the waist down.

London.

It was from his hospital bed in London that Paul wrote to Hetty asking her to come and see him. His letters home had always arrived long after events unfolded but not this letter. And of the many he wrote, there was only the one to Hetty. When it arrived at the end of May '44, Ethel shared the contents only with her husband.

'Please come and see me, I want, I need to see you one last time', Paul pleaded, 'I've not said anything to anyone about wanting to see you', he assured her. 'It's just between the two of us'. And after hinting at the seriousness of his wounding, told Hetty 'I will be waiting for you ... with love, Paul'.

"She's done enough harm to that boy already," James Eaglestone said, agreeing with his wife that Hetty should not be told, "It'll finish him off, seeing her pregnant."

June in London felt more like winter had returned and Hetty wrapped her light summer coat around her to walk to the Harrow Road shops.

"Where's the summer gone?" everyone was asking, falsely believing as they did every warm spell that it might actually continue.

'That's it till next year', her father always joked and often wasn't far from the mark.

Hetty was optimistic as usual and despite her mother's warning wasn't dressed for the rain that started to fall as she turned the corner from Rundell onto Marylands. She had received Dalton's last letter, the one posted by First Lieutenant Donaldson far quicker than the rest, for it came courtesy of the Royal Mail uncensored except by the vigilant Lieutenant. Now she would post yet another to him, intending to write every day in the hope that sometime, somewhere they would all catch up with him. The rain started to spit at first and then became a downpour as the wind picked up along the grey street, willing her to return home. Perhaps she should have left it to her mother to post? She was strangely cold by the time she walked but a few yards down Marylands, as if she had a fever. Getting a little wet had never made her feel so shivery before. But then she was getting a lot of headaches lately and she never used to have headaches before either. And stomach pains, which the doctor said was nothing to worry about.

The bomb sites always looked bleaker to Hetty in the rain, a stark reminder of what they had all gone through. The houses along Marylands between Rundell and Oakington, hit by the landmine three years earlier had all been cleared - the area no more than a long pit with scattered bricks and timbers ignored by the workmen and becoming toys for the boys who built dens and fires in their new playgrounds.

In the years following the Blitz, there had been relatively little bombing, with just the lone aircraft or two, dropping their bomb loads and making a dash back across the channel. The only period of consistent threat was at the beginning of the year. The 'Baby Blitz' as it was called or 'Operation Steinbock' had hit London as it had other cities like Exeter. Despite targeting tourist sites, there was the inevitable overspill and even Paddington caught some of the tonnage, which strategically would have been better used for Hitler's more pressing priorities.

The Eaglestones had finally received a shelter of their own, a Morrison, free of charge, because the household earned less than £350 per year. In fact they received two, which James Eaglestone stacked one upon the other. Everyone Hetty knew had just the one and had replaced their dining table with it, ready to dive under in a raid. Hetty would never forget the night Dalton was visiting and the air raid siren sounded. Her mother insisted she and Dalton take refuge in the lower Morrison, whilst her mum and dad lay in the one above. Not Dalton's idea of a cosy night she recalled with a smile. Just over six feet in length and little more than two feet, six inches high, the steel cage with mesh sides wasn't the best location for a couple who saw each other infrequently. But then her mother told her 'that sort of thing' wasn't any good for a baby anyway. Little chance of 'that sort of thing' Hetty thought, with Mum and Dad lying half an inch away, beyond the steel plate which formed the roof of their encasement.

It felt like March weather as Hetty neared the Harrow Road. Her shivering worried her for it wasn't cold as in winter cold. Dalton often said that the English were 'never happy with the weather, either too hot or too cold'. And he was right. Afterwards she had noticed it. In May people were saying 'can't stand this heat' whilst the previous month it had been 'I'm fed up with this cold weather'. Dalton liked the heat, could sit out in it all day, so it seemed to Hetty. She couldn't stand the heat, preferred the shade, 'wait till I take you to Virginia', Dalton had said when she moved into the shade of a London Plane in Green Park.

As Hetty slipped Dalton's letter into the post box the rain eased so Hetty decided to 'nip down' to Bradley and Perrins. The department store sat on the opposite corner to the Prince of Wales pub where Great Western Road hit the Harrow Road and it had a baby section. Hetty liked looking at the baby things and she might just buy some Terry Towelling nappies, after all, she could at least prepare for the baby; a boy, her mother said, 'cause it was all at the front'.

As Hetty walked past the linen department Mrs. Cretchley from number 33 was talking with another neighbour, each like Hetty, a little wet from the rain.

"Hello," they said, almost in unison.

"How you feeling and how's baby?" Mrs. Cretchley asked, as if everyone knew. Hetty relaxed a little, even though she had come over very tired with the extra walk. Unusual she thought; for normally she could have marched all the way back from the Kilburn High Road, laden with bags.

"Expect you're upset about Paul," the other neighbour commented on noticing Hetty's weary face, then realising her mistake, added, "but don't you go worryin, he's bein well looked after."

Hetty was shocked, speechless, something had happened to Paul. Sickness welled up in her, legs weakening even more, hands shaking, emptiness overcoming her delicate frame.

"He's alive, bin wounded," they said quickly, trying to calm her. Hetty gripped the counter, dizziness filling her head.

"Ere are luv," Mrs. Cretchley said supporting Hetty, "I've got you."

"Where is he?" Hetty whispered.

Mrs. Cretchley hesitated. "Why don't you go and see Mrs. Brooks, she'll tell you everything."

Hetty instantly pulled away and headed for the shop doors without another word. "Hang on luv, wait till you feel a bit better." But Hetty wasn't listening, determined to go straight to Oakington Road despite the rain which had started to fall again.

The steps up to the street door were an effort, her chest tight as if in a vice, anxiety and guilt gripping her beyond measure. What had she done to him? Poor Paul, oh poor Paul, she kept saying as she came closer to the door which separated her from the news she dreaded. Please God be alright, she pleaded as the door opened and Mrs. Brooks stood in the blackness that was overcoming her. Mrs. Brooks looked at the pale, bedraggled girl standing before her. There was no way of softening the news. She was in no mood to try. Her words were cold, brutal, like daggers to Hetty's soul and drove out any remaining breath, to cause her to collapse upon the concrete steps ...

"Paul died last night."

Chapter 29

Turbulent Water

5th and 6th June 1944.

The Empire Javelin pitched and rolled in the heavy seas as it moved away from the safety of the coast. It had slipped out of Weymouth on the night of the 4th, only to return within the hour. But now twenty-four hours later, at the tail end of the storm, she ventured once more into open water. The shuddering vibration of the oil fired engines transferred through the welds, plates and beams of the ship and its new consistency conveyed the message that there was no turning back this time. The manoeuvring had ended, everything was in place, the six thousand vessels assembled. Passing through a corridor in the English Channel, hopefully swept clear of mines, the Javelin heaved in the swell just as it heaved with the hopes and fears of the young soldiers it carried.

Having moved from Dewlish to the converted cargo ship on the 1st June, 1st Battalion had been cooped up for four days. After little sleep on the night of the 4th with the expectancy of landing, the adrenalin again flowed to keep many awake for a second night. At 1a.m. Dalton lay on the middle bunk of three with his head just a few inches from that of Paul Kennedy.

The hastily built cargo ship had been sectioned off fore and middle into shallow decks. The decks were in turn subdivided into dormitory like rooms, each furnished with triple bunks around the perimeter and capable of accommodating a platoon, some 40 men. 3rd Platoon had moved in with buoyant confidence; their banter and energy typical of a fit and well trained unit that had been together for so long. Whilst on board they had received more briefings, mustered on the upper deck, practised procedures, checked and rechecked equipment. Free time had been passed as best it could: wandering the decks, playing poker, smoking, reminiscing and talking of their plans when they got out of the army. On the night of the 4th, then again on the 5th, men had searched out buddies from other platoons, slapped backs, wished each other luck, 'see you on the beach', 'see you in Paris' they had said. But now during the first hours of the 6th, they were confined to their quarters, quiet, subdued, drifting in thought on a ship moving with such certainty towards the enemy. Listening, an outsider might never have realised that all 800 men of the 1st Battalion were on board. Even Smiler eventually became quiet and as the last hours approached, he just stared at the bunk above him, wasting most of his cigarette as it burnt slowly towards his motionless fingers.

At 2a.m. and some fourteen miles from the French coast, the Empire Javelin slowed imperceptibly to a halt; out of range of the German coastal batteries and west of the other two 116th Infantry transports, the USS Thomas Jefferson and USS Charles Carroll. The men felt the engine vibration fade to a background noise as the anchor was dropped, holding the vessel's position at the forefront of the vast armada. Now the ominous thudding of the large waves as they hit the keel could be heard reverberating through the hulk; sending a warning of menace before rolling on towards the landing beaches. The waves and surf were too high for the comfort of the officers now surveying the scene; it was clear to them that there would be casualties simply because of the weather. Landing craft were easily swamped in rough conditions and would sink without a trace with their heavy loads. And the beach obstacles with their mines were treacherous in the best of conditions, but in strong surf would be almost impossible to negotiate.

There had been no option but to delay for twenty-four hours, however Eisenhower could delay no longer. Weather forecasts had predicted improvement during the 5th through to the 6th, but worsening conditions for the 7th June. The landing therefore either had to take place on the 6th or be delayed until the next occurrence of a full moon and early morning low tide. The first to enable manoeuvring at night, the latter to give the longest possible operational hours on the first day of the assault and maximize the surprise. Further delay might jeopardise the secrecy of the whole operation. With all the equipment and men loaded and the armada of ships waiting, a risk had to be taken. Operation Overlord was given the green light - the invasion of Europe would commence.

The heavily defended section of beach they had seen on the maps at Dewlish played on Dalton's mind, such that it felt like stone rather than a living, thinking organ. He kept visualising the walk across the sand and the bullets flying everywhere. It would have to be a walk, for they were too heavily burdened. In some ways he wished he hadn't seen the maps with the cliffs, machine gun and artillery emplacements all marked out. Had he been honest with his buddies, he would have admitted to being very, very, scared. His list of fears endless, they turned over and over in his head, an inner turmoil which starkly contrasted with the exterior quietness which had befallen him. He wished he was sitting at the kitchen table at the Slaughter home place, eating his momma's hot biscuits with Hetty and his family around him. He remembered the hugs and tears on leaving home that last time when the division was recalled. 'Food for the journey', his momma had said, it had been a hell of a journey. And 'see you soon' she had lovingly added.

"See you soon Momma," Dalton said quietly into the dim cabin remembering her standing alone in the yard waving him goodbye. He rolled over on his bunk and looked almost straight into Paul's face and felt comforted; the closeness of buddies, five good buddies, they would do for now.

"We're gonna get through this in one piece," Dalton reassured Paul.

"Drink together in Paris," someone said. "A reunion in Covent Garden," said another.

"You won't have to go looking after Hetty," Dalton told Paul again, "find a pretty English girl for you and head home to good ol' Virginia together," he told his best buddy with a country drawl that drew a shout of "Country" from somewhere in the dormitory.

Paul's face broke into a smile that temporarily removed the seriousness which it had portrayed for so long.

"I know Slaughter, so you keep telling me," he quietly replied, "and I'd drink to that if Drummer had brought some booze to share." But not even Drummer had broken the rules since departing Dewlish.

Outside, the occasional escape of moonlight through the overcast skies revealed white caps on a twelve foot swell. The waves raced across the dark uninviting water, still buffeted although by a diminishing wind. The full moon had little impact on the gloom of the hour and the silhouette of the Empire Javelin mingled with the charcoal grey of its surroundings; sea, sky and ship merging on this dreary, rain-swept night. The eighteen LCAs festooned around the deck like the lifeboats of a cruise liner, rocked in the swell as they waited for the men, their cables squealing for relief as the waves struck the ship.

Sometime around 3a.m. the LCAs started to be occupied, not yet by soldiers but by the four man British Royal Navy crews who made final checks and preparations to receive the men from the decks below.

Not long afterwards, John Holmes worked his way round his squad. Like the other B Company staff sergeants, he started to rally the men, telling them to make a final equipment check and ensure everything was secure.

"Yea, we ain't comin' back this way," someone said.

"Smiler, don't forget your French letters," Austen quipped.

"First thing I packed," Smiler retorted.

Holmes started cajoling one of the guys who was beginning to shake with nerves; an authority underlying the quiet manner in which he spoke. Compassionate and calm, Holmes could always be relied upon and the younger men took heart from his composure.

Dalton checked his kit three times, pulled on every strap twice almost tearing them along the seam and then sat and waited for the order to muster on the open deck. After Montgomery and Eisenhower's message was read to the men, many felt more subdued than uplifted; for the weight of expectation seemed immense. 'You are about to embark on a Great Crusade' the message commenced, 'the hopes and prayers of liberty loving people everywhere march with you ... the free men of the world are marching together to victory ... and ... we will accept nothing less than full victory'. The message ended with 'Let us beseech the blessing of Almighty God upon this great and noble undertaking'. And after doing just that, Dalton prayed for his family, Hetty's safety and the safe delivery of their baby. He would be 25 years old in 25 days time, June 30th and he just hoped he would live to see it and the days beyond, to one day return to the life he now cherished.

At 3.25a.m. Sub Lieutenant Green was ordered to get going right away, half an hour earlier than planned to compensate for the heavy seas. Green was in charge of the eighteen LCAs and would lead the first wave of six. Five minutes later a voice crackled over the ships intercom and summoned the first wave troops to their loading stations; the announcement being preceded by 'attention on deck' as opposed to the American, 'now hear this'. The 187 men of A Company would be first to leave the ship and first on the beach. They carried their laden frames out of their quarters and trudged along the narrow gang ways and stairs to their mustering stations. The sound of kit scraping the walls and foot falls on the boards could be heard by the B Company men, but little seemed to be said.

Then, all too soon, it was B Company's turn. Dalton hoisted his kit and checked his pouches one last time. Dalton, Paul Kennedy, Staff Sergeant Holmes, Ted, Clayton and the five other privates who were joining Lieutenant Pingenot held back as the rest of 3rd Platoon walked out. Smiler, Austen and Allbritton were the last to turn out of sight and gave just the hint of a nod to the men with whom they had been so close. Without speaking, Holmes simply waved his arm and the remaining group followed on.

Confined to the ship for so long, everything seemed heavier, the stairs steeper and the gangways longer. After the narrow corridors and stairs, Dalton stepped through the double blackout curtains into the night air behind Paul

Kennedy. Paul had been made Sergeant the day before, promoted from Private First Class. Allbritton had also been promoted, from Pfc to Corporal, whilst the rest of the buddies remained as Pfc. But here on the dark deck, all men were shadows, equal among shadows.

The deck was a moving mass of subdued men. The customary smell of burning fuel oil had been replaced by the simple smell of the sea. The wind hit their sun bronzed faces and covered it in spray. Their clothes became damp and their faces moistened as though with sweat. The ship at anchor rolled in the persistent swell and the sound of the water carried up to the men and was louder than any sound they made.

One hundred or so miles back in the direction from which they had come, the hospital wards were already prepared for them. Rows and rows of empty beds with bright white sheets and recently washed blankets; the patients moved to hospitals further north. Pristine wards cleaned by the nurses at the direction of the matrons. Trolleys and operating theatres waiting and the nurses as quiet in their wards as the troops on the deck. As the ward clock ticked into the early morning hours, they thought of the soldiers as they had been before they left. Just young men lounging in the sun with their tops off and muscles tensed for the benefit of the nurses as they walked past. Smoking, talking and relaxed, the soldiers had lazed on the grass soaking up the uncharacteristic early summer sunshine. Yet now in the dimly lit wards, as the nurses looked down the rows of empty beds, they knew that the broken bodies of those same young men would start to return.

"Cigarettes out and no lighting up on the way in," came the well clipped voice of a Royal Navy Officer. He was standing at the bow of the landing craft and together with a sailor at the stern, the two were ready to guide the men on board, two at a time, one at the stern and one at the bow. All the men of B Company were now on deck, each man allocated to one of six LCAs, three on the starboard side and three on the port.

At just after 4.10a.m. the last of the A Company LCAs

slipped from view and B Company started to board. The small contingent of men from 3rd Platoon found Pingenot and his Staff Sergeant Padgett waiting for them. Clayton was the first to board and Ted the last. At four inches taller than Dalton, Ted's long legs had no difficulty in straddling the gap between the deck of the ship and that of the LCA, for each craft had been pulled in close to the side of the ship by ropes to enable the soldiers to transfer with relative ease. Slaughter and Kennedy had climbed in with their 60lb packs to sit on opposite sides of the craft. Dalton on the left side nearest the ship and Paul over onto the right side of the landing craft, a row of men between them; three rows of ten men straddling the long narrow benches. As Ted stepped down from the three foot wide deck of the LCA he sat between Dalton and Paul and immediately raised his right hand to his breast pocket and tapped the pictures inside for luck. He would look at them again once he was safely on the beach he told himself. All were now ready; Pingenot had given no orders, for no orders were necessary, the men did exactly as they had been trained, and no one this time attempted to light up, not even Clayton.

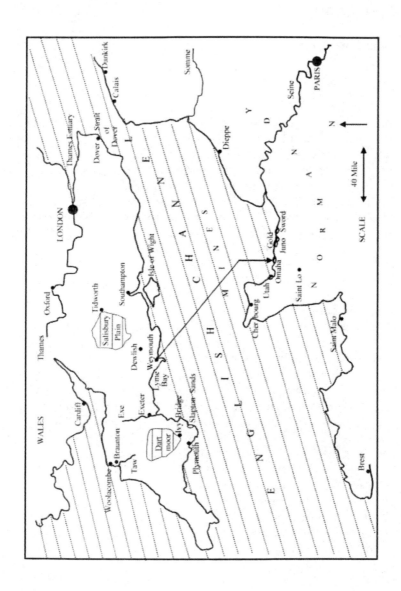

Chapter 30

Just One Life

6th June 1944.

Hanging by two cables over the side of the ship, the landing craft oscillated like a compound pendulum. A pendulum that was driven by the force 7 gusts of wind, to create a rhythm that was then superimposed upon by the natural roll of the ship as it was buffeted by the waves.

The two thick cables holding the LCA were each attached to a metal ring embedded into the craft, one at the stern and one in the floor of the craft at the bow. Hooked into the rings via a block and tackle, the cables then ran up to the davits, the strong arms which curved seaward and were fixed into the deck of the ship. With the davits taking the brunt of the weight, each cable continued on to a deck mounted winch.

The coxswain settled himself into his cockpit at the starboard bow. Protected by armoured plates with slits to view through, he was more likely than anyone to survive the beach welcome. The Royal Navy Officer still standing at the bow gave an affirmative nod to the British Merchant Navy men who manned the winches and working in unison, the two teams of experienced seamen started lowering Pingenot's boat into the dark of the early morning hour. If one of the winch crews were to unwind their cable quicker than the other crew, then the craft would enter the water at a dangerous angle making it impossible to control in the huge swell. The soldiers waited with baited breath as the human silhouettes against the grey deck structures were replaced by the formless grey of the hull, the hull appearing to slide upwards like a blind working in reverse to obscure the view.

The coxswain communicated to the stoker via the telegraph and with the craft half way to the water, the Stoker fired up the two V8 Thornycroft engines. The lease of life was both a relief and a jolting reminder of events to follow. For despite having disembarked this way several times, the circumstances and rough seas created a tension amongst the men that made even the expected turn of events seem threatening. The Stoker had taken up his position long before B Company came up on deck. Squeezing down into the cramped engine room via the small claustrophobic hatch at the stern; he had long made his final checks of the engines, fuel lines, controls and telegraph. He was confident even if the soldiers were not.

The craft neared the water. It was level and Dalton felt the sudden deceleration as they encountered the buoyancy of the water. The currents were strong and the waves raised and lowered the craft like a cork, testing the winch crews; the movement also causing a rolling action towards and away from the ship's grey hull. The stern winch crew unwound more cable and on cue the engines were engaged to hold the craft steady, the extra slack allowing the stern cable hook to be unleashed from its ring on the LCA. The sailor let go of the cable with its block and tackle to swing menacingly away, its path unpredictable amongst all the movement to rise up out of sight; one down, the second attachment to go.

At this point, two A Company craft had collided, damaging the stern of one craft and the bow of the other which subsequently sank; for in the water the LCAs were as close together as they had been hanging from the davits and within just a few feet of the ship's hull. Thankfully the experienced crews were unlikely to be thwarted again and held the LCA steady as the bow cable was released as quickly as possible after the stern cable. The naval lieutenant bent down to unhook the last attachment and with a combined sigh of relief from all on board, the craft moved safely away into the 4.30a.m. gloom.

As the bow ring was folded away into the floor, making the way clear for the soldiers when the bow ramp dropped onto the beach, the three LCAs from the port side joined up with the starboard craft. Then with a signal from the senior naval officer in Zappacosta's boat, the coxswain put the telegraph to full ahead and thus commenced B Company's fourteen mile journey to the beach; a journey which would take almost two and a half hours following a zigzag path across a rough sea.

By the time the Empire Javelin became indistinguishable against the dark northern sky, the men were already psychologically preparing themselves for the landing. A faint dawn light started to appear on the eastern horizon and it reminded Dalton of rising early to work the fields. He wondered what his momma would be baking the men for breakfast and then his thoughts rolled, pitched and tilted onto Evelyn and her boys. At Dewlish, Dalton had received a letter from her with news of a fourth child and first daughter. Jean Evelyn Ashley had arrived on April 5th. Four children, now that was a ... the craft jarred to the side by the impact of a large wave ... good number Dalton thought. Sea sickness was already starting to creep up on him, despite his determination to ignore it. Lieutenant Taylor had told the men when practising at Woolacombe to think of something nice to keep their mind off the sickness. Smiler yelled out 'sex' and got plenty of laughs, but there wouldn't be any laughs on this trip. However the war hardened British crewmen seemed to take everything in their stride, jovial even, as if the whole thing was an exercise.

The craft suddenly left the water, bounced back and nosed through the next wave sending water across the bow to flow in and drench the men at the front. Wet and getting colder by the minute, Dalton tried to ignore the elements and thought of Hetty returning with him to settle on a farm near the Slaughter home place. But he was finding it harder to ignore the incessant pitching of the craft in spite of the general issue sea sickness pills he had taken. Spray was coming in at every pounding and together with the strong gusts of wind pushed body temperatures lower. Water started washing around his feet and sometimes Clayton pressed his helmet into Dalton's back as he tried to suppress another vomit.

Dalton ignored his buddy, maintaining his isolation; Evelyn had 'gotten' it right he thought, a home near Momma and the children attending Wares. Clayton suddenly vomited again, breaking Dalton's thoughts and the smell of a warm spring as he ploughed the Virginian soil changed to partly digested food. Soon the sound of several men vomiting joined the cacophony of wind and rough sea hammering the craft and the drone of the 100 octane petrol engines.

The planners wanted the first waves to land at low tide to avoid the beach obstacles. Having delayed the invasion by a day, low tide would now occur at 5.30a.m. an hour before A Company was due to land. But it was still hoped that despite the swell, the landing craft would not encounter the beach obstacles.

With the dawn light it was considered inevitable that even A Company's approach would be spotted long before they beached. In June at this latitude of 50 degrees, equivalent to northern Newfoundland, first light occurred at around 5a.m. less than six hours after last light at 11p.m. Early in the war Britain had moved to British double summer time, where the clocks were moved forward two hours instead of the customary one. The short summer nights and equally long winter ones seemed strange to the men from the southern states, where in midsummer, first light would not be seen until after 6a.m. and it would be dark by 9p.m. Most of the enlisted men hadn't realised just how far north they had travelled when they left the US. Like Dalton, many only had a vague awareness of their geographical location. As far as they were concerned the Queen Mary had headed east out of New York Harbour; they had been at sea for too long and knew without question that they were too far away from home.

At 5.30a.m. B Company's journey entered its second hour, destined to land some 30 minutes after A Company. The sea had calmed, with waves around six feet, but still more than high enough to cause havoc to nervous stomachs and there was still another eight or so miles to go. With sick washing around his feet, Clayton leaned forward to shout at Dalton.

"Who in their right mind would have dropped us this far from the beach. Crazy, God damn crazy," he shouted.

It had been several hours since many had consumed a good meal and others were regretting the frankfurters and beans, doughnuts and coffee they had been offered in the small hours. Paul Kennedy leaned back to look past Ted to catch Dalton's eye; the two exchanged knowing looks, managing just the hint of a smile for their best buddy. Paul was not a sun worshipper but his face was now paler than Dalton had ever seen it.

The water in the bottom of the craft seemed to rise around Dalton's legs and then fall away as the craft tilted in another direction. He became colder, stiffer and more worried about capsizing. Life vest or no life vest, he was convinced that if thrown into the sea, he would go under within seconds. Although not heavily armed, B Company riflemen were heavily laden. Every man had his impregnite OD uniform, made of cloth specially treated to prevent penetration by gas. Over this the men wore a special landing jacket, the so called assault jacket. This had four huge pockets in the front and two equally huge pockets on the back. With the standard issue Garand M1 Automatic Rifle came an allocation of ammo: 96 rounds plus two or three bandoleers of ammunition around the neck.

Each rifleman also carried a half pound of TNT with primacord fuse and several grenades: five of the fragmentation variety and four smoke grenades. For sustenance, three K rations were allocated to each man: a breakfast, dinner and supper, and three D bars. On the back of the assault jacket were placed the rations, raincoat and what was called a paratroops packet, simply a pouch holding a syrette of morphine and a tourniquet. This was for the individual's use, not for use on someone else. Over the assault jacket the men wore a navy type life saving belt, the type with two tubes which were inflated by the breaking of two capsules containing pressurized carbon dioxide.

Around the neck and under the jacket went the one inch band of the gas mask. Apart from the entrenching tool, effectively a short handled spade, smaller equipment items and possessions of a personal nature were stowed away in the large pockets. All this amounted to some 60lbs of equipment and Dalton's fear of submerging, even with the life vest, was well founded.

The sea reflected the dark grey above and the trail of white water behind the LCA could be seen, as though rushing north over the hilly watery landscape to then be attacked by the white capped waves and thrown into disarray. The blue smoke from the exhausts at water level travelled for no more than a few feet across the wake, before being driven eastward by the strong westerly wind.

To Dalton's left and east were the three other landing craft of B Company; the two groups of three craft, line astern following their indirect route to Omaha. Beyond and well behind B Company were other less easily distinguishable craft - some Higgins landing craft carrying troops and other types carrying heavy equipment, the LCTs. To the right and west there were no craft.

The coxswains struggled to keep their LCAs on course. Together with the north-westerly wind, the three knot eastward current was carrying some of the force away from their beach landing zones and consequently away from the targets each unit had been briefed and equipped to attack. But B Company were faring better than most. The LCA was heavier, lay lower in the water and had a slight keel which gave it stability and the front narrowed to the single exit door to make it a little more pointed at the bow. This helped it cut through a wave and maintain its bearing, rather than simply butt against waves like a Higgins.

Built for calm water and short journeys, men in several Higgins boats were bailing out water with their helmets as they were thrown around, struggling to stay on their feet for the duration. They would be on their feet for hours with heavy kits in rough seas; an unnecessary ordeal so Clayton thought as he tried to stand and look eastward, his knowledge of military hardware a curse at this moment. The poor light and early morning mist which had replaced the rain, cut visibility to no more than 100 yards and Clayton could only imagine the chaos. Unseen, Higgins were bouncing and butting from one wave to the next, losing ground, several sinking before reaching the beach.

The gloom only added to Clayton's feelings of weariness. After being cooped up on the Javelin for five days, the two nights of little sleep and the two hours of incessant pitching and rolling, pessimism was creeping into most of the men.

Dalton felt lethargic, his legs seemingly tired and he was of the opinion that landing on the beach would at least be a relief from this torment. He wondered how long it would take him to get to some kind of protection. As Clayton had remarked, a man with so much weight on his back wasn't exactly an assault soldier. But if anyone had the stamina to make it across 300 yards of sand, Dalton had. He was inherently resilient. After a long exercise and little sleep on uneven ground, Dalton would get up, stretch and then tend to cooking breakfast as though he had just got out of a duck down bed. The words tiredness, ache or pain rarely passed his lips, 'give Dalton a hoe and he will hoe all day', Kelly had said of his son. And Dalton recalled the words and told himself that compared to working all day in 90 degree heat and intense humidity, this was going to be a walk in the park.

Just under an hour before landing, they heard the drone of USAAF B24 Liberators flying towards the French coast. The liberators belonged to the Eighth Air Force, 2nd Bomber Division. Unbeknown to the men in the water, four immense columns, each of 100 aircraft flew over their heads. The planes were deployed in V formation, three liberators to each V and together, they carried 2.3 million pounds of bombs. Within minutes came a terrific rumble as the crews unleashed their payloads onto the German defences. 'It was like the sound of thunder' but heavier and more foreboding and before the sound of one rumble could die away, it was joined and merged with another, then another so that it seemed as though the French coast might crack off and fall into the English Channel. At the tail end of the aerial bombardment, the big guns of the battleships opened up on the beach defences; and the morale of the men improved considerably.

Behind A and B companies followed the remaining 1st Battalion companies, C, D and Headquarters; all 800 men destined for the Vierville Draw section. 2nd and 3rd Battalions of the 116th were targeted to land further east of Vierville. Beyond them, the battle experienced 1st Infantry Division was to land, 'The Big Red One' as they were called and to whom the 116th had been attached for the invasion. The other two regiments of the 29th Division, the 115th and 175th would come in later under the auspices of their own division.

But the 1st and 29th Divisions represented just a small piece of the huge war machine about to bear down on the Normandy coast. In addition to the aircrews and seamen involved and the 24,000 airborne troops dropped over night, 130,000 ground troops were heading for France; to be landed from an armada of over 5,000 vessels.

Five invasion beaches would be stormed; Sword and Gold by the British, Juno by the Canadians and Utah and Omaha by the Americans.

It was hoped that by nightfall a 60 mile wide track of land, 10 miles at its deepest would be in Allied hands; 5 miles deep at Omaha. The serious planning for the invasion of Normandy, Operation Overlord, which had commenced with the appointment of British Lieutenant General Morgan in March '43, had evolved into the most complicated battle plan the world had ever seen; with more hardware involved than at any time in history. Pingenot's boat team was therefore but a very small facet in the whole scheme of things and Dalton was just one dispensable infantryman - just one life, among so many.

As the sound of battle started to break through the other noises, Dalton reached into his tunic and clasped the coins Hetty had given him, for love and for luck; given to him outside Ivy Bridge Camp as Colonel Canham approached in his jeep. Dalton had made small holes into the shilling, sixpence and thrup'ny coins and strung them onto the chain of his dog tag. At quiet times, as when turning over in the night, Dalton could hear the quiet jingle of the coins as they moved over the smooth bulbous links of the chain, to stop and rest in a new position and gently lie against his chest. The sound reminded him of her, of her laughter, her love and of her vulnerability.

Staff Sergeant Holmes carefully replaced the picture of his family back into the pocket he had reserved for the few precious mementos he carried, carried to maintain his spirit in the trauma awaiting him. Then turning to Dalton he said, "Bet I'll be the first hit."

Dalton dropped his head and unaccountably focused intently on his own boots, pretending not to have heard the man he had always respected. Dalton's boots sat brown, polished and ready, enveloping the feet that once walked bare in the squelching sticky mud of the Dragon Run. He looked down at his boots, laced tight to his feet, attached to his fine strong legs by tendons and bone. Brown boots in dark water, water that carried the worries and discomfort of men.

For those who stood up to look, they were now close enough to see their beach landing zone and dread replaced any optimism fashioned by the bombardment.

Less than half an hour earlier, A Company had landed fifty yards from the edge of the obstacles and just over 350 yards from the sea wall. But because of the high tidal coefficient, strong surf and the fact that the beach sloped at just one or two degrees to the horizontal, water now covered the first band of obstacles; stakes with mines strapped between them. Waves were pushing right up into the hedgehogs, tetrahedrons and log ramps which had the dreaded teller mines attached, capable of blowing a landing craft out of the water. Behind the obstacles lay another 100 yards of sand and shingle, smooth, featureless, devoid of bomb craters or hint of protection.

Defining the edge of the beach and separating it from a narrow coastal road was a sea wall ranging in height from four to ten feet above the level of the beach. It would offer good protection if a man could reach it, but would prove very difficult to move beyond. The sea wall ended as the road swung sharply inland and passed through a narrow river valley and on through the village of Vierville. Referred to as the Vierville Draw, this vale represented 1ˢᵗ Battalion's only means of escape from the beach. To the right, as viewed by the soldiers, were the cliffs rising quickly to over 100 feet high. To the left, behind the sea wall and road, were dunes and ridges of sand rising to a similar height. The natural defences seemed to run forever in either direction; the limestone and marl cliffs spread to the right for over a mile to Pointe et Raz de la Percée, before turning out of sight towards Pointe Du Hoc. To the left the dunes and sand ridges continued perhaps 2,000 yards before dipping down to another river valley, where the coast road turned inland along another draw.

Just before B Company was about to land, it was apparent that few soldiers of A Company had progressed past the beach obstacles, and none had reached the sea wall. The defences at the Vierville Draw were all seemingly intact, not bombed to hell as the lieutenants had said at Dewlish. Protecting the Vierville Draw were three concrete machine gun emplacements - pill boxes.

Each pill box contained at least one German Maschinengewehr 42, the best machine gun design ever evolved. Its recoil operated roller locking system and fast barrel change made it an effective killing machine. Quick, easy and cheap to produce, the spot welds, stampings and drop forgings that were involved in its manufacture meant that it could be churned out in ever increasing numbers. And Rommel had sent a few extra to Omaha just in case. Robust and reliable, the MG42 was capable of firing 1,500 rounds per minute. And as B Company approached, they were mercilessly being sprayed across the beach. The 7.92 mm diameter, 57 mm long bullets leaving the barrel at 1,800 miles per hour were carving up flesh and bone as easily as Dalton's hand had carved through the still water of Lake Serpentine in Hyde Park.

Above the three pill boxes and embedded on the cliff tops were the Widerstandsnests, or strong points, WN71, WN72 and WN73. These did not comprise of just one building but an accumulation of emplacements: bunkers to house men and the larger 88 artillery piece, concrete pods for the

75mm ack ack guns, mortar and machine gun nests and pill boxes. The Widerstandsnests were linked to each other by trenches and further trenches ran along the edge of the cliffs and back inland to provide safe routes for the defenders. The gunners in these semi independent strong points had exact measure of low and high water marks. They were having no difficulty in accurately placing their shells.

The emplacements attached to these strong points were cleverly positioned in folds of the ground so that they were virtually invisible to naval observers and nearly impossible to destroy by naval gun fire. Their locations permitted fire down the length of the beach rather than directly out to sea. Ominously the range of structures on Omaha were massive by design, with sloping concrete faces several feet thick and penetrable only by a direct hit from a substantial shell.

Behind the sea wall with its pill boxes and also blocking the route up the Vierville Draw sat a fourteen feet high, several feet thick, concrete wall; an immense barrier designed to prevent vehicle movements off the beach. If 1st Battalion reached it and were able to breach it, they would then be free to run the gauntlet of the mine fields and machine guns up the length of the draw.

Chapter 31

First Step onto French Soil

Just the sand banks to negotiate and Dalton would be in the fray. Two sand banks some 500 yards apart lay four or five feet beneath the water. Positioned 250 yards from the beach they caused the waves to partially break; the white water pushing across them, before returning to the roll of a wave and finally breaking fully onto Omaha.

The wake of Pingenot's boat bisected the unbroken water between the banks as the heavily defended sector of Dog Green loomed up ahead of them. From this distance the stretch of yellow from the beach obstacles to the sea wall seemed but a short walk, just a few more steps through life. But not a single man from A Company had yet made it there; they were still pinned down amongst the beach obstacles and suffering heavy casualties.

B Company would not be able to land in shallow water unless their craft were taken well into the mined obstacles. And unlike with A Company, the machine guns would hit the B Company boys from the moment they stepped out from their LCAs.

A signal was given by the lead British naval officer for the LCAs to move into line abreast from line astern - this was it. "Heading into the beach!" the naval officer on Pingenot's boat declared, and Clayton rolled his eyes as if to say, really, what a surprise.

Training replaced the natural instinct to cower down and hide as each man prepared for the landing. The din was heart stopping, numbing the flesh with anticipation. The sights, sounds and smell of battle transfixed Dalton's thoughts. He could hear the machine gun and rifle fire in the all too brief lulls between artillery shells and see the smoke drifting and concealing, then revealing again, before rising upward to finally depart the scene. Disbelief filled him, for how could such awesome aerial and naval bombardments have failed?

The crews of the USAF Liberators flying at a speed of 250 miles per hour were now climbing down from their planes on the airfields of East Anglia. The three, twelve year old boys of Holton Saint Peter, adopted members of 489th Bomber Group, would likely already have been invited into the Officer's Mess for breakfast. And no doubt bright eyed Eric Bacon would be the first to ask where they had been this morning. He like the other boys had heard them take off and had rushed to his bedroom window to watch them rise into the dark, early morning sky. 'To France and back' the airmen would reply. And 'to bomb the hell out of Jerry' they would add.

But their bombs had missed their target, not most, but all. For flying above the heavy cloud cover they had been unable to get a visual sighting of the shoreline. They therefore had to rely on the twenty pathfinder B24s which had led groups of aircraft into the drop zone. Equipped with the new H2X Mickey radar, the operators in the pathfinder craft picked up sharp returns from the coastal bluffs of Omaha Beach. However, the air crews were acutely aware of the proximity to the beach of their own landing forces and so often had they been sternly warned to avoid accidental short bombing, that the bombardiers had delayed release. When the Pathfinder craft dropped their payloads, the other B 24s in their group followed suit. The delayed release together with the inaccuracies in the system meant that the bombs landed between 300 yards and 2 miles in land.

Earlier, British Naval Officer Jimmy Green had watched as another softening of the beach defences ended in complete failure. The A Company landing craft had just passed the nine rocket armed LCT(R)s when they begun to unleash their weapons. The display predicted by General Bradley to be the 'Greatest Show on Earth' culminated with the rockets falling short of their target, displacing only seawater some 400 yards from the shore.

The Navy had promised to dig the foxholes for the infantry boys, but all they had achieved with their shelling was to set the dune grasses on fire. Equally devastating for morale, most of the tanks had not arrived. Many had been inexplicably launched from LCTs thousands of yards out in the strong swell and were now settling into their watery home, the silt so disturbed already precipitating back onto their surfaces. It was now down to the troops with minimal support from hardware to make the invasion of Omaha a success.

As the beach got real close, feelings of sea sickness, tiredness and fatigue rapidly left Dalton's mind. The lurching craft with its sea water and vomit now seemed the epitome of comfort. Mortars and anti-tank pieces were hitting the water around the boat, someone nearby was shouting but who it was and what was said Dalton could not make out. Beyond Paul Kennedy on the right hand side of the LCA, there were no other craft; and it was almost as if battle lines had been drawn and agreed that Paul would demarcate chaos from calm. Ahead and to their left it was mayhem at the Vierville Draw.

Staff Sergeant Holmes twisted round to look at Dalton sitting behind him, to look into the face of a friend, a face that was now stone grey and said, "Good luck Slaughter."

"Good luck Sarge," Dalton replied.

Dalton's buddy Bob Sales, the youngest member of B Company, had been selected by the B Company Captain to train as radio operator. Zappacosta was not an officer to negotiate with and Sales went obediently to radio school. "Stay with me at all times," Zappacosta told Sales as they neared the beach.

Huge by comparison, Sales stood by his captain in the Headquarters LCA, one of the three LCAs that had been on the port side of the Empire Javelin. Furthest to the left was First Lieutenant Williams' boat with part of the heavy weapons platoon to protect the left flank of the company. With him were ten riflemen from 1st Platoon. Next was Lieutenant Taylor with the rest of 1st Platoon, then Zappacosta's Headquarters unit with ten riflemen from 2nd Platoon. The captain would thus be left of centre of the six craft as they beached and be able to communicate with his company and possibly the next adjacent one. The rest of 2nd

Platoon under Lieutenant Donaldson was to the right of Zappacosta, then 3rd Platoon and finally Dalton's LCA, the furthest right of all. In total, 8 officers and 185 enlisted men of B Company were now rushing into the carnage at Dog Green.

Like Williams on the far left, Pingenot's half of the heavy weapons platoon was to protect the right flank of the company. Somehow or other, Dalton and the other nine riflemen from 3rd Platoon were to protect and assist the 4th Platoon guys in setting up; only a few seconds now before those carefully laid plans would be thrown into chaos.

Dalton knew that Allbritton and Austen were just yards away in the next LCA. That they were likely sitting close to each other and providing the same mutual and unspoken comfort as Ted and Paul were doing for him. But once that ramp dropped, every man would be on his own, with his own destiny. As the beach neared, isolation and dread closed in further, then adrenaline started to close down even those emotions.

Zappacosta and Donaldson's boat teams, the middle two of the six, were the first to beach, right in front of the Vierville Draw. When their LCAs were 50 yards from the obstacles, bullets started to ricochet off the sides and front ramp, whilst shells continued to explode on the sand and among the obstacles, shaking the men cowering there to senselessness. Metal shards and bigger clumps with ragged edges were racing across the surface in all directions from the impact, triggering mines and throwing out heavy pieces of wood at horrendous speeds. The ramp of the Headquarters' boat dropped into water rising to neck height in the swell. Leading his men from the front, Captain Zappacosta was the first to step out.

Sales followed as fourth man, but instead of walking forward he fell off to the side, driven not by some explosion but by his foot catching in the ramp. Twisted sideways, he plummeted to the sea bed and was held there by the turbulent water and the 95lb combined weight of his radio and pack. To save himself from drowning he had no option but to discard the precious equipment. As he surfaced he saw Zappacosta standing no more than ten feet away with his back towards the beach, blood pouring from his mutilated frame. "I'm hit, I'm hit bad!" Zappacosta shouted, the pain mixing with disbelief in his voice.

Sales moved towards him but within seconds the company commander had slipped beneath the waves and was gone. Men from Zappacosta's boat continued to step off the LCA into the maelstrom; to do their job, for honour and for their country. Selfless acts of self-destruction. What final thoughts flashed through the minds of these men? For the machine gun bullets ripped into them and some took not one step down the ramp. Sales watched them die, powerless to help the men he had known so long.

Buffeted and pushed by the surf, Sales discarded the rest of his equipment. A stake dislodged by an explosion offered his only protection and he inched forward behind it, still struggling in the chest deep water.

The LCA to Zappacosta's right, 1st Lieutenant Donaldson's boat team with Charlie Conner on board, landed virtually at the same time. Donaldson and his Staff Sergeant Ralph Jennings led the men from the craft, with Charlie Connor following as seventh man. Bullets and shrapnel hit flesh, shingle, metal and wood to create their own spectrum of pulses. Shingle thrown up by the explosions carried so much momentum that they smashed bone. Disorientated and confused, wading and firing Connor became aware of bodies and bits of bodies impacting onto the sand ahead of him. Donaldson was down, hit by machine gun fire. Turning to look back at the LCA, to what now seemed a refuge, Connor saw a shell land in its midst, blowing the few remaining men inside to pieces.

In addition to the weather, absence of tanks and the failure of the bombardments, another dreadful development had taken place to conspire against the men. Unbeknown until the 4th June, the 352nd German Infantry Division had been moved forward to reinforce the 716th Static Division defending Omaha. The 716th had a low standing, numbered little over 600 men and were mainly drawn from the occupied countries. It was predicted that they would fight less than enthusiastically against an army intent on liberating their homelands. But the 352nd were of the highest combat category, better equipped and battle hardened. When they moved to Omaha in March 1944 they completely transformed the beach defence capability.

The third LCA to come in, the one carrying the rest of Dalton's platoon including Austen and Allbritton snagged on an underwater obstacle in front of the draw. Despite being in deep water there was no option but to drop the ramp. On cue the men ran forward and off the craft. Several soldiers were hit by machine gun bullets, some of those who lived to touch the water, sank into its depths. Discarding much of their weighty equipment, surviving men struggled in the waves whilst others left their packs in the craft and went in over the side to try and swim for it.

With ten feet of water beneath Dalton's boat it suddenly veered sharply to the right almost throwing Ted onto him. At first he thought they had hit something or something had hit them but the new course was maintained unabated. Perhaps a minute or so later, Dalton's LCA again turned, this time to the left and headed straight for the beach. The three steel runners on the hull could be heard scraping against the sand and then the thud as the craft embedded itself at full throttle into the beach, jolting the men forward with the weight of their equipment. With this they were familiar from the exercises at Braunton and Slapton, but what surprised them, was the absence of obstacles. Pingenot's men were in Charlie Sector, earmarked for the Rangers, some 300 yards to the right of the Vierville Draw. [1]

The beach as far as they could see to their right was quite simply empty, just a sandy beach, devoid not just of obstacles but of any craft, soldier or item of war. If this had been a film and the scene frozen, the sound of battle extinguished, then the view would have been the epitome of tranquillity. Yellow sand sprinkled with pebbles and boulders that stretched eastward for 500 yards and then a

---

[1] See map page 346.

wave cut platform pushing out towards the sea. Beyond that, more rock jutting out still further and over which the surf was now pushing, the salt water running in the clefts, basins and channels of the eroded limestone. Salt water carrying food to and maintaining the life there; to the mussels and limpets, to the grass kelp and moss clinging to the rock, surviving in the environment of the foreshore. Yet panning round to the left, the camera would have presented the brutality of battle, the sand stained with human fluids, dead and wounded men, bits of men and landing craft, helmets and all the other debris being washed around by the surf. Yet amongst it all there were living men, still clinging to life.

In front of Pingenot's craft rose 130 foot high cliffs which stretched in both directions. To the left they continued for some 300 yards before quickly sloping down to the Vierville Draw, whilst to the right they seemed to stretch forever, a natural and impassable defensive wall.

The enemy's attention soon started to focus on the isolated craft, moving the battle westward, catching up with them like a summer squall racing across the beach. Quickly came the sound of mortars, bullets hitting the sand, zipping into the water, pinging off the scattered boulders and making a hollow ring as they hit the sides and front ramp of the LCA. The rounds were coming from the last of the beach level pill boxes. But situated 200 yards away from them and being just the one, the fire was less intense than in front of the Vierville Draw. Above Pingenot's boat team, German soldiers were rallying from the trenches and emplacements which stretched right along the cliff top from Vierville to Pointe et Raz de la Percée. Surprised at the arrival of the craft at this westward section, they began to fire down on Pingenot's men.

When the bowman dropped the ramp into the two foot six inches of water, few of the men could have recalled which way they had run. In theory the soldiers to the left side of the craft, Dalton's side, should have peeled off to the left and the men on Paul's, should have peeled off to the right. When Dalton's turn came to leave the craft, his equipment became very light, his mind disengaging from his actions. The overbearing noise of battle, the shouting and screaming of men and the explosions of armaments became muffled; like the screams and shouts of friends when under the surface of the cooling waters of the Dragon Run. Colours and shapes became difficult to distinguish; there was just the band of yellow, the cliff face and grey above. Dalton's legs carried him forward. Ted and Paul Kennedy had already left. Holmes was just starting down the ramp. Dalton was next to exit, to step forth, onto the ramp to then take his first step onto French soil.

But they were not his legs that performed the task, for he could not feel them, nor could he feel the ridges of the ramp or the coldness of the water. He felt nothing and though some would say that the legs that carried him were those of a hero, Dalton would have said that they were the legs of a petrified man. With his mind bombarded by a confusion of terrifying noise, he raised his rifle above his head and waded through the ever changing depth of water as the waves rolled in. Clearing the deeper surf and lowering his rifle, Dalton's finger pulled the trigger. Whether his rifle fired or jammed he could not have said. He just aimed at the line where the buff colour of the cliffs turned to grey.

Seconds had passed since he stepped off the ramp and Dalton was still on his feet despite all the incoming, but the cliff was too far, he was going to be hit. Strangely the water deepened, a runnel threw him, it ran parallel to the beach and water washed along it as the tide raced in and swept sideways; Dalton staggered in, water again at his waist and dug deep to drive himself up the slope to again reach shallower water. A few more steps and a form, a shape, a blur in his vision, curled up and fell right in front of him. Dalton stepped round the crumpled body stepping to the right or was it to the left and struggled on. Bullets from the cliff top and from the machine gun cut across him; bullets that indiscriminately struck sand, boulders and bone, entered eye sockets, stomachs and groins. More soldiers to his right and in front of him fell out of view, their cry of pain and their screams inaudible. It was a mile or ten miles not

300 yards, and like a nightmare the cliff would never be reached. He would be struck down long before the eight bullets in his rifle were spent. His legs pumped, pumped harder than they had ever done in his life, his arms so tense they could have ripped ligament from bone. He was running despite the sand and the weight he carried, body wet with exertion but more from fear. He now passed shingle and boulders more densely strewn, shouting and swearing without consciousness, eyes blazoned with horror. Then, like a wall appearing out of a dense fog, Dalton came up against the hard rough surface of the cliff face. In the few seconds it had taken him to reach there, the lives of so many families back home had been changed forever.

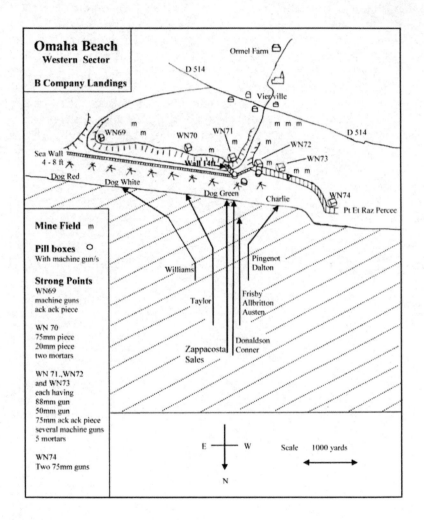

Omaha Beach
  Western Sector

B Company Landings

Ormel Farm

D 514

Vierville

WN69   m
        m
WN70   m   WN71
                 m   m m
                          m   WN72
Sea Wall   m   WN73
4 - 8 ft   Wall 14h   m   m m

Dog Red
        Dog White
                    Dog Green   WN74
                              Charlie   Pt Et Raz Percee

D 514

Mine Field m

Pill boxes o
With machine gun/s

Strong Points
WN69
machine guns
ack ack piece

WN 70
75mm piece
20mm piece
two mortars

WN 71.,WN72
and WN73
each having
88mm gun
50mm gun
75mm ack ack piece
several machine guns
5 mortars

WN74
Two 75mm guns

Williams

Pingenot
Dalton

Taylor

Frisby
Allbritton
Austen

Zappacosta
Sales

Donaldson
Conner

E ——+—— W

N

Scale   1000 yards

Chapter 32

Different Paths

Dalton didn't know how he'd got there; everything had been automatic, sub-conscious almost. He threw off the heavy assault jacket in disgust and the pathetic buoyancy aid, his breathing coming in short gasps as if a bullet had pierced his lung. Men were still arriving at the cliff face, like Dalton, sweating profusely, disbelief on their faces; disbelief at the strength of the beach defences, the lack of bomb craters and the vulnerability of their position. Crazy, God damn crazy men were saying as they arrived and more choice words besides.

Dalton was directly in line with the LCA, which having dropped its cargo was pulling away from the beach, the rising tide assisting it. The departing LCA left the B Company boys isolated for no more craft seemed to be arriving at this far western end of Omaha. Both Dog Green and Charlie sectors of Omaha had been closed by patrol craft 567.

Dalton and the other men took shelter beneath an overhang of the cliff, in some places no deeper than the thickness of a man's torso, but it was all that was needed. It was life saving and a blessing; an inconsistency in the rock that in peacetime would have been inconsequential. Formed by the work of pebbles that in a previous age had been blasted off the cliff face by a tempest, to then be thrown back against the rock countless times, shaping, sculpturing, particle by miniscule particle ready for this day. The Preacher at Wares Church would say, if ever told of the story, that the pebbles were guided by the hand of God. And if Dalton lived to have the opportunity to listen to such a message, he would be the first to shout 'yes sir'. It protected him against the incoming fire, prolonging his life beyond the moment, which was all he cared about, for what might happen beyond that was too far away for him to worry about.

Dalton frantically checked himself for wounds that adrenaline may have prevented him from feeling; disbelief and relief mixing, for there were none. No blood, no gradual realisation of pain or that his body was not as it should be. Under the temporary protection of the overhang, Dalton could pull himself together and start to interpret detail in the confusion which had previously engulfed him.

Towards the Vierville Draw and beyond, dead and wounded men littered the shore line. There were beached landing craft with fuel tanks burning, heavy equipment smouldering near the water's edge and all manner of infantry equipment, helmets and rifles strewn around, surplus now to requirements. Bodies were being rolled around in the surf like rag dolls; the turbulent water removing clothing, washing away personal items and pushing sand into every crevice. Smoke drifted across the beach which was still being pounded by German artillery as well as machine gun fire and to Dalton there didn't seem to be any chance of Austen, Allbritton or anyone else surviving in front of the draw. The invasion had surely failed.

After landing under just artillery fire, A Company had first taken up a defensive line on a shingle bank 50 yards below the obstacles. But the tide had quickly pushed them closer to the machine guns and the German defenders opened up to wreak havoc upon Captain Fellow's men, of whom many came from Bedford, Virginia. A few minutes after A Company, two C Company Ranger boats had landed to A Company's right about 100 yards into Charlie Sector. Many were lost in the beach crossing, but those who survived had worked their way along the foot of the cliff away from the draw and towards where Pingenot's men were now gathered.

When the patrol craft 567 had drawn near the beach and realised the butchery there, it had attempted to redirect all of B Company LCAs away from the carnage, but it had been too late for the three which went straight in. However, Williams and Taylor's boats had swung left and east, whilst Pingenot's had swung right and west; the most westerly of any landing.

Dalton could see LCAs and LCVPs and the bigger LCTs attempting to reinforce the first and second waves further down the beach, but none in Dog Green and Charlie. Looking around and seaward he became aware of the casualties closer to hand - the quiet, almost peaceful corpses on the sand, if that can be said of dead men with mayhem surrounding them, lying as though resting after a difficult walk. Some of the wounded were screaming, with pain contorted faces, bloodied unrecognisable faces, emitting sounds to haunt even the hardiest soldier for a lifetime. Smiler had been washed in, he had virtually been decapitated and one of his arms had been cut off. At the water's edge, right behind Dalton, Staff Sergeant John Holmes was still moving. He had fallen right in front of Dalton a few seconds after they had left the boat and not far from dry sand. A bullet to the stomach had doubled him up and he had gone down, probably the first to take a hit as Holmes himself had predicted. Dalton knew that he'd stepped past him on his way to the cliff face and he now felt very guilty. He started to weigh up his chances of running back and pulling Holmes from the rising tide, dragging him to the safety of the cliff. Persuading himself that he would again be lucky, compassion developing an overwhelming urge to make a run for it and save the man for whom he had so much respect.

Dalton's lieutenant had recommended him for promotion to Sergeant but a senior NCO had disagreed, saying that Dalton didn't always think through the consequences of his actions. Loyal, hard working, a strong sense of duty and obeying superiors without question were all characteristics in Dalton's favour. But his impulsiveness might 'endanger the men in his command' the NCO said and so he remained as private first class.

Dalton considered that the bullets were less intense now, with definite lulls; lulls during which he might sprint 20 yards or more. But distracted by shouting as C Company Rangers came in amongst the B Company boys, Dalton was momentarily released from his dilemma. When he next looked seaward, Holmes's body had been engulfed by the sea and he made no further movement, other than that caused by the natural rhythm of the waves.

Chapter 33

Cliff Edge

To B Company's left, the rising tide appeared to race past the soldiers as they inched their way towards the Vierville Draw and by 8a.m. all the beach obstacles were under water. The three teams of 146th Engineers destined to clear 50 yard gaps through the obstacles at Dog Green, had all been carried eastward by the driving wind and currents. Thus not only was Dog Green still being subjected to the most intense fire but it was also extremely hazardous to approach, simply because of what still lay under the surface. The later landing craft including the larger equipment carriers were therefore still being directed eastward, well into the morning.

The new arrivals found themselves on an ever narrowing strip of sand and anything operational soon attracted attention from the German artillery. But the half tracks, tanks and jeeps rendered useless at least provided some protection for the otherwise exposed soldiers.

With no reinforcement and nothing to distract the enemy, Lieutenant Pingenot's men were in a precarious situation and soon came under fire if they ventured from the base of the cliff. Paul Kennedy somehow found himself next to Dalton and good he had, for the overhang was more protective there. A landslip to their left also gave some protection from fire laterally along the beach. Moving out from the safety that the rock face provided, those that were able, fired up towards the cliff edge. Darting out and falling back, triggers were pulled with tensioned bodies, the choice of timing and direction proving well judged or otherwise. The 3rd Platoon riflemen were powerless in offering the protection 4th Platoon needed to set up their mortars and machine guns. Pingenot could do little more than encourage his men to take evasive action; the protection of B Company's right flank meant nothing now. In the planning B Company was supposed to be mopping up targets and although trained in the use of a wide range of equipment, most of the soldiers were only carrying the equipment of riflemen. No soldier could lob a grenade up a 130 foot cliff and no rifle bullet could pierce the concrete and sandbagged emplacements. The Garand rifle was not easy to wield in tight situations and without telescopic sights, was powerless to infiltrate enemy positions.

It was C Company, the 2nd Rangers on Charlie Sector which changed the course of Dalton's morning. Forty or so of the sixty-five Rangers made it to the base of the cliff and they immediately reorganised to initiate one of the first break outs from Omaha. The Rangers had been assigned to eliminate the Widerstandsnests, between the Vierville Draw and the headland promontory of Pointe et Raz de la Percée. These strong points with their variety of concrete emplacements had a commanding view over Omaha and were still dictating events there. The Rangers' preferred route to them lay via the Vierville Draw but since that was still heavily defended, plan B, scaling the cliffs, had to be adopted; for which they had brought knotted ropes.

The Rangers wanted to replace their losses in order to ensure the cliff top trenches could be cleared as well as the emplacements and as 'fortune' would have it, Pingenot's boat team were right there on Charlie sector to lend a hand. The B Company men were placed into Ranger squads and given a rushed and soon interrupted briefing, for the Rangers were quickly on the move. Dalton and his buddies were told to discard their assault jackets and take only their rifles, ammunition and grenades.

"The rest can stay on the beach," a ranger said, "you won't be needing anything else for a good whiles!" But Clayton shoved a few cigarettes into his pocket just in case and Ted would have done the same with some rations but wasn't given enough time.

The long cliff face stretching from the Vierville Draw had just one chink in its defensive armour; a blemish that had been carved out long before this day, possibly several hundred years earlier. A plane of weakness in the coastal strata together with the under cutting wave action had caused tons of rock face to subside and slide onto the beach. Over the centuries much of the fallen rock had been washed away by the sea, but the subsidence had left a V shaped indentation in the cliff. The gradient here was less and about 90 feet up, the slope levelled off into a hollow before rising again to the cliff top. The subsidence must have been stable for generations because a well-heeled family had built a house on the flat area of the hollow. The Germans hadn't fortified it but a direct hit from a naval shell had caused severe damage. Without grapnel hooks fired from mortar like devices as provided to the Rangers at Point Du Hoc, this route to the cliff top was the only alternative to the Vierville Draw.

Following the Rangers lead, Dalton and the other 'volunteers' started to drag themselves up the steep slope towards the house. Small arms fire whistled past them, a man was hit to Dalton's right and fell back. The knotted ropes seemed to have dissolved into thin air and Dalton resorted to using the barbed wire which dressed the slope; hauling himself up the steeper, more slippery sections with one arm and then firing his rifle as best he could. A stick grenade flew past him and exploded somewhere below. Haphazard sub-machine gun fire emanated from left of the house and rifle fire from the surrounding trenches. The cacophony of small arms and shouting mixed with the boom of German artillery pieces, whilst inside Dalton, fear mixed with gut determination and the drive to survive. Several bullets hit the rocks and clipped the barbed wire as he reached the lip of the hollow. Someone else was hit and dropped like a lead weight, but the predicament of others for the moment mattered little to him.

The beige to brown rocks over which Dalton passed were deposited 200 million years before, during the Lower Bathonian period in Jurassic times. A period commencing with limestone, formed in a calm, clear, warm sea and made up entirely of the shells and bones of once living creatures. But then over thousands of years the waters were muddied, the depths darker, even the shallows less hospitable as fine silt from ancient rivers clouded them. Life struggled, yet the mudstones that were formed contained still many shells and bones; so much so that the mudstone could not be called mudstone, but marls. Thus the B Company boys moved from the limestone into the marl, from firm to crumbly footholds, up through the millions of years to younger rocks above. And as they were wounded, grazed and cut so their blood gave colour to the pale ancient life forms. It was as such that Dalton passed where the marls became limestone again in the higher regions of the cliff. And just like the waters had cleared to form it, so Dalton's way became clearer, for there were trenches leading off from and around the hollow into the cliff top terrain.

On reaching the shattered, empty house, Dalton followed the Rangers another thirty feet up, to pass a concrete bunker to the left - its defenders ripped open, dead and dying. Seconds later he stepped into the trench beyond it and came beside Clayton. A dead German infantryman lay facing down some steps and beyond him lay the bodies of several GIs; bits of uniform and human flesh clung to the edges of the access ways. Clayton and Dalton had moved onward but a few steps when suddenly, puffing and panting Ted scrambled off the slope into the trench behind them. He was the last man to leave the exposed slopes. Clayton looked at Dalton and they knew instinctively what the other was thinking; predictable that Ted was last to make it up, and what a damned good feeling that he had.

The trenches on the cliff top threaded their way along the edge of the cliff in both directions. Subsidiary trenches peeled off joining the different units within the strong points as well as joining one strong point with another. Dalton and some of the other B Company men accompanied by Rangers made their way eastward along the trenches into WN 73. After the oppression of the beach landings, of being pinned down for so long and of losing so many men, the foreboding seemed to release its hold. Without his assault jacket and on firm ground, Dalton felt that he was moving faster than he had ever moved in his life. Chasing an enemy in retreat, glimpsing grey uniform, firing at grey blurs, the slosh of feet, the shouts to advance, to fire, throw a grenade. A success, then another, then a man down and then another. This was a new sensation of combat, his training at last seeming relevant. Dalton's feet nimbly picked their own way around discarded equipment and bodies; the same feet that on entering a hallway at home might have tripped on the first discarded pair of boots. They came across concrete pods with artillery pieces, ammunition bunkers and some emplacements with both artillery sites and machine gun slits. All perched on slopes facing along the beach and from which the GIs could now view the mayhem those very guns had caused. Bunkers were set deep into the back of slopes and appeared so black inside that light seemed to be incapable of penetrating them and equally incapable of escaping.

Turning back westward now and passing the house in the hollow again, the trench curved round the far side of it to follow the line of the cliff. There was just the lead Ranger and another B Company man ahead of Dalton now. Amongst the terrible noise and intense adrenaline, Dalton caught sight of something that made him slow up and interrupt the chase. Around the curve in the trench, a grey uniformed arm had flexed and released a stick grenade; its trajectory calculated and direction well judged. It descended in front of the B Company man ahead of Dalton and as the grenade fell to chest level it exploded, tearing the man apart and throwing him backward. When Dalton reached the spot he slowed imperceptibly, stepped round the lifeless form and ran on.

With just the one Ranger still in front and firing sporadically, the GIs flushed out the remaining defenders. A few hundred yards beyond and west of the house they came to what seemed like the end of the main trench system. Open ground to the left, agricultural land in its day, stretched out before them. Here the Rangers left the B Company men and headed forward. Dalton was soon joined by Paul Kennedy and later by Clayton and Ted. They scrambled through some vegetation beyond the trench and lacking orders, took up a defensive position lying prone on the ground just yards from the cliff edge. Conscious of the mine fields which littered the areas behind the strong points they had no intention of venturing too far; but the field in front of them seemed empty, abandoned almost. Looking across at the hedges on the other side of the field and the slight rises of earth in between, Dalton suddenly felt uneasy with the thought that eyes might now be watching him. Paul's pale complexion, his mellow brown hair and calm, retiring character contrasted so much with Dalton's almost auburn curls and lively disposition. Two handsome young faces, grimacing faces, splattered with sea salt, dust, mud and grime artistically interwoven by beads of sweat. How must they have looked to the watching eyes?

As Paul lay there regaining his breath, he told the others that he had given up hope of ever getting off the beach alive and the rest confided in having thought the same. Ted lay on his back with the grass pushing up into his helmet and panted hard, his huge muscular chest rising and falling as though an eruption was about to take place in its depths. With one hand on his rifle, Ted moved the other to search out and press against his left breast pocket, checking that the pictures were still safely inside. He hadn't yet had the opportunity to look at them, but then he had promised himself to look once he was safe and he didn't yet feel safe. Lying on his front, Clayton manoeuvred down into his pockets, extracted a poor bent up excuse for a cigarette and would have tried to light up had his matches not been wet.

To their left as they lay facing inland, the air of battle on Omaha had slightly diminished in intensity, whilst here on the cliff edge there seemed to be a different atmosphere. A different battle loomed here, similar to that of a waiting predator watching his prey and deciding when to strike. Lying prostrate on the French earth, the GIs could smell the soil and feel its moisture, just a few yards separating them, buddies with bonds so strong from the three hard years they had spent together.

On the other side of the uneven field, the green hedge was thriving from the wet weather; the hawthorn, dog wood and blackthorn thickly intertwined with the occasional maple growing higher than the rest. The GIs scanned the lower stems and places where the foliage was thinner but could see nothing of note. To their far right and some 150 yards across the field was a farm gate, providing a way through the hedge to the next field and a view which again provided the impression that no one was around.

Visibility had improved through the morning and as much as they could make out the detail in front of them, so too could anyone concealing themselves behind the hedgerow. The B Company men were not members of the Special Forces or the Rangers they had been designated to support. They analysed the threat but did not fully appreciate it. The B Company Boys were leaderless and not veterans of previous battles, unaware of the ways in which the enemy could ensnare them and from what distance. Lying and looking, their heads were sometimes slightly above the mound behind which they lay. They exchanged comments and felt more secure than since leaving the ship, they were off the beach, only just, but they were off and their spirits were raised.

The four B Company men watched and waited, waited for orders that wouldn't come, close to God's earth, its proximity a comfort, yet they were so near to being absorbed by it.

Looking through his Ziefernrohr telescopic sight, the German sniper had a clear view of the GIs. His Mauser bolt action rifle was likely made in Oberndorf, though it could easily have derived from earlier times; for the Treaty of Versailles did little to stem rifle manufacture. The Germans simply licensed other countries such as Russia, Czechoslovakia or Poland to do the work for them. The sniper watched and waited, the wooden butt pressed firmly into his right shoulder, his left hand under the telescopic sight supported the weight of the rifle and the first finger of his right hand cupped itself around the trigger. Who would be easier to hit, the soldier to the right or the one to the left, or another. The magazine was full, five rounds, but just one of the 3.5 cm long bullets would be needed to obliterate the skull of the man he selected. Which soldier bobbed his head up higher, more often or was more exposed. He had a choice of four targets and with the improving light he was unlikely to miss. With the choice made his finger tensioned, pulled the trigger and unleashed the 7.92 mm bullet at 2,500 feet per second. The shot was just one sound among many; just another sound in the surrounding cacophony. The bullet skimmed across the surface of the field in less than 0.25s and struck the soldier in the middle of the forehead, just beneath the rim of his helmet. Paul Kennedy's skull bulged on the impact; the entry hole clean, round and red. But on hitting the hard bone the tip of the steel cartridge flattened compressing its lead core. Thus on reaching the other side of Paul's skull the bullet caused the back half of his head to explode. Dalton looked round at Paul and saw only the clean bullet hole and the trickle of blood with Paul's head resting as though asleep on his arms. Dalton crawled over to hold his best buddy, heavy in his grasp. Blood poured down Paul's bent neck, over Dalton's hands, to soak into the soil of the French field. There was no life in the face of his friend, or thankfully pain and he knew that Paul was gone. The bullet had wiped out youth, middle age and old age; it took everything that was Paul except in the memories of the few remaining soldiers who knew him.

Chapter 34

Head Count

A hand on Dalton's shoulder and the look on Clayton's face, made him realise he should quickly gain better cover and the three buddies slid away to where they thought it would be safer. They moved extremely cautiously now, frightened of the next bullet, the sniper surely still in place and having good measure of their new position. They lay static for long periods, looking at each other, unsure of what to do next. Then slid still further eastward, repeating their start stop, indecisive movements.

Along with the cold reality of war came the physical cold, of being wet and sea sick for so long, of no food and the fear and exertion of hours of battle. Over six hours had passed since they had left the Javelin and after being trapped on the beach and then clearing the cliff emplacements, it felt as if a week had passed. With no contact from the Rangers, nor the rest of the boat team, the three buddies decided they had best locate someone, an officer, NCO, anyone who might know what to do. Keeping low, they made a dash for it and recovered the safety of an enemy trench, going 100 yards before coming across a few Rangers and a couple of other men.

"The reinforcements have arrived," a Ranger joked and told them to join up with their boat team further east.

They passed concrete chambers cut into the limestone to act as shelters for the guards of Rommel's Atlantic Wall, the insides appearing as black as night. Dalton and his buddies just hoped they had been cleared and weren't still harbouring enemy soldiers. Moving still further back eastward they came level with Pingenot on the far side of the field; he was getting the remnants of his boat team to dig in near the hedgerow. Spotting his men, Pingenot sent a runner to them.

"No one's where they oughta be," the runner told them.

"Pingenot's got less than twenty men with him and he doesn't know where the hell the other boat teams are, just a mess, could be pushed back into the sea at any minute ..."

"Just what we wanted to hear," Clayton replied looking at Ted and Dalton, with Ted sticking a finger through a bullet hole in his pants and wondering how in the world he didn't have a hole through his leg. "And the radio's bust!" the runner added as if he hadn't relayed enough bad news. But Clayton was smiling, Ted was now completely distracted, he had found a piece missing from his rifle butt where a bullet must have hit it. With a shrug of his shoulders, Ted sat down on the mud and removed the precious pictures from his top pocket, "Guess I'm as safe as I'm gonna be," he said to himself, looking at them.

The runner looked at Ted as if he had gone mad, but he continued regardless. "Pingenot wants you guys to find another officer and let them know where we are and get hold of some more ammo. Pingenot's shouting at everyone, shit scared we're gonna get a counter attack."

"Yea, well I just wanna eat," Ted said, surprising his close buddies by his insubordination. "Just took my first piss in France and could hardly lift myself out."

"His first piss outside his pants," Clayton corrected and everyone laughed for Ted had not been the only one.

The landslip cliff section didn't seem so steep on the descent. At the top of the hollow they could see right along Omaha; it was 11a.m. and what had been a real mess was slowly transforming into organised chaos, the tide was finally turning against the defenders.

Stepping onto the sand they passed the etchings of the battle. The waves still washed around the dead, rolling the bodies this way and that; someone had shifted Staff Sergeant Holmes onto the boulders to keep him clear of the water. Beneath the cliff some dead had been laid side by side. A group of wounded soldiers further along towards the Vierville Draw were receiving attention from medics and from their buddies. B Company man Mach Smith's eye was out of its socket, lying on his cheek. Bob Sales had placed a rag over it. More seriously wounded men were grouped together nearer to the draw, again at the foot of the cliff.

Of the three B Company landing craft beaching closest to the Vierville Draw, there were perhaps twenty or so able bodied men and not a single officer to be found. Though untouched by wounds, they simply leant against the rock face or sat at its base; numb from being in the water for hours, from inching their way up the beach and numb from the sights they had witnessed. They were leaderless and static.

Of the Headquarters craft, Bob Sales was the only survivor. Only three men from Lieutenant Donaldson's boat made it: Charlie Conner, Harold Baumgarten and Roy Perkins. The other B Company men were from Dalton's own 3rd Platoon whose boat had snagged on an obstacle. Allbritton had made it but Austen was wounded and the tenacious Sergeant Campbell was there, despite being in the sea long enough to be as wrinkled as a prune. First Lieutenant Winkler, like Donaldson, had been killed and 3rd Platoon's Second Lieutenant Frisby had been wounded; whilst the fate of the boats led by Lieutenant Taylor and Lieutenant Williams was yet unknown.

Dalton, with Ted and Clayton, started to pick up bandoliers from men who would no longer need them. They were careful to avoid the more brutalised men where the ammo belts had become as one with the ribs and inners. It was then that Dalton realised that one of the wounded men lying at the base of the cliff was the Company Chaplain. The Chaplain was the link with the woman who kept Dalton's soul alive and images of Hetty, which had been driven deep by the experiences of the day, came to the fore and made the horrific more so.

The Chaplain reached out to take Dalton's hand but was barely able to squeeze it. They spoke to each other, though what was said Dalton soon forgot for as he headed back to the land slip, the US Navy started to bombard the remaining German emplacements along the Vierville Draw. One of the shells fell wide of the mark, hitting the cliff above where the Chaplain had lain and sent rock cascading down upon the wounded men.

Climbing away from the shoreline, Dalton, Clayton and Ted forgot about collecting their assault jackets which they had discarded on the beach that morning. Possessions mattered not and even food was for the moment way down even on Ted's list of priorities.

Over 18,000 troops had been landed on Omaha by 12.30p.m. and during the afternoon they pushed their way ever so slowly inland. Ordinary men had become heroes by necessity and the terrain became littered with them. Thankfully, there were those with whom luck ran and thus by the evening of this long Tuesday in June, a strip of France some 4 miles wide and just 800 yards inland at Vierville and 2,000 yards inland at Coleville had been taken. Just as they could never have anticipated the carnage on the beach, so the men had little perception of the experiences to follow; oblivious as to just how treacherous each and every further step in Normandy would be.

Pingenot's boat team stayed by their hedgerow until the light started to slip away in the west; setting beyond where the English Channel reached the Atlantic and then still further towards a calmer and safer place.

When Dalton, Clayton and Ted rejoined the boat team with their unwelcome news, Staff Sergeant Padgett told them to dig their foxholes and quick. They were being harassed by the occasional sniper as well as mortar fire and without reinforcements, Pingenot was still adamant there would be a counter attack.

Dalton started to dig a foxhole close to the hedge and encountered great difficulty in achieving any depth to protect him from the shrapnel that came with the mortars. Normandy had experienced the same fine weather through May as the south of England. The earth was dry beneath the muddy surface, the limestone having drained away the water and Dalton's first strike sent a pulse vibrating up his arm and through his tired joints. The ground seemed as hard as concrete, not at all like the Devonshire soil so easily displaced in spring. Several inches deep, Dalton encountered the roots of the hawthorn and if breaking up the surface wasn't difficult enough, driving a short blunt spade through half inch roots brought him out in another sweat. The salty beads ran off his brow and created still more streaks down his already grubby and lined face. The day was stretching out real long now; normally Dalton would have dug without stopping, dug until the hole was sufficiently deep and broad to provide good protection for two men. But at about eighteen inches in depth he passed the spade to Ted, and took his turn in keeping guard, waiting for the counter attack. Ted dug a further foot and with the displaced soil surrounding the hole, the two soldiers decided it would have to be deep enough as it was. The first mortars had fallen on the abandoned emplacements and Pingenot had been right in moving away from them and digging in by the hedge. With German snipers and scouts moving up and around the surrounding fields, it wasn't long before mortars were falling closer to the mark and the protection of the foxholes was needed. But the fire was sporadic and succeeded more in keeping the men on their toes than providing any strategic intent for the 'Krauts'. With night closing in, Dalton wasn't sure which was worse, the reality of daylight harassment or the anticipation and fear of what might loom out of the darkness.

Hunger finally filtered into Dalton, Ted and Clayton's consciousness sometime after dark. But with their rations in their assault jackets, food had to be scavenged from whence it was available - the German emplacements and the bodies of enemy soldiers. Even stale German rye bread was tasty to a stomach that hadn't consumed food or drink for twenty-four hours.

Sometime after midnight, illuminated by the moon's rays which penetrated the clouds still scudding across a heavy sky, Pingenot's boat team started to make its way back down the cliff to the beach. They had been ordered by Colonel Canham to regroup with the rest of B Company in Vierville. The locations of their dead were marked by attaching the bayonet to the man's rifle and then inserting it into the ground where they lay with the man's raincoat used to cover his body. But otherwise they were strictly to be left untouched; left for the Grave Registration Department to collect. They would be identified by their 'Dog Tags', one of which the Department would leave on the soldier. Down on the beach they had already placed some of the dead in body bags, but it would be a long time before they reached the men on the cliffs. The bodies would later be transferred into caskets and then as soon as feasible, to a temporary cemetery. Sometime in the future, on a clearer and calmer day, a decision would be made, hopefully by the family as to where their boy would be permanently laid to rest.

The wind had dropped and the sea calmer as the men stepped onto the quiet beach. The sun and moon were pulling the sea away from the shore again and soon there would be another low tide, before yet another the following morning and so time moved on. The surf washed up the beach and little by little, the scene changed. The dull light rounded the shapes, blurred the edges and took away the colour. The debris stretched across the widening expanse of sand, as though several huge ships had sunk off shore and all their contents had been thrown onto the beach. In an hour or so the moonlight would be lost and make all appear as one, just like boulders and rocks, a continuum of the shore line of Normandy.

The 116th 1st Battalion were to regroup close to Vierville, on its northern edge and north of the quarry where the 29th Division command post had been established. It was at this command post, just 150 yards inland, that Colonel Canham, the regiment's commander anxiously awaited the arrival of the rest of B Company; so few had yet reported.

In the darkness, Pingenot walked his men up the Vierville Draw past the remains of the sand bagged emplacements and the mine fields. They were bedraggled and tired. Uniforms, faces and hands were dirty and dusty with mud and blood stains; blood from men hit close by and from their own cuts and grazes. Salt encrustations from the sea water and sweat dressed their skin. Clothing was ripped by the barbed wire on the cliff, rocks on the beach and splinters from the wood of the trenches. Stains and smells from human excrement and sweat, faces smeared by the wipe of a hand, working hands at the end of working arms, hands that spread the grime in among the fine light hair that grew unobtrusively from their young chins. But more telling than anything, were the looks on their faces. This had surely been their longest day.

About the same time as Pingenot's men arrived at the company rendezvous, Lieutenant Taylor with some of Lieutenant William's men walked down the road from the north of Vierville. Thus with the arrival of Taylor and Pingenot all that were coming back, were back.

It was an emotional reunion for the surviving men, pleased as they were to find buddies safe, yet deeply concerned and insecure at the absence of others. But priorities had to be right; set up a defensive position, dig the foxhole, eat then talk, if the enemy allowed it. The company moved up to the crossroads with the D514 where Dalton and Ted paired up again to dig yet another foxhole, their tiring arms shifting what felt like ten cubic yards of soil. The soil was softer here and without roots proved much easier to dig. But at a depth that was clearly inadequate, their empty stomachs and tired limbs refused to co-operate further. They pulled out a chocolate bar from a D Ration and then set about opening a C ration can containing 10oz of stew hash and beans. It was a feast, finished off with a few dry crackers and water.

Basic training in the States had focused on care and feeding of weapons and if a rifleman hadn't learnt in training that his M1 rifle was his best friend, then it only took a couple of minutes in battle for the message to sink home. It had been drilled into them to keep it clean and they had become proficient in taking it apart and reassembling it blindfolded. It was well after midnight but it hadn't yet become fully dark. The last of the moonlight was still piercing the clouds to provide a subdued illumination, more than sufficient for a well trained rifleman to clean his M1. Dalton started what would become a daily ritual and a compulsive endeavour to keep his rifle dry, clean, oiled and loaded. Then whilst men settled down and either finished their food or like Dalton, cleaned their weapons, events of the day were recounted. With strained and muffled voices, news of the fate of each LCA passed along the grapevine; from group of men to group of men. Some of the information was accurate, some inaccurate and some a soldier's tale. Dalton listened whilst he unlocked the trigger guard from the trigger housing, separated the two sections, pulled out the trigger housing and set it aside.

Dalton already knew something of what happened to the three LCAs beaching at the Vierville Draw; of Bob Sales and the Headquarters LCA, of Charles Conner, Baumgarten and Perkins LCA and of the main body of his own 3rd Platoon. With the muzzle of his rifle pointing down, barrel to the left, Dalton separated the rifle stock from the barrel and receiver, separated the operating rod and removed the spring.

Much was said of the losses, of best friends and of good soldiers. Eight Officers and 185 enlisted B Company men had landed eighteen hours earlier, and in looking around at those remaining, Dalton could see that the company was seriously depleted.

He used the tip of a bullet to remove the operating rod pin and removed the bullet guide, operating arm and catch. Working the operating rod handle loose from the bolt, he slid the bolt free and lifted it out.

It seemed that Lieutenant Taylor's LCA beached on the far eastern edge of Dog Green and only three soldiers were lost in crossing the sand. By around 11a.m. the platoon had moved up the bluff to the edge of Vierville and then on through the village towards Ormel Farm. Drawing small arms fire from a field to the left of the farm, Taylor's platoon had attacked with rifle fire and grenades. The engagement was said to be swiftly concluded when the dozen or so Germans surrendered, with no losses to the B Company men.

Dalton pulled out his little kits of wipes, linseed oil and ramrod style barrel brushes. After pushing a damp cloth through the bore, he ran the barrel brush through several times to remove any sediment. Taking a dry cloth and making sure it was absolutely clean, he pushed the cloth through the barrel to dry it and then lightly oiled it to ensure it didn't rust overnight.

After dealing with the prisoners, it appeared that Taylor led his platoon to the crossroads just beyond the Farm. Here two German trucks stopped several hundred yards further down the road and soldiers off- loaded to take up positions in the surrounding fields. Taylor apparently lost four men in the subsequent fire fight and pulled back to the farm buildings. The walls of the farm were slotted and the men were able to repulse the first attack, then with the arrival of some 20 Rangers, the farm was said to be comfortably held. Taylor did not withdraw until ordered by Canham to regroup at Vierville that evening.

Dalton treated the rifle chamber in the same meticulous way he had attended to the bore; all metal parts were cleaned with light coatings of oil, except for bolts, springs and rod cams which were cleansed with graphite cup grease and wiped off.

The 40 or so B Company men already at Vierville before Taylor and Pingenot arrived, must have been made up from the three landing craft beaching at and near the Vierville Draw and some from First Lieutenant Williams's craft. Williams had beached still further to the east of Vierville than Taylor. The British Naval crew were described as 'cool cookies' and had bided their time, continuing until they found a 'calmer section' and eventually landed their human cargo between WN 68 and WN 70 in the vicinity of Dog White. Reading between the lines, Dalton gathered that few casualties were incurred in crossing the beach.

It was at Dog White that Colonel Canham and his Command Team also sensibly landed, perhaps 30 minutes after Williams and set up a temporary command post there. Accounts of Canham's bravery in motivating the men pinned down on the beach stirred the men's pride in their regiment. The Colonel had apparently helped initiate one of the first penetrations inland; thus together with other units, Williams's platoon moved up the bluffs at Dog White and tackled the German emplacements.

Dalton had been told that as much care should be taken of the wooden parts and strap as the mechanical parts of the gun, to lightly apply linseed oil to the wood, to wash the sling, dry it and lightly treat it with neatsfoot oil to keep it pliable. But Dalton felt that would have to wait, maybe forever.

Lieutenant Williams was at first said to have been hit by two grenades and several bullets, but the story settled to him being lightly wounded when he crawled forward from his men to drop a grenade into a machine gun emplacement. Apparently Staff Sergeant Frank Price led the platoon on towards Vierville whilst Williams was picked up by medics. Price entered the village around the same time as Taylor and joined the lieutenant in the push to the crossroads and Ormel Farm.

Thus unbeknown to each other, the three B Company units had been involved in some of the earliest break outs from the western half of Omaha. The first being Pingenot on Charlie, then Williams at Dog White, shortly followed by Taylor on the eastern edge of Dog Green.

"Shame they didn't have us all land at the softer spots," Clayton remarked. "Wonder who thought it a good idea to make a full frontal attack on the Vierville Draw?" he asked, but no one replied, they had no idea, hadn't even questioned the rationale. "Could have come from behind and taken the emplacements out from the start," he added.

Dalton dwelt a while on Clayton's words, then tried to make himself feel better by assuming that the people who knew best, must have had good reason to attack from the front.

The whispering and the story telling petered out, eating and cleaning done, the men fell quiet as the early hours slipped by. 2nd Lieutenant Taylor had reported to Divisional Command at the Quarry. As Acting Company Commander, Taylor returned to do a quick head count before dispatching a runner with a note. The runner was Marshmallow of course, his first real job of the day. He had turned in sick on the afternoon of the 4th and had arrived on Omaha at 6.30p.m. clean and 'as fresh as a daisy'. Marshmallow's note carried the news that 5 of the 8 officers and 100 of the 185 enlisted men were missing.

N.B.
(C Company of the 116th who were to follow B Company in at Dog Green, actually landed 1,000 yards to the left and lost only 20 of their 194 men in crossing the beach.)

Chapter 35

The In-Laws

Paddington, June 1944.

Paddington Hospital, situated on the Harrow Road, was just a stone's throw from Thorngate and lay opposite where Marylands Road joined the busy road and tram route into London. Hetty was in a ward at the back, where those well enough could look out over the grimy Grand Union Canal and the railway tracks running into Paddington Station. Their familiarity reminded her of better, carefree days, of living on Ranelagh Road and taking picnics to Regents Park. How things had changed, the fun-loving Hetty, guilt ridden and doubtful of carrying her baby to full term.

The ward was clean enough and the staff efficient, though they scowled should anyone ask for extra attention. Hetty had refused to use the bed pan but Matron's threat of a sedative, persuaded her otherwise.

"Our difficult patient," the Matron said, pointing at Hetty as she floated ahead of the doctor as if wafting away any slight inconvenience that might delay the great man; moving from bed to bed, ticking this and that, making notes and responding, "Yes doctor, of course doctor." The doctor grunted, tapped Hetty's chest and back whilst listening with his stethoscope, then placed the cold contraption on her tummy and listened again, moving on with barely a nod to the feeble girl. Hetty wanted to ask if her baby was going to be alright but didn't like to trouble him; perhaps Matron would come back and speak with her later, she thought.

"Toxaemia," the Matron said the following day, after she had checked that bed pans were clean, the sheets changed and bed baths carried out. "The only cure for toxaemia in pregnancy is to get on and have the baby," the matron explained. But it was too early; there were still two months to go. It was the high blood pressure that had been giving her the headaches and high blood pressure wasn't good for the baby, 'caused problems for the placenta' as far as Hetty could understand.

Edith had told Hetty that a friend of hers had died of it, 'had a few fits, then a massive stroke and was dead, quick as that'. Just what Hetty wanted to hear. Did children pay for the sins of their parents, Hetty asked herself, or was she so wicked that God was punishing her for what she had done to Paul.

"Everything's a mess!" Hetty told Pat Harrison when she came to see her. "I am useless, even hurting my own baby ... should never have got pregnant in the first place," she told her cousin with absolute conviction. Pat remembered their visits to Ivy Bridge and was convinced Hetty must have become pregnant on their November visit, right there in that upstairs room of the Kings Arms. She had still been dating Roy Perkins then, fun days she told herself, recalling the noise in the adjoining room that had kept Roy and her amused. Squeaky metal bed springs. Whoever invented them, Pat asked herself? Hetty had been happy then, what with her new found freedom away from home and away from that 'controlling Mother of hers'. The complete abandonment and youthful optimism that had been present when her child was likely conceived, gave Pat hope that Hetty would once again become the cousin and friend she once knew.

Pat had hoped that Roy would propose to her like Dalton had to Hetty, but as Christmas '43 had approached with no proposal forthcoming, she had pressed Roy on the subject. Roy declared that he could never love her as she loved him so Pat finished the relationship.

"I do miss Roy," Pat said to Hetty.

It temporarily pulled Hetty from her woes. "I know Patsy," Hetty said comfortingly. "He was the love of your life wasn't he? You never know, after the war he might realise what he's lost and come back for you."

"Maybe," Pat said, "but there's plenty more fish in the sea."

"Perhaps Paul wouldn't be dead if he could have come back to me," Hetty said in such a disconsolate manner that it frightened Pat. "If I had at least visited him in hospital, I could have told him I still cared about him ... as a friend, you know, and made 'im feel better. Perhaps he would have forgiven me for what I'd done to him?"

"Come on Hetty, no good thinking like that," Pat said.

"Told my Dad I would have gone to see Paul and maybe things would have been different if I'd seen him. But do you know what he said?" Pat shook her head, even though she did know, Hetty had told her at least a dozen times already. "Don't you think you'd done enough harm to that boy without him seeing you pregnant?"

Pat tried to comfort her cousin but Hetty was off again.

"Glad Mum didn't give Paul's brooch back after all. Didn't feel I could wear it, not with marrying Dalton. Gave it to Mum to take round, but I found out she sold it and kept the money. Now I am pleased she did, it would have been another smack in the face for him."

There was a long pause, Pat didn't know what to say, this was old ground. Ethel shouldn't have sold it, probably spent the money on the horses Pat thought, but she knew the Eaglestones well and wasn't going to criticise.

"Look sweet'art, getting all upset isn't going to help yer blood pressure."

"I've been so bloody stupid," Hetty said again and started to cry.

"Hey, come on now," Pat cajoled, "baby's going to be okay and Dalton will be back as soon as 'im and Roy have given the Germans what they deserve."

"Jimmy says if I'm lucky, Dalton will come back a cripple and serve me right ... unlucky and he'll come back in a body bag."

Pat couldn't help herself, "Bastard your brother, always 'as bin," Pat retorted angrily.

Hetty looked surprised at her cousin's venom.

"He's got problems of his own," Hetty said defending her brother.

"Yea like wantin' his own way all the time, thinks the universe revolves round 'im."

Hetty stayed silent and Pat refrained from further comment. Jimmy sometimes made her blood boil. The whole family knew how much Ethel had spoilt 'Young Jimmy'. Young Jimmy, what a bloody stupid way to refer to a grown man, Pat thought. Him and his bloody cricket, 'game for girls' her Dad said and of Ethel, she had 'a sickness' or was it 'bloody neurotic' either way, she had dressed the container but left it unfilled.

Pat changed the subject.

"Terrible about all these pilotless planes," she said commenting on the gossip after a heavy weekend of bombings.

"I know, the air raid sirens keep going off. Nurses were disappearing for a bit but they just carry on now, just too many alarms to worry about," Hetty said.

"Dad says they're called doodlebugs."

"Doodlebugs?" Hetty questioned grinning and then started tittering.

"Yea, stupid name init. Heard a kid call 'em 'bumble bombs' the other day." And with that both girls started laughing.

"Dads and the names they make up," Pat reflected.

"Wonder if they're using 'em against our boys in France?" Hetty asked her cousin. "It's been two weeks since the invasion and I haven't heard from Dalton yet," anxiety again colouring her tone. Edith had told her that if 'yer don't get a telegram, then there's nuffin to worry about'. But Hetty couldn't help but worry. Seemed like all she did lately was worry. Lay awake at night worrying: about Dalton, the baby, where they would live after the war, and not least, about what she had done to Paul. Hetty wasn't sure if she would receive a telegram anyway. Dalton's mother was on his Dog Tag as next of kin. Fleda would write to her of course but with the time it takes for letters to travel from America, it might be weeks before she heard anything.

The nation knew that the invasion took place on the 6th June. Churchill went to the commons to announce that the 'first of a series of landings upon the European continent has taken place ... everything is proceeding to plan'. Announcements were made in shops and factories, later edition newspapers carried the 'Invasion' headline and the churches were fuller than they had been for years. Some even holding impromptu services throughout the day to cater for those who wanted to pray for a loved one. An old porter came up to the ward and announced to everyone that the allies had landed in Europe, and in almost bloated pride declared, 'Long live the King!' Matron wasn't amused.

"What a mess," Hetty said again to her cousin as she pictured the long journey her bad news might have to travel. She wondered if Dalton's family even knew about the invasion.

"If yer want to see a real mess, come with me up town," Pat said trying to divert Hetty's woes. "At the weekend Doodlebugs were fallin' everywhere. They'd aimed one at Buckingham Palace, but it hit Wellington Barracks instead. Hit the Guards Chapel ... killed over 100, so Stan Kirby's friend said."

Stan Kirby, now there was a name Hetty hadn't heard for some time. "Lost his stripes 'cause of me," she reflected. And with that, Pat decided it was time she got off to work.

Launched from fixed ramps in northern France, the 25 feet long V1 or 'doodlebug' was always targeted on Tower Bridge, at the start of the docks. Yet they were falling over a wide area of the city. With a speed of 350mph and an altitude of 2,500ft, simple guidance systems kept the winged craft on track and once the preset 140 mile distance was reached, circuits closed down the jet engine. Plunging to earth it delivered one ton of explosives to produce a surface blast wave which caused extensive damage.

One landed right by the Paddington Recreation Ground on Ashworth and Grantully Roads, a third of a mile from Thorngate. Another just as close, fell on Westbourne Square and Ranelagh Road, already severely damaged during the Blitz.

In the few days Hetty had been in hospital, 700 V1s hit the capital, damaging 100,000 buildings and killing over 500 people. It was with bated breath that the Eaglestones listened to the whining hum of a Doodlebug approach, willing it to continue on past their home before the engines cut out. Two fell near Paddington Station, one hit a hospital in Kensington and others killed shoppers on both sides of the river. The city was again gripped by fear and another evacuation was already underway.

In the days that followed, Hetty learned from Jimmy that her mother had gone to see Paul in hospital.

"She told Paul you were too ill to visit ... just a little white lie," he said, mimicking his mother perfectly; then raised his bushy eyebrows as if to await Hetty's response. But she didn't have one, didn't know what to say, her brother was so upset at losing his best friend. Just back from the funeral, still in his suit, dust on his trousers from the wall he'd been sitting on, alone in contemplation, his face flustered, eyes watery and wringing his hands as if it might help him find words harsh enough to express what he was thinking. But he said no more, it could wait. There would be plenty of opportunities if Dalton actually did make it back, though he'd put his month's wages on him not to; the hospitals were filling up with casualties and the telegram delivery boys were very busy. He might have asked Hetty for a few bob, but their mother had warned Hetty against taking money into hospital with her. "I'm off," he said, seeing Edith walking down the ward, removing her head scarf as she approached.

Hetty soon poured out her woes to her sister as she had done to Pat. She was still getting headaches as well as stomach pains and it made her feel scared. The only answer to toxaemia at this stage in her pregnancy was to get plenty of rest, but rest eluded her.

"You're making things worse by worrying so much," Edith said with diminishing sympathy. "Blood pressure's not goin away if you're up tight all the time. And what's done is done. You didn't really luv him sweet'art and that's that."

"He was lying on his death bed waiting for me and I never came," Hetty said, starting to cry again in her sister's presence.

"It's Dalton you should be worried about ..." Edith cut in looking around her, a little embarrassed at the attention they were starting to draw from the other patients. "He's your husband," she continued in a hushed voice. "Don't know why you chose him mind, I didn't want you to. Stupid man if you ask me. But you could have done better than Paul, boring he was."

"I AM worried about Dalton," Hetty said emphatically, not sure how to respond to her sister calling Dalton 'stupid'. "I think about him all the time ... I don't know what I'll do if I lose him," she added, getting even more upset.

"Well I'll tell you somefin for nuffin, you're gonna lose your baby as well as Dalton if you keep on like this," Edith warned as she made her excuses to leave ... "and don't forget to write to his Muver, keep in with the in-laws; you'll be bleeding living with em soon."

Chapter 36

Down the Road

Normandy, 7th to 9th June 1944.

Working in pairs, with two hours on guard and two hours off, the 1st Battalion made the best of their first night on the narrow band of liberated French soil. Sometime after everyone fell silent, Charlie Connor walked to the edge of the bluff to take a nature call and in the dim light saw a German machine gun team scurrying past. On returning with several of the men, the enemy had already slipped into the gathering gloom. But the sighting led to an edgy rest, with sleep hard to come by and short in duration.

In the last hours of the short night, a thin veil of sea mist moved onshore to shroud the bodies and debris littering the beach. Pulling itself across the widening expanse of sand, it lay low and then crawled up the Vierville Draw, swirled and sunk into foxholes, clung to uniforms and to the exposed skin of the men and formed a cloak around the night watchmen - the silent watchmen who stood peering into the gloom with just their thoughts for company.

Dalton had slumped down into his foxhole sometime after waking Ted, around 3.30a.m. Ted was on last watch. The light levels appeared to increase well before 5a.m. but the promise of a new day dragged on until the anticipation was lost and trepidation again replaced hope. One night, whilst training on Salisbury Plain, Allbritton had commented to Dalton that the sun 'in these parts seems to hover below the horizon for a while' as though there was some debate as to whether it should rise.

By 6a.m. it was as light as the day was probably going to get, the sky still overcast and the mist vaporising away. Trucks, jeeps and a few tanks started to make their way up from the beach and along the road through Vierville. Dalton slept despite the noise, deeper asleep than at any other point in the night. For having woken to see US vehicles moving inland, he had felt more secure. Sometime after first light Sergeant Campbell came down the ranks and told Ted that he could stand down; Ted immediately slouched over and fell asleep.

Clayton was the first of the platoon to rouse himself and the first to break open a K ration; the paraffin coated khaki box had done its job, holding together despite the damp. Pushing aside the coffee, soup powders and the crackers, he picked out what he was looking for, the precious cigarettes. The first few draws gave him the lift he needed; he got up and made his way over to a water pump in the back yard of a shell damaged building. Dalton woke to see him crossing back over the road with his helmet half filled with water. Clayton splashed his face clean of the previous day's grime, before lighting the wick of a Coleman stove with his Zippo lighter. He then placed his helmet with the remaining water over the flame until the water was hot enough to add the coffee powder. Allbritton, Ted and Dalton joined him and the four soldiers sat without talking and watched as more vehicles and men moved up the Vierville Draw. The coffee was the best they had tasted in a long time.

Of the new arrivals, the Sherman tanks were the most welcome sight. With their 450 horse power Ford engines, each of the 6m long hulks grated slowly up the incline. At 28 tons in weight, their maximum speed on the flat was just 28mph. It would be the first action for the fresh faced crews, five men per tank: the commander, gunner and loader in the turret and the driver and bow gunner in the hull. Though massive in appearance, Clayton commented that there was precious little room for five men, for once you take away the engine, tracks, the bogies and all the suspension units, there was little space left. Somewhere in amongst the crew were stored 97 shells for the main 75mm gun and all the ammunition for the three mounted machine guns. Dalton felt claustrophobic at the thought and preferred his chances in the open air. However with all its weaponry and armour plating, it looked an awesome and reassuring weapon to have on their side. Though little did they know how powerless it would be in the Normandy countryside and feeble by comparison to the German tanks. Between the tanks came the jeeps, a few M8 Armoured Cars, half-track personnel carriers and the important supply trucks.

By around 9a.m. under the orders of Colonel Canham, the three battalions of the 116th Regiment had been mustered and prepared to advance from Omaha. It was essential to break out from their tentative toe hold before the enemy counter attacked, though fortunately German armoured and infantry divisions were still being held in their reserve positions. The high command still believing that the Normandy invasion was a feint, with Pas de Calais the actual target of the Allies.

1st Battalion, comprising of what was left of A and B companies and the less depleted C and D Companies were to push west along the D514.[2] They would be accompanied by 2nd and 5th Rangers. The column of some 550 men, 10 Shermans and a sprinkling of other vehicles did well to leave Vierville at around mid- morning. The road ran parallel to and no more than one thousand yards from the cliffs which stretched from Vierville, past Pointe et Raz de la Percée to Pointe du Hoc. It was to Pointe du Hoc that the column was heading to relieve the three companies of 2nd Rangers who had scaled the cliffs there and who had since been pinned down by the 352nd German Infantry.

Walking in two columns, one on each side of the road, the men passed the high stone walls of the outlying buildings of Vierville. They passed huge substantially built houses, like manors with equally huge barns made from the same beige stone as the cliffs. The buildings surpassed anything Dalton had seen except perhaps the few stately homes they had come across in England. Some were intact whilst others had suffered the bombs destined for the beach. With the road rising slightly for three tenths of a mile to reach open

---

[2] See map page 401

countryside, the men got into their stride. The small fields bounded by hedgerows made them feel as if they were back on manoeuvres in England; the countryside equally lush green and the plants identical, with the May blossom and cow parsley. The tanks rumbled and clanked along the hard surface and threw up clouds of dust which covered the infantrymen. It lightened the mud patches and stains on their uniforms and it filled their lungs. Those who walked close to the tanks, believing they were safer there, also struggled with the exhaust fumes which made them feel light headed.

Ditches lined either side of the road, hedges bordered them to act as a fence to the field and farm buildings frequently interspersed the route, telling the farm boys amongst them, that this was fertile ground. The barn walls sometimes sat right along the edge of the road, the slit windows appearing as if designed for military defence.

Now the naval bombardment was in evidence at every turn: more damaged buildings, shell craters, dead cattle in the fields and wrecked German vehicles with the dead still occupying them. The smell of bloated carcasses was sickening but worse was the smell of the soldiers decaying. They had seen many dead but not like these, for the oxygen had long since left their bodies, not pink, nor pale, or even blue, but purple and swelling. Swelling beyond recognition of the men they once were. Liquids oozed from their wounds and openings to grossly exaggerate their distorted shapes. The smell was as foul as the sight and the two created a nauseating concoction.

Problem was that unlike yesterday, Dalton had time to contemplate what he saw; the unique images drawn, sketches of horror, created and hung as if in a living gallery. A paratrooper caught up in the branches of a tree, suspended like a tasteless symbol, limp and motionless, to portray war in a way words cannot. The living passed the spectacle by and carried the image with them until their memory faded into their last breath of air.

The column stopped up ahead and the line of men, like the body of a caterpillar, shuffled and concertinaed to a halt.

The land to their left fell away to the Aure valley and the slightly raised nature of the road made the work of snipers that much easier. A sniper had hit for a second time and someone at the front was going to do something about it. A staff sergeant and a few riflemen slid off down a hedgerow, the trees beyond it perhaps concealing the dedicated man. Most of the column sat in the ditches on either side of the road, some lit up and some fell asleep. The ditches were well trimmed as was the custom; to the French landowner, a good ditch was as much an indication of good breeding as it was of good land management. The depth and shape of them and the softness of the tended grass was strangely comforting and Dalton also grabbed what extended to a fifteen minute nap. A burst of small arms fire acted as a signal to fall back in and the column continued, delayed by just one man. Further along the road, Dalton passed Charlie Connor lying in the ditch as still as death, hit by the sniper so he presumed. By the time Connor woke up, B Company were almost out of sight.

About a mile further down the road, a German machine gun team opened up on the lead men and again the men took cover in the ditches. This isn't so bad Dalton thought as he lay down and tried to catch another nap.

"Beats yesterday," Clayton said, taking out another cigarette, more than happy to take in the brightening sky and warmth that had started to pierce the cloud. The German gun crew had done their job and held up the column. Having been left isolated, good sense prevailed above valour and they filtered off into woodland. The column continued with one less private as though nothing had happened, without pursuing or further pursuit from the German machine gun team.

Sometime after midday the battalion snaked into St. Pierre du Mont, a 1,000 yard ribbon of buildings, some of which were again huge, perhaps 100 feet wide - like Dewlish house but bigger and Dalton wondered if the Normans were renowned for being wealthy. At the limit of the village the land stretched out on either side again, with the village church way over to the right and what seemed like another very large residence to the left of it. The view might have been insignificant had a German artillery unit not used the last house of the village as a range marker, perhaps guided by a spotter in the church tower. With the shells raining in, the guys hid behind the tanks, scattered over garden walls and into front yards. Dalton leapt over a low stone wall, Ted virtually threw himself over and landed on Clayton's leg nearly breaking it. Thinking something more sinister had struck him, Clayton screamed out and his overreaction tickled his buddies' sense of humour. But any inclination to chuckle was swiftly snuffed out by the screams of men who really had been hit.

Mortars fell and 88 mm shells shrieked in to explode on and around the road, causing craters and hitting buildings. Without foxholes, the men simply clung to the earth and pulled themselves ever closer to it, luck and prayer their only protection. After the relatively calm start to the day, Dalton had managed to fool himself that things would get better, but now, caught in the open, amidst butchered men, he knew it wasn't going to. With the terrible noise and smell of cordite came the shouting of officers and non coms. Fire was returned, mortar crews pulled themselves together and the tanks started to pound the area from which the shelling emanated. But the tanks had little manoeuvrability on the narrow road and rather than risk losing them, the column pulled back 800 yards. During the encounter B Company went down to just two officers, losing 2nd Lieutenant Pingenot, hit by shrapnel. Staff Sergeant (Toad) Padgett found him in a shell crater and helped carry him to the care of medics. Roy Perkins sustained shrapnel wounds serious enough to end his combat days; to be shipped back to England and perhaps Pat's loving arms, the best of the options on offer so it now seemed to Dalton.

The dead were pulled into the ditches and the column entered the fields between the village and the cliffs, digging in for the night within the sound of the waves. They were only a few hundred yards from Point Du Hoc, but the battalion had suffered another thirty-five casualties and the 2nd Rangers would have to wait until the next morning to be relieved.

A cloud burst, though short lived, turned the surface of the churned up fields near St. Pierre into a thin layer of mud which caked onto boots. And in a way that only mud can, mysteriously spread onto almost every section of clothing and equipment as the men established the emplacements and dug their foxholes. D Company, the heavy weapons unit, set up their water cooled Browning automatic machine guns and 81mm mortars so that the centre and flanks of the battalion were covered. 4th Platoon, the heavy weapons platoon of B Company, did the same with their air cooled Browning and 50mm mortars to protect the integrity of their own B Company men.

The digging in was undisturbed by the enemy or further downpours and long before dark the men started to get some food in their bellies, clean their weapons and establish watch routines. Sitting on the edge of his foxhole, Dalton spread the bouillon soup powder from a K ration onto the spam C ration to give it a more palatable tangy flavour and for good measure opened a tin of spaghetti. With his stomach comforted, he placed another priority before the care of his weapon this night, the care of his feet; to the foot soldier the care of feet was vital. They would have to carry him from battle to encounter to engagement, along roads, across fields and likely many miles in the days to come. Dalton removed his boots and socks to air and hopefully dry and saw Ted doing the same. It reminded him of the way his momma used to prepare little Virginia Mae for an outing. Any bits clinging to the socks were meticulously removed, the material smoothed over the foot to iron out wrinkles, not just once but several times. Finally he pulled the laces to just the right tension, no tighter and no looser than he knew would ensure a comfortable mile or many miles, whatever was required of them, at whatever the time of day or night.

On his first two hour watch, Dalton peered through the hedgerow as dusk killed colour and shape. The cluster of bushes, the spinney or the wood beyond, perhaps concealing nothing more than cowering mammals scared of all the new noises and smells, or perhaps they concealed the enemy waiting to strike. The vegetation provided dense cover, the deciduous trees like oak, maple, birch, ash and elm spreading over hardy thistles, nettles and other plants growing below them. So different to a Virginian pine forest, for it offered concealment and yet also concealed the enemy. Allbritton had paired up with Clayton as Dalton had with Ted and they too would be taking turns at peering at something or nothing, real or imagined - their first night in the moist Normandy countryside. The only mammal bold enough to venture out that night was a solitary bat, which swooped across the field beyond where Dalton was standing; devouring the flying insects which seemed to proliferate in the abundant terrain. There were no birds or bird sounds, likely driven away by events. But as night descended completely so came the scratching and scraping of insects, heard loudest by the men in their foxholes; for the insects searched in the humus, the earth their home and life source. Intermingled with these natural sounds were the grunts of men getting comfortable in unfamiliar surroundings, of whispering, the tinkle of metal, the flap of a strap or the reassuring sound of a human nature call. These intermittent sounds were themselves enveloped by the distant rhythm of the waves, waves which indiscriminately maintained their assault on the Normandy cliffs less than a mile to the north.

With the enemy perhaps only a few hundred yards away to the west and with casualties of the day fresh in their minds, the guards stood alert, guns ready and fingers twitching. In the small hours, two soldiers fired at an 'approaching' intruder who failed to respond to their clicker code. The M1 Rifle fire woke all but the most exhausted however with no return fire, nerves soon settled, eyelids drooped, muscles relaxed and weapons were laid back down. In the morning a bullet ridden cow lay a few yards from where the guards had fired.

By 5.00a.m. only harmless light pierced into the subconscious of the sleeping soldiers; then a naval bombardment of the German positions several hundred yards to the west finished the wake up call.

Dalton sat up in his foxhole and brushed off the slugs that had crawled onto his raincoat with the early morning dew; the grass and hedgerow were wet with it and he was glad he had drawn the coat up to his helmet before falling asleep. Two short periods of sleep, perhaps three hours in all, made a total of no more than five hours in the last three nights. Allbritton dragged himself out of the next foxhole and threw Dalton a chocolate bar. Tucking a few precious squares of olive drab toilet paper inside his helmet liner webbing and picking up his entrenching tool, Allbritton walked off for a nature call. His uniform was still patchy from the mud accumulated the previous day and by the time he came back, was muddier still with fresh wet mud and bits of leaves attached.

Clayton had somehow managed to collect enough water for the four of them to share coffee and sitting on his pup tent canvas he looked a wiry old soldier. The men washed back the hot liquid and surveyed their surroundings for the first time in the light. A chilly wind had picked up and a fine drizzle fell from the grey sky to quietly penetrate their clothing.

"Just as cold in June as winter back home," one remarked.

"Yea, just like England," said another, whilst Clayton laughed at the use of his pup tent ...

"We need a water proof ground sheet, not a God Damn tent," he chuckled.

A few soldiers had been detailed to remove the dead GIs from the field and their movement distracted the buddies. Two of the dead had already been there when the company entered the field and had given rise to the smell which had pervaded the air during the night. A third soldier had been hit by a sniper during the early morning. The four friends watched as the swollen, putrid bodies were placed onto woollen GI blankets and with soldiers holding each corner, dragged over to the road and left in the ditch for collection. With the dead, thankfully also went the smell and the buddies drew strange satisfaction from its dismissal.

"That coffee sure tasted good," someone commented as the

last body was dragged out of sight and mind; dismissing them as real soldiers must.

With the growing light the men made ready to move west towards Pointe du Hoc and prepared for the day's likely encounters. The naval bombardment continued through the first part of the morning and then quietened as it focused on targets further west. Rather than returning to the road and facing whatever now lay waiting there, the battalion struck out across country. The pace was slow and cautious as they walked across fields, through woodland and pushed through hedgerows. Slow not least because they had to carry all their weapons as well as all their worldly goods.

The naval bombardment had done its job in scattering the enemy encircling the 2nd Rangers and the 116th 1st Battalion joined up with them at Pointe Du Hoc without incident. But before the milling men could come to some sort of order, they were suddenly attacked with machine gun fire and mortars.

The 116th 3rd Battalion had come up to support the 1st and approaching Pointe Du Hoc from the south had mistaken the American position as German. The onslaught was short lived and the casualties few but the incident left a nasty taste in everyone's mouth, their first of friendly fire. With a respite of a couple of hours, casualties were dealt with and Dalton and his buddies consumed their remaining rations and grabbed what sleep they could in yet another foxhole; dug into stony ground.

The two remaining B Company Officers met with the other battalion officers in one of the least damaged German gun emplacements. A captain talked with the Regimental CP on one of the scarce SCR 300 radios whilst other less senior officers scanned a creased and dirty map. The SCR 300 was used at company and battalion level, whereas the handy-talkie, the SCR 536, was used at company and platoon level. Surviving 536s were also few and far between after the landings but in B Company their scarcity had not been such a problem. With well under half the men and just 2nd Lieutenant Taylor and 2nd Lieutenant Varadian remaining, communication wasn't exactly complex.

Around midday, 1st Battalion, rejoined by half a dozen tanks, was ordered to push three miles along the coast road towards Maisy.

The Naval guns could now be heard again in the distance, bombarding the coastal town of Grandcamp Maisy and in so doing, attempting to make life easier for the approaching infantrymen. Pushing through Grandcamp and just several hundred yards from Maisy the column passed an old French couple. They stood on the doorstep of what must have been their home; a house partly in ruins, surrounded by a ravaged farm. They watched the men pass, the occasional soldier nodded to them and the couple returned the acknowledgment, the tears squashed by smiles on their lined faces. The quiet step of the rubber soled boots on the road was intermittently drowned by the next tank to trundle past, then when the last soldier passed by and the tanks were distant, the couple were left alone, to start the first day of the rest of their free life.

Maisy, like Grandcamp, had been devastated by the naval bombardment. The great coastal guns, the Maisy battery, had been silenced, emplacements and civilian homes damaged and the defenders demoralised. Some initial resistance was answered by the tanks, which fired on the few positions still manned and working. However, with the threat of further shelling, the Germans surrendered to the dirty, sweaty and dishevelled men of the 116th. Unshaven, unwashed, with frayed nerves to match their frayed uniforms, the guys were daunting in appearance and intent. With terrible losses so fresh in their memories, written across their faces was the message to co-operate or else. Most of the captured Germans obeyed and were thankful for their lives and those that didn't weren't a problem for long.

The 1st Battalion remained in Maisy during the night of the 8th June. Despite the attraction of sleeping in and around the buildings, the units sensibly dug in and set up defences in strategic open areas. Remaining resistance was dealt with in the early morning and the men made ready to head further into France. However, a heavy barrage of artillery onto the D514 south of the town forced them west of the road and down towards the wet coastal plain. Crossing then the low lying fields and hedgerows they captured the small village of Géfosse Fontenay around mid morning.

At Géfosse Fontenay the men were still no more than 2,000 yards from the sea, however by early afternoon of the same day, they had finally started to push into the Normandy countryside. Heading south-eastward they reached the higher ground above the Aure Valley and followed a contour with dark woodland beyond. Just what did the darkness harbour Dalton wondered as he blindly followed his officers. Well before dusk and some three miles from Géfosse, the battalion dug into the fields above the village of St. Germain du Pert. That evening all three battalions of the 116th Regiment were ordered into division reserve; it had been a long and costly first few days.

B Company Casualties

6th - 9th June 1944

Enlisted men and Officers

Compiled from B Company morning reports, National Personnel Records Centre, St. Louis, Missouri.

By the morning of the 9th June, remaining B Company Officers had managed to produce more reliable lists of casualties. But they did not distinguish between losses on the 6th with those on the 7th, 8th and 9th June.

Abbreviations used

Pvt	Private	KIA	killed in action
Pfc	Private first class	SWA	seriously wounded
Sgt	Sergeant	SWA*	Later died of wounds
S/Sgt	Staff Sergeant	LWA	lightly wounded
T/Sgt	Tech Sergeant	MIA	missing in action
Lt	Lieutenant	MIA*	later confirmed KIA
Capt	Captain		

In the heat of battle, with often fraught communications, distinguishing between LWA and SWA wasn't always an exact science. Mach Smith for example, listed as LWA had his eyeball knocked out. In contrast, some men listed as LWA returned to the company within a relatively short time. However it was invariably the end of the war for a man listed as SWA.

Name			Rank	Classification
Austen	Robert	J	Pfc	LWA
Barnes	John	G	S/Sgt	KIA
Barnett	William	D	Pvt	MIA*
Bercholz	Joseph	M	Pfc	KIA
Bray	Claude	V	Pvt	KIA
Bratten	Thomas	E	Sgt	MIA*
Brooks	James	C	Pfc	KIA
Brown	Staunton	M	Sgt	KIA
Brulotte	Roger	G	Pvt	MIA*
Brownell	Claude	H	Pfc	KIA
Butzko	George	M	Pvt	SWA
Byrnes	Charles	T	Pvt	KIA
Carnrike	Frank	E	Sgt	KIA
Cartwright	Francis	E	Pfc	SWA
Chesney	Benjamin		Pfc	KIA
Cheek	Frank	J	Pfc	KIA
Childress	William	H	Pfc	SWA
Chipps	William	R	Pfc	KIA
Churchill	Joseph	B	Sgt	SWA*
Cicerona	George		Pvt	SWA
Collins	Charles	L	Pfc	LWA
Colvin	Frank	H	Sgt	SWA
Couch	Francis	J	Pvt	MIA
Dearing	Leonard	F	Pvt	KIA
Dirtoma	Frank	J	Pvt	MIA*
Dittmar	Robert	L	Pvt	KIA
Donaldson	Harold	C	1st Lt	KIA
Drumheller	William	A	Pfc	KIA
Eckardt	George	F	Pfc	MIA*
Edney	Walter	A	Pvt	LWA
Eiseman	Henry	M	Pfc	LWA
Evans	Joseph	D	Pfc	SWA
Ferrell	William	E	S/Sgt	KIA
Felix	Joseph	A	Sgt	LWA
Frisby	Ralph	B	2nd Lt	SWA
Fridley	Thomas	H	Pvt	KIA

Garbett	Robert	L	Pfc	MIA*
Godwin	James	D	Pvt	MIA*
Harlow	Willis	M	Pfc	SWA
Hawn	George	A	Pfc	KIA
Holmes	John		S/Sgt	KIA
Jennings	Ralph	E	S/Sgt	KIA
Johnson	Hogan	M	S/Sgt	KIA
Kafkalas	Nicholas	S	Pvt	MIA*
Kennedy	Paul	M	Sgt	KIA
Kernoll	RussellT		Pvt	KIA
Kincer	John	T	T/5 Med	KIA
Knight	Alva	J	Pfc	MIA*
Kolouch	Leonard	F	Pvt	SWA
Koshinski	Francis	E	Pfc	MIA*
Krummert	Aloys	R	Pfc	SWA
Kucera	William		Sgt	MIA*
Kufta	Conrad	V	Pfc	MIA*
Kulka	Francis	J	Pfc	SWA
Laffin	William	C	S/Sgt	KIA
Latin	Peter	P	Pvt	SWA
Lee	Basil		Pfc	KIA
Linton	Charles	K	Pfc	LWA
Lurie	Harry		Pfc	MIA*
Macaluso	Eugene		Pfc	KIA
Maffe	William	J	Pfc	MIA*
Magila	Edmund	M	Pvt	SWA
Malmberg	Kayo	T	T/Sgt	MIA*
Mandino	Vincent	J	Pfc	MIA*
Manning	William	A	Pvt	SWA
Marks	Thomas	J	Pfc	MIA*
Marshall	John	W	Pvt	SWA
Martin	Douglas	M	Pfc	LWA
McCarthy	William	J	Pvt	KIA
Melanda	Stanley	L	Pvt	SWA
Messer	John	L	Pvt	KIA
Minor	Michael	W	Pfc	SWA
Nickol	Dallas	A	Pvt	MIA*
Nuzzo	Frank		Pfc	MIA*

Odee	Charles	W	Pfc	MIA*
Overman	Clifford	C	Pvt	KIA
Palmer	Robert	E	Pvt	KIA
Pellegrini	Joseph	L	Pfc	SWA*
Perkins	Roy	L	Pfc	SWA
Pingenot	Leon	A	2nd Lt	SWA
Pisar	George		Pvt	SWA*
Pluta	Metro		Pvt	MIA*
Pott	Milton	H	Pfc	LWA
Rafferty	Laverne	E	Pfc	SWA
Reyes	Robert	B	Pfc	MIA*
Riggs	Clairus	L	Pfc	MIA*
Riley	Medford	H	Sgt	SWA
Rinker	Garnet	L	Pfc	MIA*
Roach	John	A	T.Sgt	LWA
Roach	Walter	W	Pfc	KIA
Roberson	Clarence	E	S/Sgt	KIA
Rose	Albert	C	Pvt	KIA
Sadusky	Frank		Pfc	MIA*
Schools	William	E	Pfc	MIA*
Shope	Forrest	C	Pfc	KIA
Smith	Augustus	W	Pfc	SWA
Smith	Mack	L	Pvt	LWA
Stanton	Byron	L	Pfc	KIA
Stedman	William	A	Pfc	KIA
Stoviak	William	V	Pfc	LWA
Strizak	Frank		Pfc	MIA
Svebeda	Clarence		Pvt	SWA
Torowski	Daniel	L	Pvt	MIA
Umberger	William	A	Pfc	MIA
Wade	Audy	F	Pfc	SWA
Walter	Eugene	M	Pfc	SWA
Waite	Richard	A	Pvt	KIA
Williams	William	B	1st Lt	SWA
Wilson	Jerome	E	Pfc	KIA
Winkler	Emil		1st Lt	KIA
Womack	Daniel	P	S/Sgt	KIA
Wooldridge	Lexley	L	Sgt	SWA

Wright	James	A	S/Sgt	KIA
Yarbrough	James	B	Pvt	SWA
Young	Willie	E	Pvt	KIA
Zappacosta	Ettore	V	Capt	MIA*

Henry Eiseman, listed as LWA, was confirmed KIA in the morning report of 5th August.

Krank Strizak and Francis Couch, both listed as MIA, were confirmed LWA in the morning report of 29th July.

The fate of the two other men listed as MIA is unknown to me. They may have turned up later, perhaps LWA or SWA. According to available records they were not KIA.

There is a possibility that a maximum of 4 of the men listed as MIA* were not killed between 6th to 9th June but sometime later in the campaign.

SWA* and MIA* were confirmed KIA either from later morning reports or The Roster of the Dead in '29 Lets Go, a History of the 29th Infantry Division in World War II', by J. Ewing.

Total B Company Casualties

6th – 9th June.

KIA	74
SWA	26
LWA	9
MIA	2
TOTAL	**111**

That is 111 of the 193 men and officers landing on D-Day were lost by 9th June, equivalent to 58% casualty rate over 3 days.

Of all companies landing on D-Day, only A Company of the 116th fared worse, with a 63% casualty rate over the same period. (24 of the A Company men came from the County of Bedford.)

B. Company Officers landing on Omaha, 7a.m. 6th June.

Captain   Zappacosta

1st Lieutenants   Williams   Donaldson   Winkler

2nd Lieutenants   Frisby   Pingenot   Taylor   Varadian

Officers still leading B Company in the morning of the 9th June.

2nd Lieutenants   Taylor   Varadian

Chapter 37

Amongst the Hedgerows

In Reserve, 9th June.

Dalton lay in his foxhole watching a thin layer of cloud slide under a waning moon. The dew was heavy, it covered the rye grass, the clover and the cow parsley which grew along the edge of the hedgerow, it covered the hawthorn and what was left of the May blossom and it covered Dalton's raincoat. He had drawn it up when the enemy had stopped shelling the woods just over to the right of them, but exposed parts of clothing, missed in the darkness of the night, were wet with dew and the underside of the raincoat was damp from his own body. Looking upward, Dalton's view of the sky was restricted by the hedgerow and the bank of soil on which it was planted. The soil bank rose some four feet above the lip of his foxhole and then the dense trunks and stems of the hawthorn grew upward from there. So simple the needs of a plant; light to change the carbon dioxide freely absorbed from the air and water from the earth to produce the glucose it needed for sustenance. If a stem were broken, one would grow to replace it and if a hole was punched through it, the gap would close in time.

Like the British, the French farmers had used hedgerows for hundreds of years to enclose their fields. But in Normandy the hedge was planted on narrow steep sided banks of earth and stone. A resourceful approach, the technique required only the free earth beneath their feet and the hedgerow whips to plant into it. The fields were sometimes less than an acre in area and irregular in shape; the appearance from above being one of a patchwork quilt. Small fields enclosed on all sides by high hedgerow banks, interrupted only by the occasional gate, to allow movement between one field and another or to and from a track.

The hedgerow and its embankment offered the soldiers

some protection against incoming fire and the foxholes were dug to run parallel to it and as close as possible. The soil removed to dig the hole was placed on the other three sides to further impede the shell fragments - the shrapnel. Dalton's foxhole was generally that bit deeper than most; he had shifted soil to gain a livelihood and now he shifted it to keep his life.

The moonlight glanced across the top of a large crowned oak, past the loose soil around Dalton's foxhole and across the toes of his boots as if to peer at him; its face familiar in unfamiliar surroundings. Sleep was hard to come by, what with the mortar attacks on their position late evening and then a serious fire fight some distance to the south which lasted for perhaps an hour. Later, a German machine gun opened up way off to B Company's right flank and then sometime around 3a.m. mortars fell into the nearby woods. After the shelling came the screaming and yelling, followed by the sound of jeeps charging round picking up wounded men and rushing them off for treatment - soldiers on wood and canvas stretchers, strapped to bonnets, who needed to be patched up, limbs removed and faces covered. Being in division reserve was not as Dalton had expected.

In the move to their current position at St. Germain du Pert, B Company had headed down roads, along tracks and crossed fields harassed by small pockets of resistance and sometimes just individual snipers. Arriving at the village, the regiment had moved into the surrounding countryside. B Company had marched down a road barely wide enough for a truck before turning onto an even narrower farm track. Like the road, the track was bordered by hedgerows. Some two hundred yards down, a gate to the right allowed the company to enter the field in which Dalton now lay. The whole company occupied a line of hedgerow some 300 yards long in an east westerly direction. They had dug into the northern side, its right hand side as looking from the track, with the expectation and hope that the enemy would be to the south of it.

The moon sunk further and the arms of the oak, moving in the light breeze, created dark and changing shapes across its surface. The tree acted as a marker for the point where the hedgerow met the track, perhaps it had once grown from it and been allowed to reach its current majestic size, enduring the decades and then the centuries. Ted stood in its shadow, occasionally touching his breast pocket in silent ritual as if to tell his parents and sweetheart that he was still thinking of them. Dalton was confident that the big man would not fall asleep on his two hour watch.

Dalton turned onto his side and reflected on a day that had altogether been very different. After hugging the coast for almost three days they were now heading into the 'hedgerow country' of Normandy - the 'bocage'. The company had dug in for the night and for the first time, were expecting to stop one more. Several promotions had been made and what was even more different was that the company had more men in the evening than in the morning. With all that had happened in the day, together with the night time engagements, sleep came slowly for Acting Squad Leader, Sergeant Slaughter.

What troubled Dalton most was the self doubt, of not being up to the job; that he wasn't a Staff Sergeant Holmes. Dalton considered himself too impulsive to lead men, an NCO had said as much and that's why he hadn't been promoted earlier. The staff sergeants had initially been the older men from the original National Guard units and Dalton felt too young by comparison.

A rifle platoon was divided into three squads of roughly twelve men; normally the squad leader would be a staff sergeant and his assistant a sergeant. However, with just 80 or so survivors and even less of the '42 contingent who had arrived on the Queen Mary, it had been recommended that Pfcs assume squad leader responsibilities on the rank of sergeant. If Slaughter lasted long enough, he might eventually be promoted to the rightful rank of Staff Sergeant. However, official 'Regimental' confirmation of his promotion might in itself take ten days, 'a hell of a long time' under the circumstances. Dalton thought of his mother; of how proud she would be of him, of how proud she had always been of him, even of the little things. Of when he had tied his own boot laces for the first time or found the best fruit in the vegetable garden and presented it to her. Dalton needed his momma now; he was cold and damp, he was further from home than he had ever been in his dreams, he hadn't seen his family for almost two years and his confidence was at an all time low. What would they say to him now? His sister Myrtle would tell him how it was, and that was for sure.

Gradually, from deep down, Dalton drew out of himself that which he already knew but didn't want to accept. For many of the men he had trusted and revered were dead and others had suffered terrible injuries, yet he was very much alive. Dalton knew that he must now lead as they had led him. He was far from being too young, why he was twenty-four years old, not nineteen like many of today's replacement men. He had received several times their training and they had no battle experience. He had much to offer. Lying there under the moonlight Dalton finally convinced himself that he could do the job. Ted had been made his assistant squad leader, also on a sergeant's rank and would be a 'tower of strength' in every meaning of the word. Dalton finally slipped off to sleep and left his troubled surroundings behind him. In the morning he would have his first taste of leadership, to lead his squad on patrol.

The night of the 9th was the first in enemy territory for the replacement men and they were soon introduced to life in the battle field. Men such as Richmond Bell placed in Slaughter's squad in 3rd Platoon, John Andryka and his buddy Leonard Appleby in 1st Platoon and Ted Broeckling in 2nd Platoon with Charlie Conner and Bob Sales. Lieutenant Taylor thought it a good first day's experience for Broeckling to deal with the bodies of two Germans killed when B Company first occupied the area. Broeckling and another new man were told to drag the corpses to a shed in the yard of a farmhouse just behind where B Company was positioned. They buried them in the dirt floor as instructed, camouflaging the hole with hay and straw and after finishing, Ted wondered if the bodies would ever be found. Another replacement man lying in his foxhole during the late evening mortar attack had a shell land right in the hole with him. It didn't explode; the fins simply cut his legs as the shell embedded itself in the soil. Leonard Appleby however, lost his life in that first engagement with the enemy. One of Dalton's new men asked him, "What's it like out here?" when he arrived early evening.

"A walk in the park," Dalton replied with a grin, remembering some of the comments on the Empire Javelin the evening before the invasion. But then gave a long list of do's and don'ts to the worried soldier, barely nineteen years old. "Remember your training ... keep your head down ... always keep your helmet on, day or night ... watch what the experienced guys do and don't ever move out of the darker shadows at night. We'll talk some more tomorrow," Dalton said realising that the replacement man was becoming overwhelmed.

Next morning Dalton came across his body, shot in the side of the head by a sniper. He had gone for a nature call and had crept onto the track to find somewhere more private. The 'older hands' wouldn't move an inch for such a trivial matter. A momentary clearing of cloud cover, the glint of the moon, a moving patch of lighter grey, a minor reflection from spectacles or a helmet; such small changes could reveal a man to a sniper at night.

The new men were at a distinct disadvantage and their turnover rate was already proving to be much higher. Of the replacement men allocated to B Company on the 9th, there was one in particular who Dalton thought would survive and that was Richmond Bell. Bell had soon heard the mortar shells that evening and was in his foxhole a good half a second before the others had even reacted. Bell not only had quick reactions, he was clever and had made it his business to know about tactics and armoury. On arriving he immediately volunteered to be platoon tank grenadier. Some thought him stupid because this meant having to carry a grenade launcher and a couple of anti-tank grenades and not least, to be the one who had to stand and fire at a tank. But Bell knew something they didn't. The grenade launcher attached to the end of an M1 rifle, rather like a bayonet and Bell left it attached all the time. The Germans used a smokeless powder which made it difficult to detect where they were, but the US rifles issued a small puff of smoke which gave the Germans a distinct advantage in locating them. When Bell fired his rifle however, no smoke was released, for a grenade launcher prevented it.

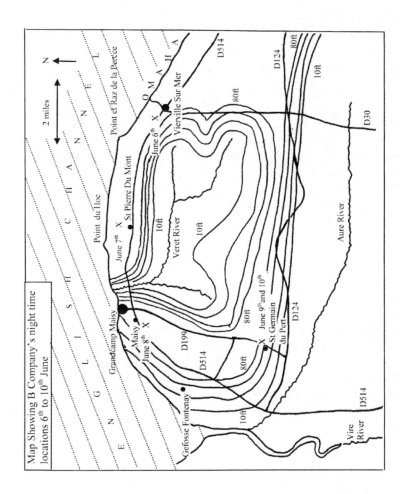

Map Showing B Company's night time locations 6th to 10th June

2 miles

N

C H A N N E L

E N G L I S H

Point et Raz de la Perée

O M A H A

D514

Vierville Sur Mer
June 6th X

D124

80ft

10ft

D30

Point du Hoe

St Pierre Du Mont
June 7th X

Veret River

10ft

80ft

Aure River

Grandcamp Maisy

Maisy
June 8th X

D199

St Germain du Pert
X

June 9th and 10th

D124

D514

80ft

Gefosse Fontenay

10ft

80ft

Vire River

D514

Chapter 38

First Patrol

In Reserve, 10th June.

Dalton peered along the farm track, checking in both directions before stepping out from the protection of the hedgerow. Ted brought up the rear and the six men, in two rows of three, moved cautiously southward over the grass patches and rutted muddy surface. The whole squad would have attracted too much attention; Dalton had picked out half his men, a mix of replacements and old hands. He would have taken Marshmallow but he was complaining of a bad ankle. The track ran level for a hundred and fifty yards or so before rising for the next hundred. The hedgerow embankments on either side of the track gave the impression of a 'sunken road'. The bank, the unwieldy hedgerow and the larger trees growing out of it, made the men feel as though the vegetation was closing in; squeezing the two columns of soldiers closer together. In places the branches of trees growing on one side arched over and met the branches from the other; creating a broken tunnel where the breaks allowed light to crash in and dazzle the men with surges of green and its multiple shades. The thicker branches scraped and snaked past each other as though conspiring to trap the strangers now entering their domain. The wind had dropped and try as they might, unwanted noises emanated - noises magnified by the tension they all felt. Who was more nervous, the new squad leader or the replacement men? Dalton led on the right, on his left walked Greg, one of the 'old hands' who always left his chin strap undone. Told so many times whilst training to fix it, yet unclipped it again as soon as he wasn't being watched and had gotten into trouble almost as often as Drummer. If he ran fast it sometimes fell off, when he dived for cover it always fell off, but when he had sex, he claimed he 'strapped it on tight'. The young, tense faced replacement men kept looking everywhere, whilst the old hands on the right watched only the right and trusted the others to watch the other flank. Ted checked behind and followed, checked and followed. The air was even cooler in the cover of the foliage. The ancient gnarled oaks and thorns shadowing the track provided dense cover. Generations of farmers had passed them by, toiling their way up the incline, to work in the fields, to check their cattle and make a life worth living. The combined ages of the passing strangers could not match their years, not even their combined ages at death, for the roots of the trees ran deep and safe.

Ted was dropping further behind as he became ever more worried about having passed the enemy and being raked by machine gun from the rear. He also checked above him in the trees, for he knew that snipers were good at concealing themselves within the branches. Ted wasn't going to let his buddy down. If the squad was caught by surprise, he didn't want it to come from his lack of vigilance.

Richmond Bell heard the enemy mortar before anyone. Then almost simultaneously, a bullet struck Greg. The 7.92mm round hit his helmet a couple of inches above the rim, tearing a piece of steel from it and throwing the helmet backward off his head. Had the chin strap been done up then Greg may not have lived to tell the tale, for the momentum of such a projectile can fatally jar a man's neck. Bell was already in the ditch as others stood aghast at Greg's luck, then remembering the metallic cough of the enemy mortar being fired, finally reacted to the threat. Greg grabbed his helmet and not for the last time, threw it accurately onto his sweaty crown as he dived into the ditch with the others. Ted had turned again to check their rear just as the bullet struck Greg; when he looked back everyone was either gone or heading for cover, leaving him isolated several yards from the rest. By the time he made his move it was too late, the 81mm shell landed at his feet.

Slaughter shouted at the men to move into the field for the enemy had precise measure of their position. The guys pushed through the thorny mass, tearing and scratching, then raced towards the German position. Dalton's contorted face portrayed the anger and fear which gripped him and transmitted itself through every sinew. It made his legs drive powerfully up the incline and his finger pull rhythmically and callously on the trigger of his M1. Each pull releasing a precious round from the limited magazine until he came upon the hedgerow which likely separated him from the hateful enemy. Taking a fragmentation grenade, he threw the lethal package with such force at the German position that its explosion might have been muffled by the soil into which it imbedded. However, in the next field they found nothing - nothing but the signs of a mortar team's imprint in the soil.

The team had likely cut and run after the first shell and bullet had been fired, to relocate and cause further difficulties at their choosing. From their position, the Germans had had a clear line of sight down the track. As Slaughter's squad had walked up the rise and the first helmet had come into view, the German mortar crew had fired and the sniper had pulled the trigger. The sniper had picked the helmet to his right, perhaps it appeared first; perhaps he just had a better view of it.

After a thorough check of the surrounding area, Dalton led his four men back down the track, retreating quickly and with less caution over what they felt was familiar ground. The raw soldiers were going to have to learn hedgerow combat the hard way. Dalton stopped at Ted's side and moved his remaining arm so that his bloodied hand lay over the pictures in his breast pocket; then striding away, pushed his dumb struck replacement men before him.

That evening, Sorrow was appointed Sergeant and became Slaughter's new assistant squad leader.

Chapter 39

Crossing the River Elle

Night of the 10th to the 13th June.

The evening of the 10th proved calm, the enemy skulking somewhere and diminishing in number. The sky cleared sufficiently to present a setting sun, the orange disc sliding slowly from the sky. Dalton sat leaning against the hedgerow embankment eating some bland rations. Ted's foxhole was now empty, his personal belongings removed. Alone with his thoughts, Dalton placed the food in his mouth without the stomach for it. He and Ted always sorted rations out together and he tried to think of better days, but Sergeant Sorrow slowly approached to interrupt his thoughts. "Men are organised for guard duties. Are we definitely stopping here another night?" he asked.

Dalton knew why Sorrow had posed the question. Moved from another platoon, he didn't want to dig another foxhole and was hoping to use Ted's.

"Yea and maybe again tomorrow night," Dalton replied, leaving Sorrow in the air about the foxhole. Then with only the hint of a grin which only a close buddy might have detected said, "Unlucky to sleep in a dead man's hole," and raised his eyebrows as if to say, do you wonna chance it.

By the time Sorrow had dug a new hole the sun was gone, the sky becoming a dirty grey spreading upward from the horizon, clouds from the Atlantic again. Apart from the ting and thud of Sorrow's spade hitting stones and roots as he inched his way into the earth, a magpie sat amongst the ribbed and bent arms of the oak; its rattle like call seemingly mocking the sweaty toil below.

The night was thankfully quiet. A few mortars were aimed their way but it was a half-hearted effort; the night patrol was on them mighty quick and shot one of the mortar team as he was running into the shadows. In the morning Sorrow waited for Dalton to get some rations together, whilst Clayton did his usual and brought over some coffee. "Here Sorrow," Clayton gestured, "you can have Ted's," he said grinning at Dalton. Clayton passed on the news that the 115th were rumoured to have hit big trouble. And the 116th were likely being moved south in support.

When the 116th went into reserve on the 9th, the other two regiments of the 29th Division, the 115th and the 175th had taken up the advance. The 115th crossed the Aure Valley on the 9th and their 2nd Battalion broke off and pushed almost to Le Carrefour des Vignes aux Gendres, where at about 1a.m. they started moving into the fields on either side of the road.[3] But within minutes of their arrival, a large German force came down the same road behind them. The ensuing fire fight was what Dalton had heard that night and with over 130 casualties it had decimated the battalion. Worse, the regiment was then moved to the banks of the River Elle east of the town of Ste Marguerite d'Elle ready for an advance across the river. They were on the move as Clayton told the story, his morning wake- up call burning between his fingers. The enemy defence was predicted to be strong and Canham's 116th were to march three miles south to Castilly, so that they were close by in case they were needed to support the 115th. All the guys, not least Sorrow, were sorry that their three day 'rest' had been shortened. They were just getting a hold on the area, starting to know the tracks and the enemy's habits and favoured spots. But orders were orders and Dalton with his squad including Marshmallow freshly back from seeing a medic, joined the lines of men snaking their way further into hedgerow country.

Following a narrow road, the D124, which ran along a contour of the valley side, they could see the dark wooded area of Castilly to the south. Like the 115th, they too had to cross the Aure Valley, passing through the marsh land and the areas strategically flooded by the enemy in preparation

---

[3] See map page 415.

for the invasion. The flooding had caused the death of many paratroopers in the early hours of D-Day and made the convoy's push southward more difficult. The convoy was restrictcd to the narrow and infrequent crossing points which made them vulnerable to attack and the men were as edgy as hell. The D113 was the only option to a several mile detour, but it stretched 1,500 yards across the flat marshland with no protection on either side for its duration.

Despite replacements, a still severely depleted B Company made the move, though the number of officers had increased; Leo van De Vort had been assigned from Headquarters Company and together with Taylor and Varadian made a grand total of three B Company Officers. Completing the three miles without major incident and in the relative safety of dusk, the 116th reached Castilly and dug their new foxholes in the surrounding fields as the dark of the 11th closed in.

On the morning of the 11th, the 115th had crossed the River Elle as planned in an attempt to capture St. Claire sur l'Elle and the high ground near Couvains. But the Elle marked the beginning of a new phase in the Normandy Campaign. Seven miles south of the river lay St. Lo, an important strategic town at the heart of the enemy's east-west communication and supply lines. The Germans had cleverly withdrawn from the coast in a way which limited their losses and maximized the disruption to the Allied forces. At the Elle however, they were determined to stall the advance and prevent the fall of St. Lo. On the south bank they set up a formidable defensive line which created the first proper front line of the campaign.

By late afternoon of the 12th June, the 115th had suffered so many casualties that they had no option but to withdraw. Consequently that same afternoon the 116th were called down from Castilly to wait on the northern slopes of the valley. Then, late that evening, when the last of the 115th had limped back over the River, the 116th were ordered to commence a second offensive.

Like Dalton, Clayton had been promoted to Sergeant and

acting squad leader, whilst Allbritton had moved to Staff Sergeant from his rank of Corporal. The corporal in each squad acted as the BAR man with responsibility for carrying and firing the Browning automatic rifle. At 13 pounds and 48 inches in length, the rifle was cumbersome and a private would be allocated to carry the heavy ammo. Allbritton assumed responsibility for the third squad whilst a Pfc, promoted to Corporal took over the BAR. It was therefore left to Slaughter, Clayton and Allbritton to lead their squads across the Elle. Dalton's buddy Bob Sales in 2nd Platoon could also be heard motivating his squad, in this, the first real offensive action for the replacement men.

In the twilight and in the shadow of the trees, the waters of the River Elle looked dark and foreboding; its surface smooth and unbroken as it engulfed the limbs wading through it. The liquid filled boots, soaked socks and uniforms, it chilled their spirits and sent shivers of anticipation through their bones. To B Company's right, downstream and around a slight bend in the river, lay the single track stone bridge. With dense vegetation on both banks together with the taller willows and alders, the low bridge was concealed from view. A road ran to the ancient structure and after crossing it curved slightly upstream towards B Company, before curving back towards the right as it climbed the incline on the far side of the valley. At the top of the incline, some 300 yards or so from the bridge, the road was bordered by farm buildings and by fields and hedgerows to the left; it was towards these fields that B Company were now heading.

The dark reflections in the water at the far bank created an ominous mirroring, for it made the water there as unwelcoming as the vegetation beyond. In the open water, the leading men felt and were very exposed. The plant growth on the opposite bank was thick and concealing in the diminishing light. To the frantically searching eye, every thicker stem became a gun barrel, paler patches became a face and thicker sections of exposed tree trunk, looked like torsos. The myriad of angles, grey shades and shapes of plants crossing and intermingling, played tricks on the frightened soldiers, mere pawns of war, whom death encircled.

The far bank, perhaps no more than eighteen inches above the water, chased off flat before running more and more steeply to finally climb at 20 degrees towards the cultivated land, maybe 30 yards beyond. When Slaughter stepped from the stream into the vegetation of the bank, the light level dropped to that of a candle.

Dalton placed one hand round the cracked purplish brown bark of an alder and started to pull himself up the slope. The branches with their sticky purple shoots and orange red intrusions seemed to sweep upward to allow him to pass; then as he started up the slope, the vegetation closed in again, the shrubs and saplings thorny and clinging. Dalton bent low and pushed through a wall of foliage, of twigs and branches and entered a chamber-like enclosure. There, in the gloom, he stumbled across a soldier prostrate on the dark ground. He was lying on his back, eyes open, the large dark pupils pointing straight at Dalton. There was movement around as the squad moved past, but in this envelope of branches, two worlds had come together to be isolated as one. The impulse to raise his weapon faded, for the man was clearly close to life's end. From the disturbance to the undergrowth, it was apparent that there had been a lot of thrashing around, the pain had likely been traumatic, but now he just stared pitifully into Dalton's face. The man's belly had been ripped open and his small intestine had unravelled across his hips and thighs, blood mixed with mud, mixed with guts, mixed with bits of leaves and twigs. His entire front was muddy as though with arms alone, he had tried to drag himself towards the top of the slope. So soiled was his uniform that it could barely be identified as German. The man whispered something and raised his bloodied dirty hand towards Dalton. Dalton quickly checked about him, no one else around, and no weapons, not even the man's helmet. He made to search for some morphine but it was too late, within seconds of Dalton crouching down, the young man had taken his last breath. The pain contorted face could have belonged to a GI, for Dalton considered that in death, as in life, he looked and was no different; 'just someone's son fighting on a different side'.

Dalton reached the top of the steep slope and the hedgerow which bordered the agricultural land; one or two stragglers finally joining him. Beyond the hedge, the land continued to rise gently for some 200 yards, interspersed with hedgerows. The undulating, furrowed surface was covered in an animal cropped, dark green rye grass. But the forms which lay there were not cattle.

D Company opened up on the next hedgerow with 81mm mortars and M2 Browning machine gun fire. The heavy weapons platoons did the same on the flanks of each company, at the corners of the line of departure. Then as the mortars ceased and the order was given to go, Dalton and the other squad leaders stood up and ran. Legs pumping, hearts racing, the squads followed their sergeants across the furrows firing from the hip, whilst the flanking machine guns fired for a time over their heads. The squad corporals fired their BARs as best they could. But at 550 rounds per minute, they soon used up the 20 round magazine. Dalton's squad reached the first hedgerow, lobbed grenades over and reloaded whilst catching their breath; sweat from exertion and fear dripping from their brows. Machine guns were set up again on the flanks and the riflemen made for the second then the third hedgerow. Coming upon each four foot soil bank with the mounted hedge, they dared not think who or what might lie over the other side. Before a grenade might land between their feet or a bullet pass through their flesh, they made sure their dosage of steel arrived first, a grenade over or bullets fired through and down onto the next field. The number-one and number-two gunners of D Company machine gun teams moved the 85-pound M2 each time, sometimes burning flesh on the hot barrel. Shrapnel punctured the water jacket of the M2 on the left flank. Designed to keep the barrel cool, the gun was inoperable without it, but still the infantry units ran for the fourth hedgerow, now encountering enemy mortar and machine gun fire.

Slaughter's feet mysteriously found their own way across the ruts and clods, ridges and mounds in the field to bring him to the fifth hedgerow. Looking round for his squad, most had made it but Marshmallow lay dead in the field, a burst of machine gun fire had drilled a large hole through his torso. Noise, screams, friendly fire, enemy fire, explosions close and far, shrapnel, bullets, orders and butchery - horrible just horrible.

There was a pause, the enemy seemed to be pulling back, perhaps regrouping; perhaps preparing to counter-attack. Men dug in and the machine guns again put in place. Incoming diminished, men regained their breath. Richmond Bell with his smokeless rifle was called over by one of the company lieutenants. Lieutenants in the regiment had become even scarcer after D-Day. There had been some replacements but they were becoming an endangered species again. They were the first pick of the snipers and for a skilled 88 crew, a challenging target. Bell, a youngster of eighteen years and with no dependants, was 'promoted' to scout and sent over the hedge and out into the open field; ostensibly to check out the situation and terrain, but really to draw fire so that the company would know where the enemy was. Bell walked to the next hedgerow, peered over, then as the men moved up, off he was sent to the next one. Bell scaled eleven hedgerows before Lieutenant Taylor picked another man to be scout. Bell returned to Dalton a relieved man. As the new scout reached the twelfth hedgerow he was shot.

Laying down artillery and machine gun fire, the twelfth hedgerow was cleared and B Company dug in to reassess their next move; they had covered less than two miles of terrain.

Whilst one man dug, the other guarded against counter attack. Slaughter shifted soil in record time, checked his diminished squad and advised the men to grab some food before new orders were given. Clayton and Allbritton had also made it, so too had Sergeant Sorrow, though Bell was dumbfounded as to how; 'Sorrow talked slow and moved even slower, with a southern drawl to beat all drawls'.

Slaughter had finished eating and Clayton was on his fourth cigarette before Sorrow finished his shallow foxhole.

The advance had made relatively good progress but unbeknown to the men, 1st Battalion had been ordered to bypass St. Claire and push a further mile south to take the town of Couvains. Shortly after digging in it rained for over an hour, the men were soaked and puddles formed in the foxholes. Men groaned and cussed; protecting their weapons from the wet, they pulled their raincoats around them, some watching for the counter attack, others trying to get some rest. When an 88 mm gun opened up, they wanted the rain back. The first shell filled their hearts with fear and sent everyone diving into foxholes - their own, someone else's, it didn't matter. One soldier landed on top of his buddy and was killed by the shell's concussion, saving his friend in the process. More shells screamed in, loud horrific screeching, throbbing pulsing manifestations of brutal power. The men pulled themselves flat, tightly pressing against the earth, willing themselves into it, bent tense fingers, arms over their heads, chests tight, hardly able to breathe - and prayed. The 88 field gun unleashed a lethal 88 mm diameter shell with a muzzle velocity up to 3,700 feet per second, almost 1,000 feet per second faster than the muzzle velocity of the M1 rifle. Ignoring air resistance, it could cover 1,300 yards in a second and at 1,000 yards, was reaching B Company in just over that.

The speed of the shell caused such a horrendous pressure wave that the noise was sufficient to stupefy the uninitiated, but the replacement men were not alone in being petrified. Dalton pushed his face down into the wet and mud, his deep foxhole seemingly as shallow as the ruts over which he had run that day. Having such a high velocity, the 88 shell was fired at a low angle, its parabolic trajectory negligible. Thus many shells came bursting through the hedgerow roots, rather than over them - the metal pieces of the antipersonnel shell bursting out at terrifying speed at every conceivable angle. The sharp, hot shrapnel embedded itself in anything and everything that happened to be in its way and thudded into the earth around the foxholes. Some shards penetrated through the ground to the tensioned bodies of the men cowering in their holes, whilst other men were hit merely by sliced off hedgerow cuttings or bits and blood of others. The screams of wounded soldiers broke the quiet between the volleys. Then when the German gun was finally silenced, the medics would do what they could. Red, the red headed medic of B Company was good at his job, but save a man shredded by an 88 shell he could not. One of Clayton's men had half his foot cut off, boot and all. He quietened after the morphine, and as Bob Sales would have said, 'half a foot is small price to pay for a warm bed with clean sheets and a pretty nurse to look after you'.

The shelling had finished but the enemy were active; exchange of fire was continuing on other sections of the line. Bolt action and automatic rifle fire, then an MG42 could be heard some way off to the right, its characteristic sound like that of ripping linoleum, now so familiar. To a man, they all feared a counter attack and strained to identify source, direction and movement of the sounds which reached them. There were vehicles on the move, but the engine noise drifted and petered out into the distance, telling them that the general trend seemed to be away from their position. Even the MG42 then fell quiet; perhaps the crew were at this moment attaching another 250 round belt, or perhaps collecting up the ammunition boxes, hoisting the 22 pound gun onto a shoulder and withdrawing to a predetermined vantage point. The delay indicated the latter. The vehicle movements, shouting and the firing of light arms diminished and the fine drizzle again turned into a heavy, noisy downpour. Peering through the hedgerow roots and the heavy rain, the men became soaked to the skin. Feet were covered in mud, movements became slow and squelching. Perhaps a couple of hours later, the rain finally eased and stopped, to be replaced by an ominous quiet. No sound of the enemy, just of large droplets forming, running and falling from the large, broad leaves to cause plop, splat a tat splat noises on the leaves and helmets below.

With the temporary peace came the inevitable - the order to advance on Couvains. One more mile to go.

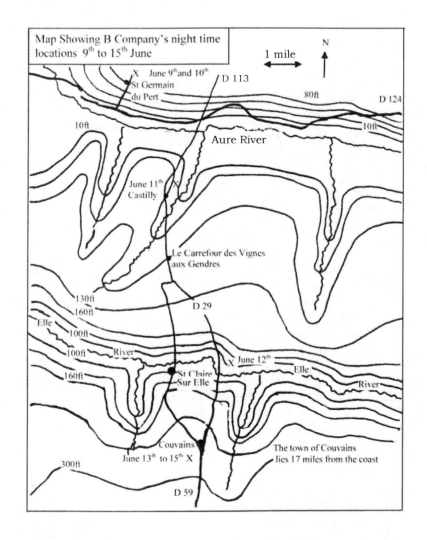

Map Showing B Company's night time locations 9th to 15th June

1 mile

N

X June 9th and 10th
St Germain du Pert

D 113

80ft

D 124

10ft

10ft

Aure River

June 11th
Castilly

X

Le Carrefour des Vignes aux Gendres

130ft

160ft

D 29

Elle

100ft

100ft River

X June 12th

Elle

160ft

St Claire Sur Elle

River

Couvains

The town of Couvains lies 17 miles from the coast

300ft

June 13th to 15th X

D 59

Chapter 40

A Bad Night

13th to 15th June.

For the final advance on Couvains the clouds cleared and the patchy blue skies became all that the infantrymen had long prayed for, allowing the Allies' air supremacy to finally come into play. German positions were bombed and troops strafed by US planes and the men walking beneath gave thanks for the airmen above and wished that they too could return to a safe base, hot cooked food and a clean, dry bed.

The soaking in the river, the rain, the subsequent mud, the pushing through hedgerows, the sheltering from bombardments and the blood, sweat and tears had made the replacement men look just as battle worn as the D-Day Veterans. All were wearing the same clothes as they had arrived with, except perhaps for a change of socks. Dalton had been extravagant and carried three spare pair of socks which he had carefully rotated, always ensuring he had one dry, clean pair. He also carried two spare sets of underwear, though he had not yet had the privilege of changing them more than once. At some point in the last eight days, faces and hands had been washed but that was as far as clean water had reached. A few men had managed a shave during their short stay in reserve. Some had half filled their helmets, rinsed out their socks and were about to put razor to face when it was announced that they were 'getting the hell out' and moving south to the River Elle.

The column of dishevelled men walked in double file, approaching Couvains from the west along a sunken dirt road. The road was barely wide enough for the horse drawn carts that plied along it in better times, carrying apples from the surrounding orchards to be made into a variety of foods, fermented into cider and distilled into Calvados, a Normandy speciality. Flanked by hedgerows and a sporadic canopy of overhanging maple and hawthorn, Dalton's first view of Couvains was of the old church and its tall steeple. Looking down at them from this vantage point, the German spotter radioed the mortar and 88 crews and the first volley of shells sent the column scattering into the apple orchards.

A shell, well directed from that place of God, sent shrapnel into one of Clayton's squad members. The Pfc had his 'family jewels' blown away, a slice of each inner thigh was taken with them and an artery severed causing blood loss to be unstoppable. Clayton crawled to him, gave him a dose of morphine and looked round for a medic, more out of encouragement for the young man than conviction. The wounded soldier kept asking if he was going to be alright, "Am I going to make it, Sarge?"

He went to feel himself but Clayton held his hands saying, "Leave it alone, there's plenty of time for that when you get back to those pretty nurses."

The comment brought temporary relief to the poor young man's face before the loss of blood weakened him further. "Oh God help me ... God please help me ... Momma, tell my momma I love her ... I want my momma ... I love her ... God help me ... God please help me," he kept repeating and repeating.

The young man became a boy again, he needed his momma, and thankfully she was not there to watch her precious son die. The boy became a child and then a baby, screaming and crying, calling for God and his momma until finally he slipped from the butchery of war into the safe hands of his God.

By the evening of the 13th June 1st Battalion had liberated Couvains, secured the approach roads and demolished the steeple using TNT at its base to bring down the tenacious observer. The termination of resistance within the streets and buildings marked the commencement of German artillery onto the town. It had first been bombed by the allies on June 7th and with the most recent action, most buildings were damaged or demolished and many civilians had been killed. With the enemy having exact measure of the remaining structures, 1st Battalion dug into surrounding fields, returned artillery fire and sent out infantry patrols.

Charlie Conner didn't make it to Couvains; Conner was hit by shrapnel and seriously wounded near St. Clair. He was in good company, 2nd Lieutenant Taylor was wounded the same day, leaving 2nd Lieutenants Varadian and Van De Vort in charge of B Company. In the push south from the River Elle to Couvains, the company had suffered twenty-three casualties. But with the allocation of a large contingent of replacement soldiers the first night in Couvains, the night of the 13th June, Varadian and De Vort found themselves responsible for 194 men.

During the day of the 14th June 1st Battalion consolidated their position, set up defensive positions and maintained active patrols. To bolster 1st Battalion, the 3rd Battalion moved south onto their right flank. On the same day and to the relief of Van De Vort and Varadian, four officers joined B Company from another unit: Captain Harrelson, 1st Lieutenants Meadows and Stern and 2nd Lieutenant Hanson. With the death of Captain Zappacosta just a few seconds after landing on the beach, the company had not had a commander other than Taylor as acting. Now eight days later, with Taylor wounded, the experienced Harrelson filled the role.

The supply jeep arrived early that evening and out of habit, the D-Day vets helped themselves to extra rations; for although the morning report was accurate in its numbers, the soldiers present by the time food arrived was usually less. This day was almost an exception, for on the 14th, just one man had been killed. Noting the increase in numbers with the replacement men, Robert Torrence, the supply jeep driver had fortunately brought a surplus. Some rations might be left for the French people hiding in the fields and damaged buildings. For unlike the American troops, the Germans had to live off the land and would take food from the farms and towns, leaving the Normandy inhabitants in short supply. Some resourceful French folk would hide themselves and their cow or other livestock in a ditch, dug deep and concealed, but most farm animals were taken by the occupying force. Over the next few days, the civilians of Couvains could start to adjust to their new lives after four long years of occupation. They hoped the men of the 116th Regiment would carry the war away from them to neighbouring fields, and to the fields of their neighbours. But Germany's forces were still strong, anything could happen in the days to follow.

After taking their K, C and D rations for that evening and the next day, there was time to really wash and brush up. Water brought up in five gallon cans was used to fill canteens; the men drank some, washed their faces and then refilled for the following day. They were privileged; Robert Torrence had been able to drive the supply jeep with its trailer close up to the men on the line. Normally they would have to creep off and haul it from a prearranged location, usually a ditch somewhere on the side of a road. When the company was under fire, Torrence would commandeer a 'half track' vehicle, throw the supplies on board and with the protection of its armour plating, drive as close to the men as he could; leaving the rifle and machine gun ammunition, grenades and mortars, together with the food and water for the men to collect. But tonight, positioned right by a 'sunken' access track, they were being spoilt.

Torrence's Ford jeep was always a welcome sight. It signalled nourishment and represented a life line, a link with more stable environs. With its blown out wind shield, lost when 500 lbs of TNT went off on the beach, its damaged 50 calibre machine gun and the holes in the hood, the jeep had become part of the family; it survived so they might survive. Torrence drove off with his empty trailer and headed back away from the line to park up and sit out the night. Snatching gas from the cans deposited on the roadsides by fuel trucks, the men knew that Torrence would do his utmost to make it back to them the next day.

Enemy harassment had filtered away. The evening was warm and the sky still clear blue with the odd wisp of white passing by in a steady and detached manner. Guards were set and men settled, most with clean faces at least. In the twilight, one of Allbritton's new men had taken up guard duty and guard he did, staring through the hedgerow roots into a formless, colourless panorama. He kept watching, looking through the same set of hedgerow roots on the same spot, looking towards the German positions, a statue of expectancy. As blue sky turned red in the west the sniper's bullet grazed past the brown stems which had run vertically up across the clean white face. It cut through the phloem tubes and xylem vessels and then crossed over to the young man and pierced the cornea, barged through the eye lens, the vitreous humour, the retina and on into the depths of his brain. He flopped backward and was dead before hitting the field. The brief complacency of the company had been lost and heightened its alertness as the sky started to tinge with purple in the east.

When a second soldier was taken out, probably by the same sniper, Staff Sergeant Bob Sales of 2nd Platoon crawled out with the intent of finding the illusive German. Usually positioned in trees, the snipers were highly camouflaged in their spring/summer coloured mottled frocks and matching helmet covers. With padded straw seats and knee pads, and some harnessed in for good measure, their aim was steady and inevitably accurate. With the immediate area devoid of substantial trees, Sales combed the hedgerows and found his man standing on a dirt road leaning against the soil hedgerow bank and aiming through the roots towards the US positions.

'Scared to death', Sales inched closer thinking that if the German heard him, he would turn and blast him. When he was close enough, Sales pumped six bullets into him.

The sky darkened and night finally came as Sales returned slowly and carefully back to his men; a false hope spreading across the company that they would now be left in peace for a while. But it had not been dark for long when Dalton, the company and likely the whole battalion, heard the dreadful noise. The smoking, clanking monster moved somewhere within the enemy positions, its destination yet unknown. When the Shermans had arrived on Omaha Beach, Dalton had thought them invincible but compared to the German tanks they were small fry. He looked at the gate to their field and imagined the huge machine crashing through it, its turret turning, the mounted gun pointing and firing. The men lay, waited and listened as it moved and grated in the fields beyond. Thirty feet in length, the Panther was ten feet longer than the Sherman and at forty-four tons, weighed over one and a half times as much. Yet it could travel faster with its twice as powerful Maybach engine and was equally mobile. Its well sloped four and a half inch thick front armour made it difficult to penetrate and with a more accurate, powerful gun, the Panther could take out several Shermans before even being lightly damaged.

The cowering infantry boys could sense a quickening of the tank's pace, the throb of the engine more rapid, the clanking a higher pitch. There was no cloud cover but the night was as dark as death and the thick, blue, exhaust smoke that bellowed out from the petrol engine was invisible in the blackness. The noise of the tank grew louder, a fearsome noise of squeaking and clanking, heading straight for them, bearing down, huge and invincible. German infantrymen were likely approaching with the tank and in another few seconds would be upon the hedgerow behind which Dalton and his buddies were situated. The entire platoon was standing now, they knew what to do, but would training overcome sheer terror? The noise started to fill Dalton's body and grip him with a fear that made his hands shake and legs wobble. Mud and stones flew out from the rotating caterpillar tracks, hitting the bushes and thudding down onto the ground. The tank came up to the other side of the hedgerow. Several men started stepping backward, fear and panic telling them to turn and run. Then when Dalton's mind convinced him that all was lost, the lieutenant opened fire and then they all opened fire, unclipped grenades and tossed them over, before firing again and again with Bell firing his anti-tank grenade. All were petrified, subconsciously shouting at nothing and no one, mouths gaping, firing in hope at an impenetrable monster and tossing even more grenades until they ran out - precious munitions wasted. And when the company finally stopped firing, the tank could barely be heard for it was at some distance and moving away from the front line. Dalton was gasping for breath as though he had just run up Dartmoor's Western Beacon, his heart likely at 200 beats per minute. But as his system recovered, slowly the clanking and squeaking could be heard to fade, the German infantry had withdrawn and just two GIs had been lightly wounded.

The men had rarely encountered a tank on the battle field for they had proved impotent and vulnerable in the Normandy countryside. The US Sherman tanks were unable to mount the hedgerow banks and short of blasting a hole through, they were confined to the narrow tracks and roads and to using gate accesses between fields. Their movements were thus predictable to an enemy who knew the lie of the land so intimately and so well concealed were the enemy positions, that a tank would often be hit before it could even fire a single shot. Prior to crossing the Elle River on the evening of the 12th June, Dalton had watched as a Sherman advanced to the stone bridge in an attempt to neutralise enemy artillery emplacements on the hill above. It was only half way across when it was hit on the second attempt by an 88mm armour piercing shell. Instead of the cluster of shrapnel contained in the anti personnel shells, the armour piercing shells were designed to hold together and pierce thick steel plating. At a range of over 1,000 yards and zero degree impact, the sixteen pound shell could penetrate over nine inches of armour. An 88 could therefore punch a hole right into a Sherman and burst out the other side. As the shell pierced the metal and entered the cockpit of the tank on the bridge, bits of the tank's armour plating were broken off and thrown around the inside at several hundred miles per hour, cutting the crew to shreds. Smoke started to pour out of the tank which now blocked the road and Dalton could hear the screams of men inside, screaming for someone to help, to save them from the heat and from burning to death. As the heat had intensified the surviving men fell silent and were cremated in their metal casket.

After the snipers and particularly the tank, the company were on edge and Dalton again found sleep avoiding him. For several nights to follow and intermittently to the day God called for him, Dalton would wake from nightmares where his legs, arms or whole body was about to be run over and crushed by a tank. He never saw the tank, it was always just the terrifying noise; it always happened on a field and always in the pitch black.

Towards the end of his two hour rest period and just as he was finally starting to doze off, Dalton was disturbed by a member of his squad. The clear weather continued into the dark, early hours and the troubled face that looked down at Slaughter was surrounded by white spots - stars painted in a black sky. The private had heard foot falls in the undergrowth of a small isolated thicket not more than ten yards away. Slaughter stood to a crouching position and listened, at first nothing, then the noise of leaves and twigs being trodden upon. If it wasn't a man then it was a large animal, though too noisy for a deer, whether roe, fallow or red.

"Have you used your clicker?" Slaughter asked the private.

"No Sarge, I thought ..."

"Well use it!" Slaughter interrupted.

The private gave two clicks and waited for a response of three, the current number. The number had been changed because the enemy had removed clickers from fallen GIs and started to use them to deceive night sentries and squads on patrol.

There was no response. The private gave two more clicks, both men with fingers poised on the trigger waited again for a response. Seconds passed when suddenly the hedgehog broke cover, running straight towards the rifle barrels that were now pointing at it.

Next morning Clayton sat on the side of his foxhole building up for the day on Lucky Strike cigarettes. He had slept better than Dalton.

"Keep a look out for hedgehogs and report any sightings to your squad leader immediately," Clayton said to Dalton's squad.

The sky had stayed clear and the heat of a summer's day was building. The early morning mists of the 15th had quickly cleared and water from the moist earth continued to evaporate.

"It's gonna be a prickly day," Clayton said loudly.

Chapter 41

The Advance to Bretel

16th to 19th June.

The stone blocks at the base of the Couvains Church steeple were split and broken; the fresh faces to be weathered and subdued, from their almost white grey appearance to the dull grey that time ensured. The accumulation of masonry lay as a symbol of the damage that four years of German occupation had caused; not just to buildings but also to the hearts and souls of the French people. The disfigured church of Couvains, like the community of almost 200 habitants, would have to be rebuilt, but for the moment created an air of insecurity rather than that of protection. It reminded the passing soldiers of the transience of possession in conflict; whether of life, health, belongings or land. For though the town had been liberated, it could just as easily be recaptured and no one, particularly the local people, would under- estimate the strength and resolve of the enemy. Success for the Allies was hanging in the balance, just three miles from St. Lo, yet stalled was the advance. Having arrived in Couvains on the 13th June, B Company remained within a few hundred yards of the small town for three nights. The reason was obvious to the infantrymen; foot patrols would return with repetitive confirmation - the way ahead was strongly defended.

The German resistance at the River Elle and the approach to Couvains had further delayed the US advance. The enemy had given themselves the extra time they needed to establish a stronger defensive line just north of St. Lo, along the high ground running east to west, north of the St. Lo to Bayeux Road. The clever, slow and well planned withdrawal across Calvados had proved lethal to the US forces. But unbeknown to the B Company boys, the next thousand yards would be even worse. The enemy would bring them to a grinding halt in front of the high ground, which rising to 600 feet, became known to the Allies as the 'Martinville Ridge'.[4]

Withdrawing German troops joined the growing forces there, the big field guns amassed, machine gun and mortar emplacements dug in, ranges measured and tactics devised. German High Command was convinced that the Allies would pursue for a truce if the advance stalled and casualties were excessive.

By 14th June all three battalions of the 116th had advanced the seventeen miles from the coast, but the remaining few miles to St. Lo would in comparison seem like one hundred. The town of some ten thousand people was strategically vital, for both sides. Taking it would mean that German supply routes to the west would be severed and the Allies could finally break out of the Calvados region. Then the road east would be open and eastward lay Paris and beyond that, the Fatherland.

On the night of the 15th June, the day ear-marked in the invasion planning for St. Lo to fall, General Gerhardt, Commander of the 29th Infantry Division informed his regiments of their targets for the next day. The 116th was to take the high ground near St. André de-l'Epine, right on the Martinville Ridge. A redoubtable task and it compounded the men's belief that Gerhardt volunteered their services too willingly for the more difficult assignments. Gerhardt was rumoured to be the only divisional commander leading a corps with one division on the line, one in the hospital and the other in the cemetery. It was certainly true that Gerhardt believed in hammering a position until it broke, but no one, not even Gerhardt knew what the 116th was taking on.

---

[4] See map page 436.

29th Infantry Division, consolidated table of casualties; missing, killed and wounded in action between June and December 1944.
(Approx 2,400 men per regiment, 12 companies.)

Rgt	Jun	Jul	Aug	Sep	Oct	Nov	Dec	Total
115th	1,138	1,414	1,222	451	615	526	216	5,582
116th	1,769	1,671	1,261	649	600	538	306	6,794
175th	1,318	1,038	1,139	750	312	853	35	5,445

Source. 29 Lets Go. J. Ewing.

The men roused early, grabbed some cold breakfast and sat on their raincoats to separate their backsides from the dew covered soil. Dalton had a new friend he declared, for as he removed his belongings he discovered a frog in the corner of his foxhole. He had befriended many a frog in his childhood. They were common around the swamps and more than once he had squelched one under his bare foot when running out into the yard. "Hiding from the French," someone said as Dalton released it from the depths of his foxhole.

By full light the men picked up their belongings and moved away from what had been their home for three days; the familiar latrine hole, the pieces of wood that had sheltered their foxholes from the elements and the trees and bushes that had become the furniture of their temporary home. Dalton, Clayton and Allbritton led their squads through the positions held by 3rd Battalion, and then on through apple orchards and pasture land to well beyond the town's border. With the terrain falling away to their left down to the Ruisseau de Branche, B Company pushed south towards La Blotrie, the land slowly but steadily rising. The apple trees were ideally placed here, for the sloping land provided good drainage and the cold air on frosty early spring nights would slip harmlessly into the Ruisseau valley.

On familiar ground close to Couvains, a scout was sent forward to check out the situation and three or four fields were traversed without incident. Now level with a large orchard to their right, the scout advanced to the next hedgerow, looked over, checked and indicated that again all was well. Slaughter and Clayton's squads were nearest the break in the bank but Harrelson waved men from 1st Platoon through. Obediently a squad of soldiers broke from cover, pushed into the next field and edged their way along, following the staff sergeant across. The rest of the men peered though the hedgerow roots, anticipation filling every cavity of their bodies. Enemy contact was evident in the distance on both flanks, for the US line pushed south over a wide front and B Company knew that soon they too would be under fire. Dalton watched as the crumpled and dirty uniforms were carried across the stones and grass of the field by fragile flesh. The staff sergeant had advanced perhaps thirty yards when machine gun fire ripped through the squad.

Those that could, crawled back under the covering fire of the men behind them. A medic bravely responded to the needs of the others and brandishing his insignia as clearly as he could, stepped out into the open. The German machine gun team were either being compassionate or had made a quick retreat, for the medic was left to do his job. With now clear evidence of enemy presence, heavy Brownings and mortars were set up and used to pound the German line. Then under suppressive covering fire, the men, firing from the hip, ran across the field and on reaching the hedgerow, threw grenades over and sprayed the field beyond with rifle fire. The gun crew and any other German infantry had long melted away. They had probably picked up their MG42 immediately after firing and moved back to the next prepared position.

Allbritton pulled back foliage from the empty German emplacement to reveal a firing trench, foxholes and slits cut into the hedgerow bank. It was so well camouflaged within its natural terrain that the scout hadn't even realised it was there. The slits enabled fire to be directed at both flanks as well as to the front. An excellent vantage point, covering a wide stretch of front line; likely just a few men had stalled the whole company for what must have been an hour. Unlike an American squad, the focus and priority of a German squad was their machine gun, the MG42. The riflemen dug the positions for it, covered its transfer between positions and whilst it engaged the enemy ensured it was continually supplied with ammo. Often the squad would quickly move their MG42 between positions on the same front line, creating the impression that the line was more heavily defended than it actually was.

In amongst the discarded ammunition boxes and spent cartridges were cards with sketches and numbering indicating ranges. "Ominous," Clayton muttered as he went over to Stern to show him. Stern immediately went over to show Harrelson and within seconds Dalton found himself running back to the cover of the previous hedgerow. In a few further seconds, mortars started to land on the hastily vacated German position. Like professional chess players, the enemy were predicting the movements and responses of their green opponents. Their retreat was a measured one, not forced. They had prepared well for the newcomers, strangers to these parts and pastimes. It took a while for D Company to set up, locate and range the incoming fire. As soon as they did, the Germans ceased fire and no doubt moved again. Then after several scouts went over to make absolutely sure they could retrace their steps, Harrelson finally moved the men back to the first German emplacement.

It was Sergeant Sorrow who spotted it, now being passed and missed by inches as brown mud covered boots pressed into the soil around it. If the teller mine went off, he was done for; they were all done for. He was an old hand and on their first day in Normandy had seen what the thing could do to a Sherman and its crew. Sorrow was frozen, staring at the metal of the teller showing above the surface. There was so much movement around it and so much noise and exchanges between the men that he felt powerless to gain their attention. It was one of the other sergeants who noticed Sorrow's stance and throwing out his arms, shouted at everyone to stand still before marking the position of the mine; no one had to be told twice to stay away. It was a miracle that the device had not been tripped, for this was their second visit to the hedgerow.

The US line pulled into the orchard on B Company's right flank. The enemy responded and mortars started to fall amongst the fruit trees. A terrific explosion threw branches and body bits into the air above the tree line, followed by the rip rip of machine gun fire, rifle fire and then lots of shouting. The front line was spontaneously coming to life in one part and dying down in another as though a wave of conflict was being flicked along a taught rope.

Sorrow's fortunate discovery really unsettled the men. On running across the next field, many found themselves paying more attention to where their feet were landing, than to where they were firing. But the distraction was soon forgotten, for there were many other more likely ways of dying.

The Germans were intent on taking advantage of every twist and turn of the terrain and made the going slow. Their emplacements were extremely difficult to find and approach and were rarely neutralised. With far fewer men, they withdrew quickly and suffered few casualties, due in part to the reticence of the GIs to take advantage of any lull, in case it was a trap. The lieutenants and squad leaders found it increasingly difficult to lead the men across the fields and through the interconnecting hedgerows; hedgerows which ran at confusing angles from and to tracks, streams and ditches.

Sometime in the late afternoon and probably no more than 1,000 yards from where they had started that morning, Dalton looked round to see the grubby, tired faces of his squad. They huddled together for comfort, another mortar bombardment had finished and for a few seconds there was quiet, no orders, no movement; a few seconds to absorb information, rather than just react to it. Realisation of thirst and hunger filtered through, for no food or drink had passed their lips for over ten, perhaps eleven hours. Every inch of ground had been nervously traversed. With mines, snipers, concealed machine guns and all the other hardware that had been thrown at them, the last thing on their minds had been sustenance. If enemy weaponry hadn't been bad enough, Dalton was convinced that men were sometimes being hit by friendly fire. A bullet hit one of his squad in the hamstring, breaking the femur. Unless the soldier had decided to turn back, a wise decision for any sane man, then the bullet must have come from the US line.

In the few seconds respite, men swigged down water from their canteens; Richmond Bell had a bullet hole in his and shared Sorrow's. A bullet had also hit his cartridge belt, exploded a clip and shredded the belt. Bell, Dalton considered, was not just clever but also had luck on his side. Many of the squad had cuts or small wounds that till now they hadn't realised they had sustained, but there would be no nursing of them.

The mortars had come from the stream bed where a gulley cut west from the Ruisseau Valley. Down and out of sight, the mortars were used to their maximum advantage, travelling in their pronounced parabolic trajectory up over the lip of the gulley to fall on the hard pressed GIs. Then using the gulley for concealment, the mortar teams slipped south into the fields below the Martinville Ridge.

The faces of Dalton's squad would have been pitiful in any situation - tired, hungry and 'shit scared' and they now had a day's battle grime to enhance the look. Perhaps their mommas would still have recognised them, but they were permanently changed in all other respects.

Five hours later at dusk, B Company had swung west from La Blotrie and as the crow flies, had moved little more than 1,800 yards from Couvains. They now occupied the gentle upper slope of a rounded hill top, at some 480 feet at its highest and just above the hamlet of Bretel. In the gloom of a long day drawing to a close, they could see the Martinville Ridge rising up ahead of them. Their target, the town of St.

André de-l'Epine still lay 1,000 yards away, nestled between the two highest points of the ridge, both significantly higher than their position. Dalton and a couple of squad members stood guard, whilst the rest of the squad dug in. Now eighteen hours since they had eaten, arms and backs were weakening and the foxholes too shallow. "Keep digging," Dalton said, taking an entrenching tool and lending a hand to Shorty, one of his squad members. Almost twenty B Company men had been wounded, at least five of them very seriously but Shorty was still hanging in there. The men dug in behind the hedgerow which followed the contour of the hill in an east west direction. It offered the best protection there was.

The land sloped southward away from the men, with fields, hedgerows and clusters of trees and gradually dropped 140 feet to a stream bed, the Rau de la Dollée. Beyond the stream the land rose again towards heights of between 500 and 600 feet. On the other side of the heavily fortified Martinville Ridge lay the town of St. Lo and the important road to Bayeux. Staring through the dying light at the formidable obstacle ahead, the men knew that the 17th June was going to be even more difficult than the dreadful day that was drawing to a close.

The digging-in finished sometime after dark, around 11.30 p.m. Watch routines had been sorted and a few men were taking their first mouthfuls of cold C rations when the company was told to withdraw from their hillside position. The front line needed realignment and 1st Battalion's position was considered to be out on a limb and vulnerable. Thus under the cover of darkness, they were ordered back across the D448 to a position about 500 yards north of Bois du Bretel, the Wood of Bretel. Here the exhausted men dug-in again. The withdrawal had been a wise decision, for around three o'clock in the morning the Germans mounted a counter attack. With the enemy moving up the Ruisseau Valley on their left flank and from Les Forges on their right flank, 1st Battalion would have been isolated and likely attacked from all sides. By luck or judgement, the line held against the counterattack and the enemy withdrew. But there was a lot of movement and no one rested.

Dalton managed to grab a couple of mouthfuls of food before first light of the 17th. The day started like the 16th with the expectation of another advance but it soon became very different. Perhaps ten minutes after the first rays of light struggled through the cloud to the east, the wretched men were subjected to a murderous mortar bombardment. Soldiers dived back into their muddy holes and pulled themselves down, for the shells fired from the edge of Bois De Bretel were well aimed. Falling with pin point accuracy, some landed directly in foxholes. Two of Clayton's guys sheltering in the same hole took a direct hit; what was left of them was indistinguishable. Many others were hit. Blood, skin and body parts were thrown out from the emaciated bodies. Fleshy bits fell into surrounding foxholes and to a man, all uniforms were spattered with the blood of a buddy. When the shelling stopped, perhaps five or more men lay dead and double that number seriously wounded. After return fire from American artillery units, the Germans were forced to retreat and the 1st Battalion were mustered for an advance; pushing south, back towards the slopes from where they had withdrawn the night before. The move was surprisingly easy, for the enemy had likely withdrawn across the Rau de la Dollée. Dalton reached the hedge and found the foxhole he had dug in the dusk of the 16th. It wasn't long before he was wishing he had dug it even deeper. Their position with the land falling away from them to the Dollée and the Martinville Ridge rising up beyond, left the men terribly vulnerable. German spotters on the ridge immediately ordered an artillery battery into action and with prepared ranges, the field guns wrought havoc on the company. The heavy artillery shells threw out horrific quantities of shrapnel; some large enough to sever a torso.

One of Allbritton's squad had his back ripped open by shrapnel, exposing much of his spine. Vertebrae and discs were shattered and the poor guy frantically tried to move his legs whilst his foxhole became a bath of his own blood. A man in Dalton's squad sat up in his foxhole, shells falling around him, looking down at his severed legs. To hear the distraught men pleading and screaming was sickening even to those who had heard it so many times before.

The 17th was a horrid day. At the end of it, thirteen B Company soldiers lay dead and twenty others were wounded.[5] Injuries were horrific and men flinched at the state of their buddies. The folks back home had little idea of what their sons were going through. There were many parents who prayed every night for their boys, asking God to bring them safely back home. Then when the letter arrived telling them he was 'wounded in action', they prayed their boy would soon be whole again. When it said 'killed in action', they prayed that the end had been quick, that their boy did not suffer.

The US line on the 17th June moved no further than that murderous hedgerow. On the 18th June there was no progress. The enemy's defence was solid, they were not intending to budge and US casualties were unsustainable. On the 18th June, the day shrapnel hit Dalton, General Bradley ordered the offensive stopped. That night, B Company and the remnants of Dalton's squad reoccupied their old foxholes on the slopes above Bretel, within hearing distance of enemy movements.

During the three day push towards St. André de-l'Epine, B Company suffered fifty-six casualties. Four of the six officers were wounded, including Varadian; the last remaining officer of the original eight landing on D-Day. Captain Harrelson was amongst those hit on the 17th, terminating his three day command of the company. First Lieutenant Stern and 2nd Lieutenant Van De Vort were also wounded but unlike the others, Stern returned immediately to the front line. On the 19th June, B Company received their fourth, though only third official Commander of the campaign, not a captain this time, but 1st Lieutenant George E. Davolt.

Two pieces of shrapnel from a mortar shell had hit Dalton

---

[5] See casualty list page 448.

during one of the bombardments suffered by the company on June 18th. Only of a size slightly larger than match sticks, yet they felt like thick hot needles being pressed into his flesh; onc in the back of his right arm above the elbow and the other in his right hip. Dalton moved back from the line to get attention and felt lucky that a quick trip to the field dressing station was all the attention he needed. Back beyond the carnage, he passed a damaged barn, its door and frame leaning at a precarious angle. Inside the gloom an older man lay dead on the floor. Momentarily a young woman, perhaps his daughter, stepped into view; a glimpse of dark hair, of brown eyes, the radiance of youth and clothes hanging limp against her feminine form. On seeing the soldier, she stepped back and was gone, but her image lingered long in Dalton's mind and gave meaning to an otherwise meaningless and brutal day.

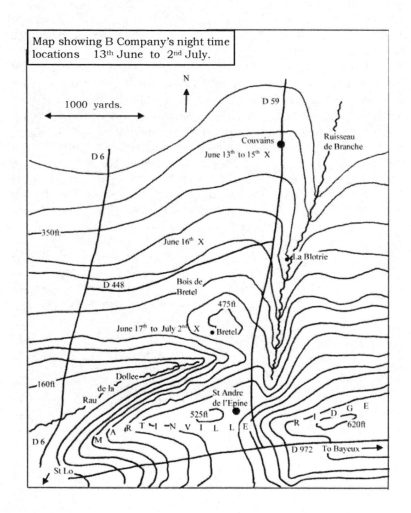

Map showing B Company's night time locations   13th June to 2nd July.

N

1000 yards.

D 59

D 6

Couvains
June 13th to 15th X

Ruisseau
de Branche

350ft

June 16th X

La Blotrie

D 448

Bois de
Bretel

475ft

June 17th to July 2nd X   • Bretel

Dollee

160ft

de la

Rau

St Andre
de l'Epine

D 6

M A R T I N V I L L E

525ft

R I D G E

620ft

St Lo

D 972   To Bayeux →

Chapter 42

News from Home

20th to 23rd June.

Later on the morning of the 20th June, Dalton returned from patrol and was immediately summoned by the lieutenant.

"Get yourself back to the CP (company command post) and grab some transport to the field hospital. Chaplain wants a word with you." The lieutenant turned away, then, as though with an afterthought, turned back, looked straight at Dalton and quietly said, "Some news from home." The look on his face and the way he said it told Dalton that he must prepare, for the news wasn't good.

Moving away from the front line, carrying kit and rifle, Dalton felt his heart turn cold. Panic gripped him, his worst fears surfaced. He thought of his momma, his fingers were numb. Thought of Daddy then of Robbie, he didn't see the ground. He thought of Hetty, and he was blind to his surroundings, passed no one and nothing. Had Hetty lost the baby? No, they wouldn't call him back for a miscarriage surely, no it had to be a death, the death of someone close like a, a brother ... a parent or, or a wife.

Everything became a blur, yet he somehow found his way through the rubble of Couvains. Could Robbie have been killed in combat? Daddy was a picture of health when he last saw him and Momma too, the image of her standing in the yard when he left as vivid now as it had been when the trees first closed her from his view. Her last letter had given no hint of illness. It couldn't be Momma. It couldn't be Hetty either, fit and full of energy. Pregnant or not, Hetty always bounced from one place to another, no stopping her, ran instead of walked, no not Hetty. And she can't have lost the baby, too far pregnant and too well. Dalton's mind was in turmoil, his senses absorbed, numbed with anxiety; he wanted desperately to get back and hear the news, to stop the misery of speculation. He started to run, then slowed for he suddenly didn't want to hear the news, he wanted to turn back, return to the front line with thoughts of Hetty and home as they had always been.

From the CP he jumped in a medic's jeep heading back to the field hospital. There were two stretchers tied across the hood and the men they carried looked in bad shape. One of their buddies had tripped a bouncing Betty, an anti-personnel mine which when tripped, would spring up to waist height before exploding. They had been walking behind and had caught some of the blast. One had his eyes covered and his facial wounds were changing the temporary bandages to a pale red colour. Their predicament became only a temporary distraction and the few miles took all too long and yet not long enough.

In the few seconds it took the lieutenant to utter those words, 'news from home', Dalton's image of home was torn to shreds. His rock that made the harsh realism of war sufferable, was sinking into the abyss of human frailty.

The news could wait he told himself, yet he jumped off the jeep and ran across to the array of tents in search of the Chaplain. It was not the same man who had known Hetty, for Dalton had seen him beneath the cliffs of Omaha. Dalton found him and together they walked away from the tents and vehicles to benches laid out behind the field kitchens. An uncomfortable silence ensued until they had walked far enough away from everyone. Finally, there in the midst of the Normandy countryside, 4,000 miles from home, Dalton sorrowfully learnt of his momma's death. She had passed away on 27th May, ten days before the beach landings. Even before he had taken his first step on French soil, she had been laid to rest in the graveyard of Wares Church.

Disbelief engulfed him and as he stared into emptiness, Wares became as vivid in his mind as if he had just closed his eyes after staring at it. His mother walked there, she was laying flowers at a small unmarked grave, whilst a child, a young boy was playing in the long grass. Seeing his mother's sombre face, the boy ran to her, stood by her side and reached up to hold her hand for the comfort it gave. Dalton and his mother walked on, passing the gravestones; their colours, their texture and the family names so vivid in his memory. Then his eyes fell upon his mother's grave and he was alone. Dalton started to cry and then he sobbed, and the Chaplain could do nothing more than leave him to his grief.

Dalton was given three days away from the front line as a form of compassionate respite from combat. On one of those, he found his way to the damaged church of Couvains, where the regimental chaplain held a service. Bob Sales and a bunch of other B Company guys attended, relieved from the front for 24hours, a front line which had become static. The men spoke the Lord's Prayer as though God himself was physically and visibly present at the altar and as they spoke, Sales recalled that 'before the war perhaps twenty men in the company knew the 23rd Psalm, yet within a few days of combat, there weren't twenty who didn't know it.'

When Dalton arrived back to the company, Allbritton and Clayton gave him knowing looks. They were the only close buddies Dalton had left and he thanked God for them.

Clayton pulled him to one side and with a cheeky smile slipped him a drink of Calvados.

"In the Chaplain's words, we need uplifting," Clayton said with a squeeze of his arm. "Compliments of an old man who wanted to thank us for his freedom."

Not the ordinary forty percent alcohol, this was the fifty percent variety that a farmer might stow away on the back of his wagon 'for emergencies!' As only a genuine Norman would say, 'it contained the true spirit of the apple'.

In the late evening a light rain started to fall from the Normandy sky - harmless stuff, just wet. Clayton always seemed to find something to cover his foxhole no matter the location. With the town buildings close by, his cover this night appeared rain proof and even shell proof. Dalton scrabbled by as Clayton was putting the finishing touches to his design, smoke from his cigarette escaping through the slats of wood.

"I haven't lost a man since you've been gone," Clayton said, "some squad leaders are just careless."

"And some are just bloody lucky," Dalton retorted and tried to demolish Clayton's elaborate roof with a thrust of his boot.

"Bloody lucky, you've been around those Limeys too much!" Clayton retorted and threw a clump of earth which caught Dalton on the back-side.

Dalton smiled to himself, for if mud was the only thing to hit him before morning he would wake a relieved man. Sliding down into his own foxhole, Dalton pulled his raincoat over himself just as the droplets of rain became heavier. The shower only lasted a few minutes before easing off and stopping altogether, the sky clearing and the temperature dropping in tune with the appearance of stars. As the patter of rain waned so the sounds of night time activity re-emerged. Not that of man, for both sides were now quiet; but the insect life that was there before, was there now and would still be there when the soldiers were gone and the war had become a distant memory. In the uncanny stillness and with tears running down his face, Dalton pulled his raincoat up to his chin the way his momma used to do with the blankets when he was little. "Good night Momma," he said towards the night sky and knew in his heart that she was in safe hands.

Chapter 43

Men Dig Their Own Graves

24th June to 2nd July.

The excessive losses incurred in reaching the slopes of the 'Martinville Ridge' had forced Bradley to stop the thrust south, but he could not remove the infantrymen from the constant danger in which they were now placed. The period following the 18th June was called the 'static period', though not by the men in B Company. On a daily and nightly basis the enemy shelled their position, snipers were an incessant threat and daily patrols, small arms fire, mines and booby traps added to the casualty figures.

On the 20th June when Dalton heard the news from home, he was also officially made Sergeant. When he arrived back at the front line on the 23rd with his 'new' rank and without a momma, his foxhole had been strengthened and dug even deeper by the few old buddies he had left. Although the slopes above Bretel left them highly exposed, their position did not change between the 17th June and the 7th July.

The situation thus developed into a 1st World War stalemate, with each side bombarding the other and patrols creeping forward to test the strength and location of the enemy. The storm of 18th and 19th June had wrecked the Mulberry artificial harbour on Omaha Beach and this left the US artillery short of ammunition. It wouldn't be until the port of Cherbourg was captured, that supplies would arrive in the quantities needed. To compound the problems of the infantrymen, the bad weather was not only making life on and in the ground miserable, it was also leaving them bereft of air support.

From being in reserve on the 10th June and up to Dalton's 25th Birthday on 30th June, B Company suffered another 117 casualties. Making a total of 228 casualties since D-Day when 193 enlisted men and officers had landed on

Omaha. Dalton's birthday passed without thought or mention, it was unimportant; to survive another day was all that preoccupied him and he gave thanks at each new morning's light. Perhaps Lieutenant Davolt found out it had been Dalton's birthday, for on the 1st July he said he was going to promote the wiry, old hand and D-Day veteran to Staff Sergeant. But the order would never be put into effect and what did rank matter when a man is on the brink of death. The promotion passed both Davolt and Dalton by and was lost in the mud of the Normandy field. Davolt was killed on the 2nd July; he had been B Company's Commander for thirteen days.

Over the course of this so called static period, the terrain was transformed into a bare, wretched landscape with up rooted trees, shell craters, vehicle tracks, ruts and mud patches over which lay broken equipment, discarded ration boxes and other personal items, shallow latrine holes and blood stains. The hedgerows were torn and stunted with gaping holes where shells had burst through. The dog rose, black thorn and holly growing in among the prickly hawthorn normally acted as a roadway for wildlife; the common dormouse, bank vole and others using it to conceal their daily routines from predators such as the kestrel and tawny owl. But the wildlife and birdsong were gone; the hedgerows now only concealed the weary infantryman. The men played their parts, predator prey, prey predator, the roles ill defined and continually interchanging to create insecurity and even paranoia. Cat and mouse, kill or be killed. Indecision, impulse, a lapse of concentration, tiredness or accidentally leaving cover and you were as dead as the humus in the soil. Thus like the twitchy wood mouse forever in fear of being eaten, the infantryman stood guard, or lay in his hole in the ground, in constant fear of being consumed by the war he pursued.

Pounded not just by 88s and mortars, 1st Battalion's positions suffered the onslaught of the big guns, the block-busting 105mm and the dreaded 150mm artillery pieces. The shell from a 105mm gun weighed over 30 pounds yet it could be fired from over 6 miles away. But in comparison, the 150mm was an infantryman's nightmare, exceeded only by the 170mm. The shell from a 150mm gun weighed 95 pounds yet it left the muzzle at 3,000 feet per second and could reach distances of almost 18 miles. When it landed, it created an explosion which shook the ground like a powerful earthquake. For a man in the open, its concussion alone could kill at 30 feet. In lull periods, men improved their foxholes, making them more elaborate, digging them deeper and taking them into and under the hedgerow embankments. They dug down the sides, placed slats of wood, tree branches or metal bars across the top, anything they could find to support a couple of feet or more of soil. Leaving just the last eighteen inches open, they would slide down into their 'burrows' and during a bombardment draw material across the opening, sliding to the more protected end of their entombments.

The night of the 1st July drew in and as yet there had been no bombardment. The mid-summer solstice had only just passed and the short six hour night had made no noticeable inroad on the long hours of daylight. The poor weather elongated dawn and dusk and the rain soaked the ground. Water seeping into foxholes made sleeping uncomfortable, but it was essential to snatch what sleep they could between guard duty and the regular bombardments. Dalton lay on the shelter half of his pup tent, lapping it partly around him for good measure. He couldn't recall which buddy had had the other half of the tent, for the tent had never been and would never be erected; it would have been suicide to have slept above ground. With the enemy so close, he laid his rifle with bayonet attached down one side of him and knife down the other, remaining alert for fear of the enemy scaling the hedge above him. With an overall length in excess of three feet, seven inches without the bayonet and over nine pounds in weight, the Garand M1 rifle was not the easiest weapon to wield if a German came over the hedge; the combat knife therefore added some reassurance. It was at times like these that Dalton would have liked a revolver. Small, light and needing just one hand to operate, they were ideal for close confrontations. It seemed that every German infantryman possessed one; for although originally intended for Officers, the versatile self-loading 'pistole' had spread down the ranks. The pistole 38 or 08, the renowned Luger, had now become part of the uniform and imparted an air of superiority. On crawling through hedgerows, guarding prisoners or hiding against an approaching enemy, the advantage it gave seemed immense. Dalton looked up at the edge where the hawthorn leaves touched the dark night sky and hoped the view would remain that way. Lacking a pistol, his hand lay against the cold sharp steel of his knife and he took false comfort from it, for it was no match for the Luger.

Dalton might relax a little once the point watch had been set, then sounds and movements would seem so much quieter and his hole in the ground so much more comfortable. Under the cover of darkness and armed with a field telephone, two privates would crawl out and dig-in to the field some yards out from the line. It was their responsibility to forewarn of a surprise attack and engage the enemy if possible. One of the Non Coms, usually a squad leader or his assistant, would be assigned to communicate with them. Fortunately the point watch of the 1st July was not Dalton's responsibility and in a few minutes he would hopefully be able to grab some sleep before the German artillery opened up. Dalton knew that the most recent replacement men would not relax all night and they would start the next day at a further disadvantage. He felt sorry for these men, whom he rarely got to know. They joined without close friends, were lonely, insecure and immediately thrust into the front line against German Veterans. The ever diminishing '42 contingent of men continued to support each other, they didn't need to converse, a look, grin or grimace communicated all, for they had lounged at the same bars and slept under the same canvas through the years of training. But now conversation had reduced to grunts, groans and gripes and it wasn't conducive to the building of new friendships. Twenty or so new men might arrive and within a week, two thirds of them had been killed or wounded. If a soldier lasted more than a week he was considered to be an 'old hand'. Dalton lost two new replacement men the day he was LWA and struggled to remember their names.

Replacement men allocated to the 116th Regiment. between 13th to 30th June. (Approx 2,400 men per regiment, 12 companies.)

Date	18th	19th	20th	22nd	23rd	24th	26th	27th	30th	Total
Officers	9	34	11	1	4	5	0	1	7	72
Enlist. men	271	205	163	112	0	148	132	112	1	1144

Source. After Action Reports. HQ 116th Inf. 1944.

The point watch never made it over the hedge, for after 11p.m. the big 150mm German field guns started to pound 1st Battalion's position again. Inside Dalton's deep foxhole it was completely black, the earth shuddered with each hit and sent soil falling in on him, sliding down between the wooden stumps he had used to support his roof. Midnight passed and still the bombardment continued, salvo after salvo, some so close that his ears were left ringing and his brain numbed. A closer hit shook his whole body, his brain felt as though it had been knocked from side to side, he was left dizzy yet had nothing to focus upon. So much soil tumbled in that he thought he might be buried alive, his hearing had gone, he shouted but couldn't hear himself, panic gripped him, he started to flail his arms upward tearing his skin on the stumps of his roof. Then another shell hit some distance away, he heard the explosion, he got a grip of himself and lay still, safer to remain partially buried than to be out in the open. Dalton twisted round onto his stomach to allow the loose soil to fall off his face.

With one hand clasping Hetty's coins on his dog tag, he squeezed his eyes tightly closed and tried to think of the woman who made his life worth living. Still the shells came in. Wounded men could not be attended to and through the night dead men started to decay in the damp earth, swelling and oozing foul smelling liquids. The huge shells sounded like they were beating the air as they screeched seemingly straight for Dalton's foxhole. Some foxholes received direct hits and body fluids and parts were spread over the tortured landscape. Living men quaked, prayed and clung to the earth. When light started to creep in through the cracks as dawn approached, there came with it the hope that soon the shelling would stop, but it didn't. It continued incessantly through the early morning hours, past five, six and then seven o'clock. Eight hours of shelling and so it continued; instilling a deep depression and desperation amongst the men. Dalton felt that he could stand it no more, yet on it went and alive he remained, despite believing that the next, then the next or the next shell would kill him. Between explosions men could be heard shouting for help, or calling to buddies, but no one answered them. Dalton passed his calls of nature where he lay. A man maddened by the terror, ran from his foxhole and was cut down by shrapnel. Another soldier killed himself with a bullet to the head. Others cried uncontrollably and continued to shake long after the shelling finally ceased. When it did, Dalton was too frightened to move, lest it start again. But the silence, broken only by the ringing in his ears, stretched on through the seconds, slowly amounting to minutes and was uncanny, unnatural, threatening. He imagined German infantry running at that very moment towards him, guns about to blaze and a grenade thrown into his hole. The thought drove him scrabbling out into the open, the light hurt his eyes, he was stiff, numb and dazed; yet he stood, crouched amongst the carnage and checked for the assault. But there was nothing, just the intransigence of the Martinville Ridge still bearing down upon them in the mid-morning sunlight.

Men started to crawl into the light from the safety of their holes and take in their transformed surroundings, changed as if they had been transported to a different section of front line. Dalton looked across at the foxholes of his platoon and the sight caused despair to well up within him and flood his stoicism. Leaning against the hedgerow bank he allowed himself to slump slowly to the earth and drop his head back against the soil. Clayton's foxhole was gone, completely obliterated.

B Company Casualties,
Enlisted men and Officers.

9th to 30th June 1944.

Compiled using B Company morning reports obtained from the National Personnel Records Centre, St. Louis, Missouri and from communicating directly with B Company veterans.

Rank column, abbreviations used.
Pvt   Private
Pfc   Private first class
Sgt   Sergeant
S/Sgt   Staff Sergeant
T/Sgt   Tech Sergeant
1st Sgt First Sergeant
Lt   Lieutenant
Capt   Captain
M   Medic

D or R column.
D indicates a D-Day soldier.
R indicates a replacement soldier with their date of arrival.
Left blank indicates that I do not know whether the man came in on D-Day or was a replacement.

LWA   Lightly wounded in action.
SWA   Seriously wounded in action.
KIA   Killed in action.
dw   Died of wounds.
All of the above with date given.
LIA in LWA column indicates lightly injured in action.

The distinction between LWA and SWA for the reporting officer was a difficult one. From the records it appears that many of the men listed as LWA did not return to combat.

Surname	Forename	Rank	D or R	LWA	SWA	KIA
Abate	William	Pvt			29th	
Abernethy	Julius	Sgt				22nd
Anderson	Allister	Pvt	R 16th		30th	
Appleby	Leonard	Pvt	R 9th			09th
Ashton	Norman	Pvt	R 15th		22nd	
Atkinson	Arthur	Pvt	R 22nd	30th		
Avery	Blane	Pfc		23rd		
Barham	Fred	Pvt	R 19th	29th		
Barile	Pasquale	Pvt	R 12th			
Benton	Clarence	Pfc				20th
Black	Robert	Pvt	R 19th		22nd	
Blanchard	Eugene	Pfc	R 15th	21st		
Bleecker	Robert	Sgt			17th	dw18th
Booz	Thomas	Pvt		23rd		
Bott	Milton	Pfc	D	09th		
Boyer	Charles	Pfc	R 16th		22nd	
Brown	Kenneth	Pvt	R 13th	17th		
Buonanno	Patrick	MSgt	R 19th		23rd	
Burk	William	Pvt	R 22nd			29th
Burns	Joseph	Pvt	R 9th			10th
Cantara	Rudolph	Pvt				17th
Carlson	Harold	Pvt		29th		
Cassell	Ervin	Pvt		9-29th		
Clarke	James	Pvt		16th		
Colucci	Daniel	Pvt			9-19th	
Conner	Charles	Pvt	D	13th		
Cooper	William	Pfc				17th
DeHerrera	Freddie	Pvt	R 12th	16th		
DeWitt	Harry	Pfc				17th
Dickerson	Cecil	Pfc		17th		
Dickey	Leonard	Pfc				17th
Dovey	Wilbert	Pfc		16th		
Duncan	Brenard	Pfc			9-19th	
Geary	John	Pvt		21st		

Surname	Forename	Rank	D or R	LWA	SWA	KIA
Gish	Strother	Sgt	R 16th	30th		
Goins	John	Pvt		16th		
Gordon	William	Pvt		17th		
Green	Obie	Pfc	R 16th	24th		
Greishaw	John	Pfc	D		11th	
Harrelson	Joseph	Capt	R 14th	17th		
Hawthorne	Jennings	Pvt			9-19th	
Hlavaty	Joseph	Pvt	R 15th	LIA23		
Hoag	Earl	Pvt	R 16th		29th	dw29th
Holt	Adrian	Pfc				17th
Horton	Robert	Pfc	D	12th		
Hughes	Joseph	Pfc			17th	
Hunt	Raymond	Pvt		16th		
Iannarilli	Mario	Pfc				17th
Ira	Donald	Pvt			16th	
Johnson	George	Pfc		16th		
Kane	Thomas	Pfc				17th
Keiderling	Donald	Pvt	D	10th		
Keller	Clarence	Pfc		18th		
Kemper	Kelly	Pfc	D	10th		
Kosala	Michael	Pfc		LIA20		
Kovach	Chester	Pfc				10th
Leach	Eugene Jr	Pvt				18th
Lifsitz	Mortimer	Pvt		17th		
Manos	Aristeded	Pfc				29th
Marion	Caleb	Pvt			9-19th	
Mays	Elwood	Pvt		18th		
McElhone	Daniel	Pfc	D	10th		
McLough	Richard	Cpl	R 16th			17th
Mehring	David	Pfc				17th
Miller	John	Pfc				17th
Miller	Ralph	Pvt				17th
Minor	Michael	Pfc	D		09th	

Surname	Forename	Rank	D or R	LWA	SWA	KIA
Napoli	Joseph	Pfc		16th		
Newman	Lyman	Pfc				18th
Nocera	Angelo	Pfc		16th		
Osier	Albert	Pvt			9-19th	
Ott	Maurice	Pfc	R 11th			22nd
Pacholewski	Steve	Pfc	R 13th	17th		
Padgett	O'Dell	S/Sgt	D	16th		
Patton	Harry	Pfc				17th
Pauley	Robert	Pfc			16th	
Peerson	Vernon	Pvt		17th		
Pelc	Joseph	Pfc		9-10th		
Planster	Joseph	Pvt	R 16th			29th
Polito	Philip	Pfc		17th		
Pott	Milton	Pfc		09th		
Powell	Bruce	Pvt	R 16th	30th		
Powers	Harold	Pvt	R 16th	30th		
Presley	William	1stSgt	D		17th	
Price	Richard	Pvt			17th	
Price	Charles	Pfc		17th		
Procbstle	Robert	Pvt		21st		
Puckett	Chesley	S/Sgt			17th	
Ramirez	Manuel	Pfc	R 16th		29th	
Roach	John	T/Sgt	D	09th		
Roubideaux	Eugene	Pvt	R 12th		16th	
Ryder	Mervyn	Pvt		16th		
Schauer	Albert	Pfc				17th
Sicard	Louis	Pfc			16th	
Slaughter	Dalton	Pfc	D	18th		
Sligh	James	Pfc	D	sk23rd		
Sligh	Ralph		D		MIA18	
Smith	David	S/Sgt		24th		
Sorensen	George	Pvt		16th		
Sovetsky	Peter	Pfc		16th		

Surname	Forename	Rank	D or R	LWA	SWA	KIA
Stade	Arnold	Sgt	R 16th	29th		
Stern	Philip	1st Lt	R 14th	17th		
Stone	Willard	Pfc	R 22nd	29th		
Stoviak	William	Pfc	D	09th		
Strohecker	Clarence	Pfc	D	10th		
Taylor	Walter	2ndLt	D	13th		
Thomas	Albert	Pfc		17th		
Tomlin	Burt	Pfc	D		17th	
Urdenis	Mike	Pfc		24th		
VanDeVort	Leo	2ndLt	R 11th	17th		
Varadian	Varad	2ndLt	D	17th		
Wade	Audy	Pfc	D	9-10th		
Wingerd	George	Pvt	R 13th	17th		
Winschell	Walter	Pvt	R 12th		16th	
Wright	Fred	Pvt	R 13th	15th		
Wright	Samuel	Pvt				18th

Chapter 44

The Dresden Shell

2nd July 1944.

Dalton pulled himself together and searched for Clayton in the vain hope he might still be alive. But there was nothing but soil where Clayton's foxhole had once been. He looked around expecting to see him walking towards him with a hot coffee, mysteriously prepared somewhere as he had done so often. But there was no sign of his buddy. Again he stared down at the crater expecting any minute to see smoke rising from a crevice in the earth. And as the minutes passed so he started to question whether Clayton's foxhole had been there at all. Perhaps concussion had confused him and he had been situated further down the hedgerow. But eventually denial was replaced by acceptance, acceptance that another close friend was gone.

The remaining soldiers could be excused for thinking that the only American tactic was to replace men as quickly as they were lost. The June casualty list for the 116th alone ran to over seventeen hundred men (killed, missing, wounded and injured). General Bradley might have been convinced that through attrition, the enemy would be defeated, but the mud covered GIs with the blood of friends spattered around them thought differently.

Despite retreating into Poland, with the loss of half a million troops and the reinforcing of their last defensive line in Italy, the German defence in Normandy had stalled the US advance. Superior field tactics, equipment and years of battle experience gave the Germans a huge advantage over the young American Army. As important, Germany was not burdened by politics or allegiances to big business and readily copied and continually adapted weapons according to need rather than economics. Thus young men continued to be drawn from the cities and countryside of the US and poured into the fields of France, to be cut down and replaced, cut down and replaced, step by step, hedgerow by hedgerow.

As Dalton again looked out at the Martinville Ridge on the morning of the 2nd July, he was thinner than he could ever remember himself in manhood. Eating came a low second priority to avoiding death and mutilation. Cold rations, mixed with rain, sodden clothes, mud and carnage didn't give a soldier the best of appetites. With his uniform filthy, his face carrying the stubble of several days' growth and his skin unwashed for almost as long, Dalton presented the appearance of a renegade in defeat. The US front line was a mere twenty miles from Omaha and it had taken twenty-nine days to get there. They had now been in the same position since the 17th June, fourteen days of hell in the field of Monsieur Vasselin. To B Company's left flank they could see the few houses making up the hamlet of Bretel, in theory still in German hands, but really it was no man's land. Beyond B Company's right flank and over the ridge lay the town of Saint Lo which had been scheduled for capture nine days after D-Day.

Bradley was under enormous pressure to break the deadlock and planned another thrust against the ridge for the 7th July. Thus as Dalton pulled his men together after the terrible bombardment, he was told to make his squad ready for a push past Bretel towards the Rau de la Dollée. They were to test the strength and resolve of the German defence in the fields below them.

Before the off, Dalton drank a welcome coffee that for once hadn't been prepared by Clayton and tried to focus on the latest orders. But his thoughts kept meandering back to better days, to Ivy Bridge and their hut by the side of the Exeter Road, to his five buddies sitting together in the warmth of the coke stove and to the optimism and the dreams they had once shared. Clayton would not be teaching history, nor would he be returning to England with his daddy and as Dalton recollected the aspirations of his dead friends so emotional and physical exhaustion overcame him. Colonel Canham's prediction at Ivy Bridge had seemed incomprehensible, but now 29 days into the conflict, almost two in every three men were, in fact, dead. Of Dalton's five good friends Paul Kennedy, Ted and Clayton were gone. Austen had been wounded on the beach and only Allbritton and Dalton remained unscathed. So who would make it back and who would be killed to make it four out of six not to go home?

Dalton knew that the NCO had been right when he described him as too impulsive and now he was too exhausted to even recognise it. Dalton was sure he would be next, for the 'optimistic Yank' was as dead as his best buddies; as dead as Staff Sergeant John Holmes, Smiler and all the others along the way. Snipers had picked men so close, bullets had passed within inches and shells had fallen barely far enough away not to harm him. How much longer would he last?

Some men prayed for the perfect wounding, one just serious enough to end the conflict for them but not too serious as to cause lifelong difficulties. A few had taken it upon themselves to self-inflict one, it was a court martial offence, but not a soul in the ranks would now condemn such an action, for it was driven by despair and a certain amount of insanity. Dalton's friend Richard Hatton shot himself in the foot - a cast iron approach to survival Dalton thought, but it didn't sit comfortably with him.

3rd Platoon left their battered dug in positions and crossed the first field before entering the second to edge their way towards the Rau de la Dollée. Richmond Bell, with his sharp hearing, followed Dalton and Sergeant Sorrow brought up the rear of the squad. Another guy who Dalton barely knew led Clayton's men. The second field was not unlike any other they had crept through or fought over, except that down in its right hand corner stood a water pump. The men had seen it many times as they peered by day and night into the region which had become no man's land. A hedge ran down to the corner where the pump stood and the southern edge of the field was bordered by a sunken track perhaps six feet wide. The GIs had patrolled the track and so too had the Germans. Its high sides with mounted trees and hedges had become an unofficial dividing line between the opposing armies; and together with the two or so fields on either side of it, formed no man's land. Leading a patrol along it one late evening, Dalton was convinced there were Germans on the other side of the hedgerow, just feet away from him, yet no one made a move on the other, as if content with the status quo.

The field with the water pump initially sloped gently downward, then steeper as it approached the track. An unusually small bank of earth topped with broken hawthorn lay at its edge and finally the men slid down into the sunken thoroughfare, which was muddy and overshadowed by vegetation. Spreading out along it and under the cover of a short lived bombardment of the Martinville Ridge, each man dug into the high embankment which formed the southern side of what in better days was a link between Bretel and other hamlets and allowed carts to carry produce from the fields. By cutting into the earthen bank the men would have a more protective firing position and on their push into the fields beyond, could always retreat to it should they encounter strong resistance. With the habits of farming days long past, Dalton drew upon reserves yet unrecognised to excavate a deep hollow, such that no one would mistake its owner. Just a few feet behind him standing on the raised field was the water pump, as if scrutinising his work. The cast iron mechanism with its long pumping handle had for generations provided water for the farm animals, passers-by on the track and workers in the field. But now it stood waiting for those peaceful days to return, leaving the clear fresh water in a safer, unscarred world somewhere below.

With their positions dug into the bank it was time to move forward beyond the track to the third field. Pulling themselves up and over the bank they pushed through its dense hedgerow into the other half of no man's land. The platoon split up with each group moving down either side of the field. Dalton brought up the rear of the single line of men on the right side, religiously stopping, checking their right flank, checking behind and leaving several feet between him and the next man. They crept forward for what seemed like an hour, wary of mines, ambush and booby traps before finally reaching the hedgerow at the far side, crouching there and trying to quieten their breathing in order to listen for any movement on the other side. Short of dropping grenades over and broadcasting their position, the only way to check was for someone to take a look. Whilst others considered the infantryman to be expendable, good lieutenants and NCOs tried, in their small way, to prolong their stay of execution and it was the valiant platoon sergeant who took it upon himself to check. Slowly and with the skill of an old craftsman he placed himself so that he could see along the length of the other side. It was a brave and noble action and many held their breath until the sergeant withdrew his head. A few men however had simply sat on the earth, as if sick with war, ignoring the platoon sergeant's endeavours.

Not wishing to use their men as scouts, the platoon sergeant and lieutenant decided, against all guidelines, that this time they alone would move to the next hedgerow on the far side of the fourth field. "To take a quick look," the sergeant said.

The rest of the men were to provide cover as they moved out into the open. If the Germans 'let loose' then Dalton was told to consider moving the platoon back to the 'dug in' positions in the sunken track, for their current position would be too exposed.

Keeping again to the right side, the two most senior ranking men of the platoon moved slowly out into the fourth field. Their men watched, concern rising with the respect they felt and their questioning of authority diminishing somewhat. Three quarters of the way across the field they stopped for perhaps a third time, again nothing, no movement or even a hint of enemy presence. Dalton felt himself holding his breath and listening with the intensity he might have done had he been with the lieutenant himself. A butterfly skirted the hedge, passed over the head of the lieutenant and fluttered into the open field, struggling there against the early summer breeze, a breeze which brought the smell of a changing season. When the breeze died and the hawthorn leaves stopped rustling, the ringing in Dalton's ears from the long bombardment was the loudest sound he could hear.

The lieutenant and platoon sergeant moved on again, quicker now, as though they had been stalking a stray farm animal and were now making a last dash to grab it. Crouching down behind the soil bank on the far side of the field, the two men slowly raised themselves to peer through the roots of the hedgerow plants.

The German soldier must have watched the GI's progress, for he was now adjacent to the lieutenant and just a few feet of soil separated them. With his trusty pistole at the ready, the German infantryman waited for the lieutenant's head to come into view, pointed the barrel at the face beneath the helmet and pulled the trigger. The single shot split through the preceding peace, the lieutenant's head jarred backward and he fell to the ground. The platoon sergeant fired off a couple of rounds through the hedgerow. Fire was returned. More rounds from the platoon sergeant, then nothing. Seconds passed, though they seemed like minutes. The rigid stance of the platoon sergeant softened, then bending down he grabbed the lieutenant by the back of his jacket and pulled him to his feet. The bullet had entered the lieutenant's mouth and gone straight out through his cheek. Holding his face and half staggering with shock, the lieutenant was guided by the platoon sergeant and retreated back across the field. The covering fire damaged no more than a few hawthorns and left bullets in the soil bank for French lads to discover in the peaceful years to come, but it did its job. Passing Dalton, the platoon sergeant shouted, "Country, pull the men back to the sunken track."

With the lieutenant and platoon sergeant striding away from him, Dalton was left to manage an orderly withdrawal, instructing some to provide cover and others to make their way back. He knew without question that he would leave himself to last. On being told to go, most ran and never looked back, leaving Dalton and a guy called Max the last at the hedgerow. Max was all of nineteen years old and one of the most recent replacement men. He had attached himself to Dalton and in so doing had likely increased his chances. Dalton finally told Max to go and then stepped up onto a dip in the soil bank and pushed himself through a thin section of hawthorn to view along the other side of the hedge. It was an impulsive action which left him exposed, an action driven by tiredness and a fear of being shot in the back. Max was running now and probably half way across the field, a few more seconds and Dalton would likely be alone. Slaughter the Sergeant, Acting Staff Sergeant and now temporary Platoon Sergeant looked to the right and saw nothing. Then turning to the left he froze, for hunched over and moving slowly away with his back towards him was a German soldier. The man's head was tilted downward and sideways to look through the roots. He hadn't seen Dalton, why should he have? No one would surely raise themselves above the cover of the bank for to do so would present a compelling target.

Dalton hadn't weighed up the risk. Instinctively and some might say foolishly, he had wanted to quickly be sure that no one was waiting to pick him off as he retreated. To end up face down in the soil with a bullet in his spine was not the end Dalton wanted.

The German soldier slowed down, perhaps he had seen Max. Above him Dalton watched and yet did nothing for he had never killed a man so close.

Shoot him, someone whispered in Dalton's head, or he will shoot Max.

What, me, shoot a man in the back? Dalton questioned.

You have to shoot him, you have no option, came the reasoning from his seemingly empty skull.

When the German stopped and took aim at Dalton's retreating young squad member, Dalton's finger finally pulled the trigger. But the finger did not belong to Dalton for he was no more than a link in the chain of war, of that monster who rode defiantly on the actions of simple, well intentioned men.

Dropping back off the soil bank, Dalton stood for a moment disorientated. He felt sick, his body stiff as if it had momentarily been turned to stone. The fingers that once worked a hoe and caressed Hetty were still taut and curved around the trigger of his rifle. But the sight of Max darting out through the gate stimulated Dalton into action and he started running for his life. Sickness left and dread replaced it as he sprinted over the patchy grass and red clay soil, a dread that made the field seem twice as big, twice as deadly and the opposite soil bank an unachievable goal as in a bad dream, never to be reached. Then ten yards from the gate a thud shook him to the core. Not the expected rifle bullet to shatter his spine but a mortar that might tear a man apart. The first explosion was soon followed by others as mortars fell on either side of the sunken track. The Germans had good measure of the trajectory.

Dalton slid down onto the track and made for his own dug in firing position. He didn't trust the others and his own was just a few feet further. But occupy it he couldn't for Max was there. Yet Max was motionless, slumped against the bank. He had chosen Dalton's position in preference to his own. It had been the wrong choice - concussion had killed him. In the absence of higher ranking men, Dalton commanded the platoon to fire towards the enemy. He was convinced more German soldiers would be assembling beyond the far hedgerow.

The shelling continued in its accuracy and if anything became more severe. Exploding mortars issued shrapnel at over 100 feet per second, metal as different in size and shape as the faces of agony they caused. It tore through flesh like a knife and snapped bone like breaking a match.

The platoon sergeant returned to assume command but he didn't stay long. He was positioned several feet from Dalton when suddenly he spun round clutching his elbow, blood pouring down from where the shrapnel had hit him.

"You're in charge now Slaughter!" he shouted and without a pause, ran back to the medics across the field with the water pump.

Taking his responsibility predictably seriously, Dalton moved along the platoon shouting at the men to fire. Bullets and shrapnel splintered through the vegetation surrounding them, metal thudded into the earth and into the soil bank and sometimes into flesh. 'Shorty' was standing and firing as commanded but as he stood down to reload, a small piece of shrapnel imbedded itself in his neck. Blood started to pulse out from the damaged blood vessel to drench his chest as Dalton moved over to help the stricken private. Taking a rag he placed it against the wound and positioned Shorty's hand over it.

"Press hard and get the hell out of here!" Dalton shouted and Shorty didn't have to be told twice.

A shell closely followed by another landed near the water pump and the pressure waves caused the arm to rock and a trickle of water ran out from the ground below, from peace into chaos. It was as though an invisible farm worker, oblivious of the blood-letting, was summoning water from the depths.

Dalton again shouted at the men to fire, moving down the line as he did so. A shell hit a tree and pieces of shrapnel blasted down and almost tore both arms off a man. Another shell exploded behind Dalton and a large piece of shrapnel whizzed past his legs and embedded itself deep in the hedgerow soil bank. Should they retreat, Dalton asked himself, frantically considering the options? But his men would be so exposed in the open. More mortars fell, another close to the water pump. With no trough the droplets fell to moisten the soil, running but a short distance to soak away and be gone, back into safety.

The shell with Dalton's name on it started its final journey, pushing through the still air of this Normandy summer's day. It may well have been manufactured in Dresden with steel from the Ruhr, hauled by train across Northern Germany, perhaps through Paris and offloaded at St. Lo. It had been carried to the field by truck, man-handled to the mortar emplacement and fed into the tube by fair hands to be fired into the bright, afternoon sky of the 2nd July 1944.

The farm boy's luck was finally about to run out. Dalton had just moved back to within 20 feet of the water pump when the Dresden shell landed.

A large piece of shrapnel tore through the inside of his right thigh, half way between the knee and the groin. It scraped past the femur and left a gaping large wound. His leg lurched forward from the impact and he stared in disbelief at his torn uniform and the mess he could see through the shreds of material. Instinctively he pressed his left hand against the warm and bloodied flesh and limped away from the platoon's position. Struggling up the low soil bank which separated the track from the field with the water pump, he made his way up what now seemed a very steep incline. He was in shock and for the first few yards could feel no pain. Crouched over with blood streaming over his hand to run down his leg and fill his boot, Dalton's pace was slow and the open ground made him feel even more vulnerable. Should he have stayed at the hedge or moved as he was doing? Chance! Was it a good choice or an impulsive one? But to go back was as dangerous if not more so than to continue. He had made his decision, a decision partly guided by the fear of bleeding to death.

Dalton maintained the path he had chosen, its end likely no different to any other. Another shell landed in the field to his left just as he was passing a gate and a large piece of shrapnel drove into Dalton's left leg just below the knee, smashing the tibia and fibula bones. The momentum of the impact drove the lower leg unnaturally around so that it swung up and grotesquely touched his right thigh, tearing ligaments and completely breaking the knee joint. Dalton fell to the ground. He was half way across the field on the more gently sloping section, but now he could only crawl.

He was frantic and confused. Why couldn't he stand? Heart stopping pain filled him to capacity. He was in agony yet still he tried to pull himself up. But despite the strength in his arms, he merely thrashed around like a confused old man cast down by a stroke. "CRAWL, CRAWL," he berated and thus reaching out and digging his fingers into the soil, he hauled himself across the earth leaving a trail of his own blood. He crawled on what was left of his joint, the torn flesh and exposed bone pressing into the mud as he tried to shift his weight forward. Looking back, he saw his torn frame, his left leg two thirds blown off, the mess that war had made, his lower leg dragging along by the tendons which attempted to keep it a part of him, to keep the once wholesome young man whole. Inch by inch his pace slowed and each inch felt like a yard.

"God help me," he pleaded through the pain.

He thought of Hetty and wrenched himself on, he thought of his family and the land he wanted to farm and he reached another rut in the red clay field. He wanted these precious gifts so much that his tiring arms dragged his broken body ever closer to the other side of the field.

Dalton hardly noticed when the second finger of his outstretched left hand was sliced off. Though it hung down into his palm and impeded his attempt to crawl, he was more aware of another new pain that emanated from his back. A piece of shrapnel had entered him just below the shoulder blade and it was consuming his attention. He could see the other injuries but not this one. The unknown threatened him; how deep, what had it hit, how much blood was escaping inside?

The country boy was in a mess, he was done for and he knew it; the end of the field and the medics were too far, the next rut insurmountable. The shells continued to fall while Dalton's blood flowed from him, until eventually he was too weak to even hold his head off the ground. As he slumped down to fully embrace God's earth, his dog tag pressed into his chest and Hetty's lucky coins slid silently down its chain. Leaves in their prime, ripped from trees, fell down around him and blades of grass moved across his face, nudged now only by the wind.

Chapter 45

The Aftermath

July 1944.

In the days following the 2nd July, the war moved away and left the field with the water pump at peace once more; alone with the hawthorns and maples, the ruts and the blood stained soil. The scars on the landscape eventually healed; the hedgerow grew back, the farmers levelled the sunken track and fixed their broken gates. In the woods, vegetation grew over the shell craters and the plough removed all trace of them in the cultivated fields. Perhaps in time and as the decades passed, the young Norman farmers would not be aware of the blood that was spilt on their land or appreciate the fear and suffering experienced behind the hedgerows. For the wounded men however and the families of the dead, such healing and return to normality might never take place, for humans and their bodies are far more complicated.

As Dalton's body lay unnoticed, the shelling gradually petered out to be followed by a transient, uncanny silence. Within seconds men responded to the lull, with orders and requests, running and shouting, jumping into vehicles and tearing off in different directions. Dalton's consciousness wavered and sensing movement about him, somehow managed to raise his head and stare again at what to him seemed like a great expanse of field. He could see GIs moving around and prayed to God that one would soon spot him. The pain tormented him, so much so in his back and strange how his finger hanging by a thread seemed more painful than both his legs half blown off. His torso felt like lead, no way could he raise it, he was frightened, death felt so near. With no one coming even close to him, he weakly dropped his head and lay still once more, pleading to God.

"Hold on Country," a voice said close by. "I'll get the medics to you," the voice added in muffled tones struggling through Dalton's dampened senses. The voice was gruff, familiar even, it sounded like the staff sergeant from 4th Platoon, 'Toad' Padgett, but he was in no state to be sure.

Then, at some indeterminable time later, Dalton felt someone kneeling beside him, his skin punctured, his limbs manipulated and then being turned over to face the sky.

"What the hell you been doing sergeant?" joked the man from God as he attached the syringe to Dalton's collar to show that an injection of morphine had been administered.

The sky turned black, back to light, then dark again and out of the shadow, a face finally formed.

"You've made a fine mess of this field," said the man with the heavenly face and caring hands.

Dalton tried to speak but no sound came and anyway, the medic was too busy to listen. He applied tourniquets in an attempt to stem the already excessive loss of blood, poured antibacterial sulfa powder over the wounds and then dressed them to offer some form of protection before strapping the torn limbs together. Hoisted onto a stretcher, Dalton was carried across the remaining few yards of the field in seconds; then on into the fields above Bretel which he had known so well and finally placed onto a jeep. With both positions on the hood already occupied by wounded men on stretchers, Dalton's stretcher had to straddle the front passenger seat and a rear seat.

"We don't do this for everyone," his saviour said, hanging on to Dalton to ensure he remained secure.

He was barely conscious as the jeep bumped its way along the track through Bois De Bretel, passed farm buildings and crossed a narrow road to reach the battalion aid station. As soon as the captain at the station saw the extent of Dalton's wounds he transferred him to the divisional field hospital; a longer but more comfortable journey in one of the medical battalion's ambulances.

Dalton couldn't remember arriving but arrived he had for next to his bed, beneath the canvas hospital tent stood a doctor whose face he recognised; they had sat together and talked for a while when they were first drafted at the 5th Regiment Armory, Baltimore in 1941. Noticing Dalton's regained consciousness, the doctor said, "You'll be ok Slaughter."

The blood transfusions were doing their job but the morphine was still strong in his veins and Dalton felt deadly tired. He wanted to check to see if he still had legs but the effort was too great.

"Don't go anywhere, we'll operate as soon as we can," the Doctor joked, leaving to check the next man in the row of cots.

The humour suppressed some of Dalton's fear and he slipped away to a field of corn. The shoots were several inches proud of the soil and two strong legs supported him as he hoed all day with the warm sun on his bare, unblemished, sun tanned back.

"Hey Slaughter, you saved my life," Shorty called out sometime after Dalton returned from theatre.

"Shame!" said the platoon sergeant from a distant bed and Dalton knew then that he was back in good company.

The field hospital was busy and the men lying there had every conceivable wound war can inflict on the fragile human frame; but whatever their physical state, mentally they had all changed. For some it would be possible to build a new life or even return to their old, but could a young man without limbs or eyes realise his dream? Could a woman marry a man who was sickened by the sight of himself and would wives still love them?

(For what happened to Dalton's squad, B Company and the 116th Regiment after 2nd July see appendix A.)

Chapter 46

St. Leonards, Dorset.

July 1944.

With the pain killers taking Dalton from one period of consciousness to the next, the hours passed as if they were minutes and exactly when he arrived in England, he couldn't say. Flown out of Normandy on a Dakota, he returned to friendly soil via Hurn Airfield, four miles from the English Channel and the coastal town of Bournemouth. It was the 5th July, three days after being wounded. As the wheels touched down, he was not the only soldier to feel relief, for he had never been in an aeroplane before. Its structure appeared flimsy, liable to buckle at the slightest impact and the engine noise alone seemed capable of destroying the metal it gave momentum to.

The truck which carried Dalton from the airfield to St. Leonards Hospital took the same route as all the others - the forest road through Matcham's Wood. It had been purpose built to carry the wounded, enabling the trucks to keep off public roads and away from the public eye for fear of demoralising the nation. But there were locals who walked those woods even at night and told friends of what they had seen. Stories became gossip whispered over a pint in the pub, or over afternoon tea. 'Truck loads of 'em bumper to bumper, all amputations', and 'things aren't going well for the Yanks, they're taking a beating'. Most who heard such gossip thought there to be some truth in it. For the hospital incinerator and mortuary, set deep in the woods, were always busy.

In the weeks following his return, Dalton lay in a bed within one of the many long wards which occupied the large complex. The wards were single storey buildings, built parallel to each other with a large space between to reduce bomb damage. Intended to be temporary, St. Leonards was built specifically for US casualties and paid for entirely by Uncle Sam. The number of wards and their length at over 150 feet, betrayed the reality of US strategy; that they expected high casualty rates and did not believe their troops would be adequately catered for by existing hospitals. The investment was sadly not in vain. Repetitively built of red clay blocks, the wards were connected to each other and to the other buildings by covered, heated walkways. Plain block wall sections alternated with windows down the length of each ward and like all the others, Dalton's bed sat squarely in the middle of the block wall section, bordered by concrete pillars like sentinels to the wounded.

Dalton watched as other men stayed for a while and then left. The majority heading to other hospitals in England or in the States, some for the mortuary and a few who might have considered themselves lucky, returned to their units. With July slipping past, St. Leonards became yet another temporary home for him; one more in a long list since leaving his real home, the home that could not and would never be replaced by any other. But compared to lying in a muddy foxhole, with just luck protecting him during a bombardment, the clean sheets and caring nurses of St. Leonard's seemed like heaven as Bob Sales said they would. After what was said to be his last surgery in England, Dalton regained consciousness to look down his bed covers. It was near dusk and the overcast sky and blustery showers seemed to be beckoning autumn, the country's sixth of the war. Dread filled Dalton as he looked down at himself, for fear that another part of him would be missing; that the shape beneath the covers would end at his knees or worse at his hips. He delayed the inevitable. With arms lying on top of the sheets, left hand heavily bandaged and finger gone for certain, he first reconciled himself with the fact that both arms and hands were otherwise intact. With his good right hand he then slowly raised the bed covering, high enough to see to the bottom of the bed. He did not look down, not at first, but stared at the canvas like ceiling as of a tent he had created. In the hazy world that followed the anaesthetic, a white sky arched over a flat white field and rising up were two long ridges. Eventually his eye followed their line down to pink standing stones pointing skyward. The ridges ended at toes, his toes, yet still he had to feel through the white cotton to confirm what lay beneath. Dalton's hand squeezed sensitive flesh and with an enormous sigh of relief, he gave thanks that his legs had been saved.

Talking afterwards, doctors had commented that had Dalton been a British soldier, the left lower limb would certainly have been amputated and possibly the whole of the right leg. "The British like to keep to old traditions," one said with a wink.

Paddington, early August.

Hetty fiddled with the buttons on her little brown jacket as she waited in the taxi for her mother. She was still inside giving last minute instructions to the men folk as if she was leaving for a month, not just for the day. Hetty was determined to make the journey to St. Leonards. But at almost nine months pregnant and still convalescing from toxaemia, she had to discharge herself from Paddington Hospital to do so. No one knew when Dalton might be shipped back to the States and Hetty was determined to see him before he left.

Leaving the house when the taxi arrived hadn't been made any easier by the send-off. The muted conversations with her father had set her on edge and her brother's comments had felt like knives being pushed into her. About her having a 'dead fiancé' and now 'a cripple for a husband' and how she was risking her baby by travelling all the way to Bournemouth.

Worried with anxiety verging on tears, Hetty ran the tips of her fingers around the buttons of her jacket as though doing so closed out everything horrible from the circle she described.

Finally, Ethel appeared up the area steps, flustered in face and frantically checking the contents of her handbag.

"Wart'erloo Station," she demanded as she settled in the black cab next to Hetty and, "don't try goin the long way round, cos youl get no more out of me," she added.

The Bournemouth train from Waterloo was crowded and walking down the narrow corridor with people buffeting her, Hetty found all the compartments full. There were one or two seats which merely supported a bag, clearly too precious to go with the other luggage on racks above the passengers' heads, but because of their contempt at such ignorance, neither Hetty nor her mother would ask for it to be moved. Thus passing beyond the compartments with their sliding doors to the corridor, they found space at the end of the carriage and there stood and watched as bomb damaged London streets and then the Hampshire countryside slipped past. No one offered up their seat to the two women and possibly as Ethel commented, common courtesy to women was a thing of the past. The demands of war had changed the image of women and attitudes towards them had perhaps changed also.

However, Hetty had chosen her attire carefully and the plain brown maternity dress with matching jacket concealed her condition well. Flowing and fashionable with its Peter Pan collar, the dress also fell over hips which carried no extra weight and viewed from behind, Hetty's waist looked just as narrow as it had always done. But perhaps no one offered up their seat simply because accompanying the pregnant girl, dressed all in black, to include, jacket, dress and hat, Ethel not only looked equally sturdy if not so young but too formidable to even suggest she might not be so.

The express steamed through the small country village stations without stopping and headed for its final destination, Bournemouth. After an hour and forty minutes of standing in the corridor, Hetty and Ethel sensed the train slowing as it approached Brockenhurst. Before 1885 the main line with its fast trains travelled on towards Ringwood but with the growth of Bournemouth as a seaside resort, the Brockenhurst to Ringwood line had become a subsidiary. At Brockenhurst then, Ethel with her pregnant daughter changed to a carriage train and found a welcome seat for the short journey to Ringwood.

Propped up with pillows, Dalton settled down to re-read Hetty's letters and wait for her. Every day he had been in combat she had written to him. Yet not one letter had he read until they caught up with him in hospital. His last embrace with Hetty outside the camp at Ivy Bridge seemed as if from another life; with so much dread, death and despair lying between. He craved her now just as much as when he lay in the Normandy earth, fearing morning would not break for him. He longed to hold her, to smell her sweet scent, to touch her skin and feel her lovely long hair - that she might brush it across him once more, like water carrying the power of healing.

As Ringwood station came into view, Hetty recalled their last touch on the Exeter Road when Colonel Canham was fast approaching in his jeep. Dalton's hand had brushed across her tummy and she wondered what he would think of her now that she was so enormous.

Looking up from Hetty's letters, Dalton again stared at his bandaged legs. For the moment he was forbidden to walk or even stand and feared he might never be normal again. But there were other marks on him not just the physical; engraved forever in so many ways in a manner only war can sculpture. And what would Hetty think of the new Dalton? Will her words portray the intimacy of the letters he grasped, or sound as if speaking to a stranger, tinged with foreboding at what she had taken on and what the future might hold?

At Ringwood, Hetty and Ethel crossed over the twin tracks via the foot bridge to reach the station buildings and thence to the taxis outside. The black Austin 16–4s all belonged to Bailey's Taxi Service, only Oscar Parkes competed with them in the town and never parked up at the station. With mother and daughter sat comfortably in the back, the lead taxi moved from station approach onto High Town Road and was barely past the Railway Hotel when Ethel leaned forward and said, "Don't try over chargin us, we've bin'ere before."

As Hetty and Ethel approached Dalton's ward through the covered walkway, mother and daughter carried thoughts as different as their ages. Ethel noticed the heating systems installed by the US authorities to keep personnel warm during colder seasons, even as they went from one building to another - whilst Hetty fretted about her man and could only picture him as he had once been, fit, strong and very handsome. Perhaps it was because she couldn't imagine him being any different or might it run deeper than that; might she never be able to fully accept his incapacity, forever comparing him to someone else?

Dalton kept watching the door for Hetty to enter, whilst men near to him smiled at his anxiety.
"Women change for the worse as soon as they get married," an older soldier quipped.
Being pregnant would make her "motherly looking," another added, choosing his words carefully. The comment made the group laugh and Dalton relax, but only a little bit. They had only been together for a handful of weekends and stark reality was about to replace war time romance as the enfolding vessel of their relationship.

Hetty and Ethel entered the long, single storey building via the end door which took them past smaller treatment rooms and offices that couldn't be seen behind the closed doors. Doors carrying typed and hand written notices pinned to them. Scraps of paper in some cases with too much information to catch as Ethel led Hetty purposefully towards the ward at the opposite end.
A nurse opened the door to the ward and Hetty stepped in with vision blurred by her emotions and could only see rows of beds with battered, faceless men.

"Hello son," her mother said to a soldier in the nearest bed and Hetty realised that an Eaglestone kiss had already been placed upon Dalton's cheek.

Across Ethel's shoulder Dalton glimpsed the most beautiful thing he had set eyes upon in months. She stood as though rooted to the spot, her hands clasped together around her lovely tummy.

Then as Dalton's handsome, smiling and unblemished face developed in Hetty's awakened senses, she rushed forward to almost lay upon him as she knelt without permission on the bedside, to hug and kiss the man she loved so dearly.

"You look pretty good considering everything you've been through," Hetty said pulling back slightly from Dalton's still strong arms and looking into the mischievous eyes she remembered so well.

"You look more beautiful than ever," Dalton said as tears of relief ran down both their faces.

"Thank God you're back safe," Hetty replied, oblivious to the silence in the ward as everyone focused on a romance still in flame.

Chapter 47

AWOL

To October 1944.

Two weeks after Hetty had visited Dalton at St. Leonards, Ethel telephoned the hospital with the news that Dalton was now a dad. Hetty had given birth to a baby boy, born at home on the 21st August, weighing six pounds and four ounces.

Dalton found it hard to comprehend that he was now a father; of a son, a friend and life time companion, so he considered. A farm life was good for a boy he thought, for the ebb and flow of the seasons soon taught the meaning of reaping what you sow. And the more he planned his family's future, the more he came to understand his own father.

Smiling at the prospect of returning home and of being reunited with his family, Dalton pictured his momma and of how proud she would have been to see him come home, a war hero, her grandson in his arms and a pretty English girl by his side. The fuss she would have made of him; returning home might just not be the same without her.

Kelly Slaughter's grandson would be Christened, Dalton James Slaughter, with a middle name to remember Hetty's father by or so it was said. But it might best recall Hetty's brother, 'Young Jimmy'. Dalton had been a little surprised at Hetty's choice, so declared when Hetty and Ethel visited him in hospital. Was it really Hetty's preference Dalton wondered, yet what did a middle name matter he asked himself, for it was only a middle name.

At Waterloo Station, the smart older couple at the back of the taxi rank queue watched as the GI on crutches exited the terminal building. With uniform pulled over bandages and no more than a splash of aftershave and Brylcreemed hair to protect him from the chilly October wind, the GI just didn't look warm enough. Not as they were, with overcoats covering smart attire, the gentleman wearing a three piece suit, matching brogues and a trilby hat. After all, travelling by train warranted a certain appearance, as much as the need for warmth. With care, the GI made his way towards them. It was a Wednesday, 5p.m. and London was busy with commuters rushing to get home. Buses, trams and black cabs plied their trade, life seemingly a humming panic, where no one quite ran but body language betrayed a desire to do so. The soldier's path remained straight as others weaved past him and the station porter motioned another taxi towards the queue.

"Go ahead son," the elderly man in the Trilby said to Dalton as he reached the back of the orderly British queue. And as each person noticed the wounded soldier so they moved aside for him and the porter urged him forward, an inbuilt respect for 'the boys' ringing strong around the nation.

"Thanks," Dalton said as the porter helped him into the cab.

"No, thank you mate," the porter replied.

"So where to Guv'nor?" enquired the cabbie.

"Thorngate Road, Paddington, to see my wife and baby," Dalton said with a beaming smile.

The journey from St. Leonards Hospital had become an expedition, a challenge to see whether a man on crutches could make it so far. Following his clandestine escape from hospital, Dalton took a bus into Ringwood, a train to Brockenhurst and thence to Waterloo and finally the black cab across London. But slipping out of hospital had been the most difficult. Through late August to early October, Dalton had gradually gained strength in his legs, to at first simply stand for a few seconds and then to stand for longer until taking his first tentative steps using crutches, as if learning to walk again. His first venture outside had been wonderful. For having feared that he might never again enjoy such a freedom, it was like a life sentence remitted. Then on the 11th October, with strict instructions not to wander too far, Dalton stretched the 'not too far', to just as far as London. The seed of the idea had been planted during a telephone conversation with Hetty. 'I'd love to see you and Junior,' he told her. 'Come on,' she'd encouraged, 'I dare you.' And how could he resist such a challenge, he was desperate to see her and his son. Soon he would be shipped back to the States, to a military hospital in Martinsburg, West Virginia. They had to make plans, ensure their parting would be brief and persuade Hetty to bring Dalton Junior to Virginia, to settle, to farm and to live a country life. Dalton was AWOL, it might go on his record, likely pay deducted, perhaps demoted but what did he care, he must see Hetty and hold Junior before he left.

So the black cab carrying the wounded soldier crossed Waterloo Bridge onto the Strand and suddenly Dalton was back where it had all begun; the chance meeting with Maud in Leicester Square and the arrival of Hetty to partner Paul Kennedy. He thought now of how he had discarded Maud and stolen Hetty from Paul without conscience. Youthful arrogance, instinct, destiny, call it what you will, but walking into the Black and White Milk Bar with no more than the urge for a cold drink had been a life changing decision; and as Dalton looked out at the London streets, he had no idea how far from his old path this new one would take him.

Hetty had no idea that Dalton was in London. The impulsiveness and anticipation of her surprise heightened Dalton's excitement and he held the cab door release long before the Shirland Road came into view.

Little had changed in his nine month absence. Though the blackout precautions had been relaxed, the air raid shelters and bomb damaged buildings remained and fear still hung over the people in the streets, not of the Luftwaffe but of a different malice, the V1s and the V2s. After the optimism which followed the Normandy invasion in June, morale in the south-east of England was now very low and over a million people evacuated the city by the end of September. Despite the artistry of war displayed by the arrival of newly wounded at St. Leonards, the leafy environment of the hospital at least portrayed a calm to Dalton that clearly was absent in London.

A month before Dalton arrived in London, Hitler had ordered the first V2 ballistic missile to be fired at the capital. Another so-called revenge weapon, almost twice as long as the V1, weighed fifteen tons and carried 1,600lbs of high explosives. With northern France now liberated, the V2s were being fired from easily transportable platforms on the far side of the Rhine. After some 30 hits in September, over 130 V2s struck in October. The rocket would peak at 50 miles above the earth, then approach at 3,500mph with the sound of an express train and send shock waves rippling across the city. People even ten miles away assumed they were in for a direct hit. Unlike the V1s which could be brought down by anti-aircraft guns and fighter planes, there was no defence against the V2. Approaching so fast, the V2 gave brief warning of its arrival and it was impossible therefore to take shelter. With its high explosives, one missile could demolish a whole street of houses. The V1 and V2 collectively killed almost ten thousand people and damaged over a million homes. What unstoppable power might Hitler have wrought had the Russians not sapped his strength? Dalton had no experience of the German inventions but was soon to understand what living in the British capital now meant.

Dalton's taxi passed along Shirland Road, turned into Marylands, followed by an immediate right onto the block paved road of Thorngate. "Number forty-three is just around the bend on the right," Dalton instructed the cabbie, whereupon he slowed to a halt by the air raid wardens' shelter.

Then under the watchful eyes that lay behind curtains that moved oh so slightly from the breath of the onlooker, Dalton was helped out of the cab and left to negotiate the concrete steps. He knocked with a knock so similar to his first, to be opened this time not by Hetty in her bare feet and dishevelled hair, but by his mother-in-law.

"Hello son," she said warmly.

"Hetty," she called, "you've got a visitor." And with that, Dalton was ushered down the hallway.

"Don't disturb Dalny ..." Ethel whispered as they passed along the dark hallway, "I've just got him asleep."

Dalton wondered who 'Dalny' was and might have asked had Hetty not stepped out from the parlour and squealed with surprise.

Later in the evening, with his back to the fire place, the firemen and the mantelpiece clock, Dalton sat on a dining room chair in the front room. Above the clock, the mirror with its wood surround supported family knickknacks on its small wooden shelves and reflected the different worlds of the two people sitting below. Back home at Church View there was no electricity but here in the light of the tungsten lamp, and well into the October evening, Ethel changed Dalton's dressings. His wounds were sore and weeping from the long journey and the gaping hole in his right thigh had drenched the cotton. Away from her husband's eyes Hetty fed Dalny and reluctantly left her mother to care for Dalton, at Ethel's insistence.

Ethel's conversation with Dalton, planned over weeks ran this way and that, like her fingers on the piano keys, moving where she commanded and the occasion dictated. Of what type of work Dalton might gain in London, to lighter topics as of family and the weather, then back to where he and Hetty might live, perhaps in one of the rooms upstairs, if James Eaglestone was in agreement. Edith with Georgina still lived there and Tom would join them when he was released from prisoner of war camp. Young Jimmy would return to his cricketing career, she stated confidently and he too would live at forty-three.

"So why not you and Hetty," Ethel said, more as a statement than a question.

"Be luvly, us all bein together," she said searchingly.

Dalton simply stared at the piano trying to avoid Ethel's gaze. The Old Joanna stood between chimney and bay window, with the lid down, to be used again no doubt at Christmas, when the spirit in the form of gin would be flowing, Mother's ruin so they called it here. Dalton found the English spoken by the English sometimes difficult to understand, not just their pronunciation but they said one thing when they really meant another. The locals thought the Yanks rude with their direct manner, but wasn't it rude to say one thing when you really meant something completely different, he asked himself. Dalton thought he understood the real meaning of the conversation, but then he thought apples and pears were fruit. Ethel's lines continued to run with smooth rhetoric, no script, playing by ear the young mind she called son. But Dalton had grown up of late and bred in a different place with an ear for a different tune and he didn't comment. He and Hetty alone would discuss their future, even if later Hetty would have to discuss it with her parents. Yet Dalton still wore his heart on his sleeve, his face betrayed his thoughts and Ethel read them well.

The next day, Thursday, 12th October, Dalton and Hetty walked again in Regents Park. Not now just the two of them but with Dalton Junior or rather Dalny as everyone else seemed to call him, in a black Bassinet pram, which had been Georgina's. It wasn't easy to push the large contraption with its big wheels and shiny bodywork whilst using crutches. But Dalton managed, much to the amusement and admiration of Hetty who explained that she had seen, "A nice modern, wine coloured pram in Hamleys - smaller, easier to use and you can remove the carriage and use it as a carry cot ..." but Dalton wasn't listening. He had stopped and was several feet behind her, grinning, motioning her to come back to where he stood. As she came up close, Dalton pulled her to him and at the same spot where they kissed passionately for the first time, Dalton insisted they kiss again. Then with Hetty pushing the pram, Dalton followed blissfully behind. As he walked in the bright October light with colours of autumn resplendent in the park, he thought of all those B Company boys who would never sense such emotions and considered himself the luckiest man in the world.

Resting on a park bench by the pond where the ducks paddled so hard to make only slow progress, Dalton and

Hetty agreed their course. Hetty would enter the opposing current when the time was right and tell her parents that she was going to live in Virginia.

Chapter 48

Right at Home

February 1945.

The deck of the American Red Cross ship rolled gently in the unusually calm North Atlantic, whilst the deep blue sky disguised a cold February afternoon. So different was the return voyage; none of the departure excitement of travelling so far, of seeing a new and distant part of the world or the bravado of teaching the enemy a lesson. Burdened with their memories, of youth and friendships torn apart, the wounded men contemplated their uncertain futures as the convoy made its way slowly home. There were times when Dalton managed to reach the deck, to stand and gaze at the light and shade of the ocean's surface. The stillness of the water and its lazy separation to either side of the ship acted as though to suspend him in a strange detached state; a duality of not being part of the war and yet not home to face the consequences of having participated in it.

Dalton's departure had been postponed and postponed again such that he had spent a little more precious time with Hetty and his son. But the three days AWOL proved the most enjoyable as well as the most costly, for he received a hefty $40 fine, equivalent to about one month's pay and a 30 day confinement order. With each pulse of the propeller surely increasing the distance between him and Hetty, so his thoughts turned from her to the friends he had lost and of the chances and fate of his time in Normandy. With Paul Kennedy beside him, formed from the memory of when they had stood together at the rail of the Queen Mary, Dalton grabbed what fresh air he could before heading back down to his bunk.

To the uninformed army boys travelling so slowly homeward, the possibility of being sunk by a German U

Boat loomed large in their imagination. But in reality the threat was minimal; with just a handful of subs still operational, repair yards being bombed daily and supply lines in tethers, Admiral Donitz's fleet was a mere shadow of its glorious past. With the days slipping by and Europe becoming a distant land so the men relaxed more and focused on home. The feeling of security intensified as America approached but so too did the feeling of guilt - they had made it back, when so many hadn't.

Once the US coast finally came into view, Dalton watched the landscape form and grow and felt disbelief that the country before him was indeed America, that Hetty was so far away, as if from another lifetime, or a dream from which he had finally woken.

Dalton still needed to use crutches and when he was dropped outside the Slaughter home place it was for a few days only. The army had given him a week's leave before wanting him at Newton D. Baker Military hospital in Martinsburg, West Virginia. The extent of the injury to his left leg and the large area of open wounds meant that further treatment was necessary and he had been warned not to expect quick results. Dalton lingered a while on the road before opening the gate to the yard; delaying the moment when stepping in would confirm the passage of time and events. The air was still after another crisp night, the Dragon Run was frozen and the pine tops bristled with the cold as they looked down upon the soldier's home coming. The rutted road upon which he stood replaced the block paved road of Thorngate, a tapestry of tracks to be changed only when the warmth returned. Some boys ran up from the banks of the Dragon, their laughter could be heard across the tranquil countryside and still the soldier stood.

'Dalton will come home', his momma often said in the company of others and indeed he had come home ... but as he slowly entered the yard, she wasn't there to meet him.

The following Sunday, the third Sunday of February, the caretaker, Barrington Carlton arrived early at Wares to light the wood stove. It was another very cold day and the congregation were likely to have to keep their coats and scarves on even with the stove burning at its maximum. Snow still lay around Wares Baptist Church from the blizzard a few days earlier and the roof held on to some at its edges.

Barrington was always careful with the wood stove for it was the stove that burnt the old church down. Sparks had caught the cypress shingle roof alight and within a few hours the community's center of religious life was gone. Snow lay on the ground then and Barrington didn't want a repeat under his care. That was in 1919, twenty-six years to the very month and Fleda Mae Slaughter had been five months pregnant with Dalton. Incredible how the years pass Barrington thought, for the boy had come home a hero of the war in Europe and today he would be reunited with his church. Virginia had offered up some proud, strong young men and by Barrington's standards, Dalton Roy Slaughter was sure one of the stronger ones.

"What he's been through just don't bare thinking about," he told Lucy his niece that morning as they walked across the graveyard to collect water from the spring. The spring lay down in the woods and provided drinking water for the congregation. With snow still on the ground, Barrington expected the congregation to be small and only half filled his bucket. But later, as more and more people arrived so it became clear that many had made a special effort.

"To have your momma die is bad enough but to be thousands of miles away in combat when it happened must have been real hard for the boy," Barrington remarked, "sure not looking forward to when Dalton sees his momma's grave for the first time."

Lucy felt for Dalton too, but her thoughts ran deeper than her uncle's.

As Assistant Clerk, Edward would normally arrive shortly after Barrington but this day he had a more important responsibility, to look after his brother. Dalton hadn't come home after six months 'to plow that field' as Edward had said on the day Dalton left and Edward reflected on how shallow those words now sounded after three years of American involvement.

Just Edward and Kelly lived in the home place now, so subdued and quiet was the atmosphere and so different to that which Dalton could remember. Edward opened the draw string gate to allow Kelly to drive the Model T Ford out of the yard. With Kelly and Edward in their suits and Dalton in his uniform, the old Ford carried the three men jarringly along the rutted road, over the Dragon Run Bridge and toward Wares.

Parking just off the dirt road by the church, Dalton used his crutches to pass under the gum trees with his daddy and brother and up the slight rise to the front steps. The white painted wood blended with the white tinted woodland behind. Like an artist's chalk strokes on a charcoal grey sketch, the snow defined hollows, branches and fence rails to make them stand out on the winter scene. Pine with snow pads, oak, holly trees and others stepped right up close to the back of the church to cloak it from the northerly winds and to remind those who needed such, of the beauty of God's hand. Woodland from which the lumber had come to rebuild the church after the fire; for there had been church members in the logging business and they had given the wood free of charge. Thus together with other help and financial contributions from members, the church was rebuilt more on dedication than on money.

In the vestibule Dalton was welcomed by the new Preacher, James Weaver, as well as family and old friends who in warmer times would have gathered outside. Dalton was cornered by Sonny, Tommy and Bobby who thought their uncle was 'just foolin around' when he limped in. And when they were told that Uncle Dalton 'wasn't foolin', they wanted to know when he would be better so they could play in the snow with him.

"Oh my lands, it's so good to have you home," Evelyn exclaimed in her broad southern accent whilst lovingly pushing her boys aside to embrace her brother.

When an arm came around Dalton's shoulders he knew instinctively that it was his brother Amos. Just something about its familiarity and then they too hugged, just as they had always done when one or the other had left or come home after any length of time. "Come on little brother," Amos said to Dalton ushering him into the body of the church. With the last of the arrivals, Dalton made his way toward the pews instinctively searching the faces of the choir to look for Lucy. She was there smiling at him as she always had done and Dalton smiled back, for old habits die hard.

The women folk in their hats, scarves and warmest attire sat to the left of the church in front of the choir, with the men to the right, whilst the many children all disappeared upstairs for Sunday school. Wares still had a strong membership and good that it did for it survived solely on donations, including paying for the preacher's wages.

James Weaver had only been pastor since August 1944 but had gotten to know everyone real well and the members loved him; a moderate preacher unlike those of the past. James in his sermon reminded 'folks' of how they had prayed 'to the good Lord' to keep Dalton safe whilst serving their great country; that Dalton had first come to Wares 'as a baby' ... been 'baptized in the Mattaponi River as a boy' and now 'come back to us as a man and a hero'.

"Is it good to be home son?" the Preacher asked Dalton with a smile and after gaining the expected response, added, "Well it's sure good to have you home."

The hymn Glory Hallelujah roused the congregation and was followed by one which was accompanied by the 'new' piano, donated by the Walden family and it made Dalton feel 'right at home'.

After the service Amos, Evelyn, Edward and Dalton walked out with their father, down the gentle incline to the dirt road and crossed over to the graveyard. Like the church, the two and a half acre plot and its occupants were watched over by snow laden trees, as if bowing to their cause. Dalton didn't have to go far on his crutches to reach his momma, for there was room for just one more grave between her and the road. Space enough for Kelly to protect his wife for eternity from the few vehicles that had cause to pass that way. Dalton dropped his head to read his momma's name and her dates and held back the tears his father mightn't like to see.

Fleda Mae Slaughter
16th October 1885, 27th May 1944.

As much as he had tried to imagine what his momma's grave looked like, seeing it confirmed the reality. The family plot secured by Edward had spaces to the right and at the head of Fleda for several other family members and Dalton considered that if God called them in turn, surely Daddy would be the next to join her.

At the graveside Dalton learned that his momma had died in the front room of the home place. Dorothy Lee, Bertha's daughter was with her grandma when suddenly Fleda clutched her chest and fell to the floor with a 'rattling sound'. The fourteen year old ran screaming out of the house to get help. However with no telephone in Church View, Edward had to drive into Urbanna to get Doctor Vanham, whilst Kelly held Fleda in his arms ... but there was nothing anyone could do.

Whether Edward got his neck washed after throwing fertilizer that day Dalton didn't find out, for it had been to wash Edward's neck that Fleda had gone into the front room to prepare. And in the nine months that had passed since her death, most of the things which Fleda once did just hadn't got done.

Finally, as the cold started to penetrate even Dalton's consciousness, the Ashleys, Carltons, Reveres and others dispersed from the cemetery and James Weaver walked back inside his church. Standing almost alone now, a loving arm came around Dalton's waist to stop him from reading and re-reading his mother's name, urging him home for some wholesome Virginian food.

Dalton (right) with Robbie reunited after the war, sitting outside the Slaughter home place.

Chapter 49

Decisions

February to March 1945.

As a child, Hetty had often sat on her father's knee whilst he recounted stories; of family, of history and those which children just loved to hear. As she became older he talked of current affairs and thus it was James Eaglestone who had educated his daughter beyond the work of school; to politics, royalty and of being proud to be British. James Eaglestone had all the qualities Hetty had once hoped for in a husband and it was her father who above all others had made her feel very special. Yet as Hetty reflected on her life now at home, it was her father who could not accept the man she had married and so the decision to live in America seemed impossible to carry out. Dalton's few visits from St. Leonards had been tense affairs, where Hetty dreaded the atmosphere and was always both sad and a little relieved when he left.

Her dad had never liked the Yanks, not since the Great War and 'least of all an uneducated one' with no skills save for those which James would rather not consider. It hurt Hetty when her father talked like this but she understood the era from which he had grown. She knew that Dalton's loving ways and his hugging and kissing of her in front of people, did not sit comfortably with him.

On the occasion when James told Dalton to leave the house for his 'over familiarity' with Hetty, Hetty had said, 'If he goes then I go!' And that probably hurt her dad more than anything and she felt terribly guilty afterwards for bringing so many problems onto the family. Dalton promised that he would try and change his ways but he found it impossible to do so and Hetty smiled at his impulsiveness, in spite of herself.

Even the night times were terribly tense because she knew that her mother would be listening on the landing. Ethel continually warned her about getting pregnant again; to make sure she followed the doctor's advice and not have another child for five years. But then her mother hadn't heard of French letters, or she chose not to mention the 'dirty word' as her mum would have referred to it and Hetty definitely wasn't going to be the one to educate her. Not when her mother considered holding hands in public unacceptable and never uncovered herself in front of her husband.

Whilst Hetty could respect her father's attitude towards Dalton, essentially for his resolute adherence to it, she was less comfortable with her mother's because Ethel's attitude depended on who was present. She soon stopped calling Dalton 'son' and making him apple pie when Young Jimmy came home on leave from the RAF. Dalton's American accent, direct manner, openness and even his humour were difficult to understand and accommodate by the London family to whom he had become 'loosely attached'. For here 'family' meant common blood running through the veins, and where marriage was a poor, if not completely inadequate substitute.

'Some of the things he writes in his letters are just not normal,' her brother said to her and Hetty had felt so humiliated that she rushed out of the parlour in shame. She had told Dalton that his letters were sometimes read by the others and asked him to be careful what he wrote but he carried on regardless and Hetty wondered if he really cared about her feelings. Hetty knew that tact was not Dalton's strong point. When her brother had told everyone over dinner how 'the Yanks are sitting pretty thousands of miles from the war' with no civilian casualties and that Dalton's 'family wouldn't understand the suffering of London families', Dalton had replied, 'No sir, but they damn well understand they are losing their boys over here for you guys.'

Her dad had dropped his knife and fork and shouted at Dalton for swearing in her mum's presence and Young

Jimmy might have hit Dalton had it not been for her mum shouting at everyone to 'bloody well shut up!'

All this ran through her head as she lay night after night worrying about her decision to go to America. In the early days of February, possibly even as Dalton was being tenderly guided away from his mother's grave, Hetty decided that she could not go through with it. Dalton would have to come back to England and live in London with her.

After his week's stay at home, Dalton was admitted into Newton D. Baker General Hospital, in Martinsburg, West Virginia. It was a big hospital employing almost one thousand four hundred civilians and had treated thousands of soldiers by 1945. It was named after Newton Baker, the lawyer who became US Secretary of War under President Wilson during World War One. Born in Martinsburg, Baker presided over the mobilisation of four million men for the Great War, stating that he was so much a pacifist that he 'would fight for peace'. Valued not just by one president but by Presidents Coolidge and Hoover also, Baker became Martinsburg's famous man and the city, some might say inappropriately, named their general hospital after him.

Dalton remained at Martinsburg whilst surgeons encouraged his wounds to heal, so large and open were they with damaged blood vessels that new techniques were only just being developed to deal with them. Untried methods of which some failed and some came close to success, as in one attempt where one leg was laid across the other in the hope that skin would graft itself to the wound; after many weeks of lying still in bed, the process failed.

"How long before he's back?" Ethel kept asking Hetty as March slipped by.

"Makes you look like you've bin ditched," she chided. But always quick to add, "You're best off here luv, girl needs her mum when she has a littl'un to look after …

there's pleny of jobs waitin' for him when he does come," she assured Hetty. At which James Eaglestone would raise one eyebrow and noticing the gesture Ethel would round on him saying, "Well he can drive carn he?"

"No farms in London Mum," Jimmy often said with a grin, for the meal time conversation was repetitive.

Ethel always ignored such comments, even from her favoured child, for she was on a mission to keep her family intact. Everyone would understand, she thought, the end would justify the means once Dalton had settled in London.

The focus would always turn to Young Jimmy whatever the interim, even of his war experiences, yet James Eaglestone's First World War medals lay discarded, lost even deeper in a drawer. As Ethel served dessert she would pry into Jimmy's social life; the girl friend, was it 'serious?' with an emphasis on serious that only Ethel could express. Eventually and predictably, she would turn to Jimmy's plans for getting back into cricket 'now the war is nearly over'. The subject of cricket would pop up around the time dessert was finished and the flow of food, like the conversation, had seen little interruption by the war.

Long before the conversation turned to cricket and the food towards dessert, James Eaglestone would check his pocket watch and look forward to his air raid patrol. Not long now before the war would end he considered, perhaps just weeks away and another excuse would have to be found to leave the house in the evening. Perhaps he should consider working nights as a stoker and slowly evolving through his meal times, the hot dirty work became quite an attractive proposition.

Dalton's letter from Martinsburg was placed directly into Hetty's hand as she happened to be stood on the steps when the postman arrived. She could hardly breathe with anxiety, he hadn't written for so long. Looking only briefly at the strange stamps, she tore open the envelope; was he ok, what treatment had he been given, would his legs be alright, did he still love her and want her to come over or had an old flame gone to see him in hospital? Suddenly, she was immersed in worry as she nervously manipulated the product of Virginian pulp wood. He always started his letter with 'My Darling Hetty' and closed with 'All my love, all my life'. But this letter would be different she told herself, things had changed. War had swept them from their senses, he was home now, back with his family, he didn't need her anymore. She should never have left Paul Brooks, she had broken his heart, her selfishness had killed him. 'Wicked' she had heard her dad say one night when she had crept out of bed to pass by her parent's door. 'Wicked what she did to that boy', and surely it was her and Paul to which her dad referred.

Perhaps it was the way Dalton had written Hetty E. Slaughter on the envelope in what seemed like an uncaring scrawl or in his delay in writing to her. Perhaps it was just her insecurity. Unfolding the thin page, the letter started with 'My Darling Hetty' and after telling her about his many treatments, he asked her to come over as soon as possible, he wanted and needed her. Finally, squeezed into the last remaining space on the corner of the sheet was written, 'All my love all my life'. Hetty walked into the parlour that morning and said, "I've decided to go to America to live with Dalton."

"Gaud luv us," her sister said and all were silent as the Eaglestones absorbed the news.

Hetty followed the same route as Dalton had done on his arrival to England. To Salisbury Plain at Ludgershall, then the branch line via Perham Down and Windmill Hill to pass the large goods yard and finally arrive at Tidworth Station. The women were herded onto the wide troop platform and then to the vehicles, buses and some trucks waiting to take them into Tidworth Camp. Carrying Dalny in his wine coloured carry cot, Hetty made a bee line for a bus, reluctantly having to push her way on to ensure she didn't have to climb onto one of the US Military trucks. She watched women as they did so and they looked so undignified; but many found it funny and the wise cracks of the soldiers and their smiles indicated that at least some were enjoying the experience. The GI Brides were to be housed in Jellalabad Barracks and as they made their way down Station Road, bemused locals watched as this very different cargo was transported through their town. After the GIs in late '42, Jellalabad had housed Italian POWs and now the GI Brides were arriving in their hordes, for 'shipment to the States' as described by some, for they all received free passage courtesy of Uncle Sam. So many GI brides were there in fact that Perham Down Camp was later used for the overflow.

Only Delhi Barracks separated Jellalabad from Candahar where B Company had been barracked and the layout was identical. Hetty climbed the same external stairs as the 29th had done and walked the same verandas with their wrought iron railings to gain access to the same first floor dormitories. Noisy, large rooms with women smoking, chatting, laughing and some crying, with children playing, screaming and babies crying over the sound of their mothers. Never before had the Dodsdown red brick buildings been witness to such guests.

Whilst some women lounged around reading Woman's Own and Woman's Weekly supplied from Smith's on Station Road, those with younger ones were kept busy with more pressing issues. Some of the brides seemed to have very little luggage, whilst Hetty had two large trunks. The wooden trunks, each with three leather bands around, contained all her worldly goods. One with keep sakes and personal belongings that had great sentimental value: the bride and groom from their wedding cake, the cradle from the Christening cake which Dalton had never seen, her wedding dress, childhood trinkets and tokens of farewell and good luck. The final item to be laid in was 'a pretty green suit and matching hat'. Hetty had bought it second hand from an Australian girl and was convinced Dalton would love her in it.

However as Hetty's first day at Tidworth reached evening, her worries intensified. Nights were always more difficult for her; just as the day's light faded from the surroundings, so Hetty's anxieties caused her spirit to fade. The day hadn't exactly been a good one; herded like animals, the so called 'medical' which was no more than an intrusion and then the questionnaire. Prison record indeed! Name and address of the man she had married. Did they think she didn't know and after all, had she not gone through all this at the American Embassy?

The dormitory seemed even noisier as the dark closed in and Hetty struggled to sleep. She laid thinking about all the unanswered questions, questions the Eaglestones had posed her and all the answers she had failed to give. America seemed so distant, many days sea journey away and beyond the financial reach of working class families. Travel abroad was rare, except to go to war and from the Eaglestones' perspective, the working classes just didn't travel unless they were leaving forever, because they never came back.

'How you goin' to take care of yer baby, bobbin about in the sea for weeks? You get sick travelin' down to Yalding,' Ethel had reminded her.

'What about gettin' from the docks to 'is home ... how you goin' to manage with Dalny in 'is cot and all your luggage' and 'how you goin' to feed and change baby if you're on a bus for hours on end? What about yer family, don't you love em? Suppose his family don't accept you cos you're English?' And so the questions went on and on.

'You just don't know what 'is home's really like,' Ethel told her 'wouldn't it be better if you left it till he came out of hospital ... well wouldn't it ... wouldn't it be better not to go?'

Hetty turned again and again in the small bed, questions flying around in her head, making her come out in a hot sweat, indecisiveness frantically going round and round till she almost became mesmerised by her growing dilemma. Questions always spoken by her mother's voice and they buried deeper and deeper until her brain felt as if it was stuffed with cotton wool, as when she was a child and had the flu. By morning as light slipped across Salisbury Plain and with hardly a wink of sleep, Hetty's hands were shaking. She had heard that the GI Brides would likely be travelling in a cargo ship converted to a hospital ship with facilities for GI brides and that the journey might take fifteen days. There were still U Boats in the Atlantic and although the brides would be sailing as a Red Cross ship, which under the Geneva Convention should not be attacked, why take such unnecessary risks with Dalny, she asked herself. Perhaps her mother was right, it might be better to wait and go later. Whilst trying to focus on feeding and changing Dalny, Hetty's mind kept wandering to Church View. Would it be difficult living there as her mother warned, with no mother figure to help her? Church View had sounded very rural, very different to London. Dalton had once commented on how much easier it was for her mother to do the household chores with running water actually supplied from a tap in the house. The Slaughters had to raise all the water they needed from the well and then carry it into the house. The thought of keeping herself and her baby clean and fed in a house with no running water made her feel uneasy. From what Dalton had said, his family used oil lamps when it got too dark. As long as Hetty could remember, her homes had always been lit by gas lanterns. Admittedly they would not use the gas supply to the bedrooms because of cost, but it was always piped to a bracket in the parlour, the sitting room and at least one on the stairs. They had used candles and paraffin lamps at night in the bedrooms but to have to use them everywhere around the house seemed archaic; particularly now when at the flick of a switch they had electrical light in every room. As the day of her departure came closer, Hetty's worries gripped her more and more, like a vice, stifling everything except life's basic functions. Could she really leave her mother? Her whole family had almost begged her not to go and Hetty doubted now that she really had meant to. She had made a mistake. Hetty could not imagine never seeing her family again. Perhaps her mother was right, maybe she should not go, not yet.

Drawn and tired, Hetty picked Dalny up and walked into the office adjoining the dormitory.

"Can I use the phone?" she asked.

With James Eaglestone on his way down to Tidworth to collect his daughter, Hetty was called to have her interview, a mistake or procedure, she wasn't sure which. With so many women to get through there was little time to consider privacy, courtesy or tact and the interview was more like a lecture.

"Your husband very likely doesn't live in Hollywood," the young lieutenant told Hetty, nor "even in New York City," as so many of the GIs had bragged to their girls he explained.

"Well unlike some, I know exactly where my husband lives," Hetty responded, forgetting temporarily that it didn't matter, she wasn't going.

"Where's that Ma'am?" The officer questioned, interested to see if she really knew.

"Church View, Middlesex County, Virginia," Hetty said confidently.

The lieutenant smiled, "I see."

"Women have arrived in the US to be dumped on some country road in the middle of nowhere, when they were expecting to be living in a smart house in the suburbs," the lieutenant continued.

"I know exactly what Church View is li ..." the officer raised his hand so he could continue.

"Some women have even discovered that their man is already married, war does strange things to soldiers," the officer warned, with a knowing grin.

"I know exactly where I am going ... was going, I changed my mind," Hetty said indignantly, "but do you think I would have married Dalton if he was already married? My family checked that all out at the American Embassy, I assumed everyone did."

The officer was surprised for this was not the normal run of conversation.

"Perhaps you should speak like this to the women who haven't even brought cots for their babies and are using the drawers you've provided. They're the ones who aren't prepared. Why they couldn't have got a hand me down or one from the pawn brokers I shall never know. Just waiting for a hand out; isn't it enough to be given free passage without expecting everything else as well?"

The young officer was starting to think that perhaps this was one GI Bride the US would welcome.

"Well I'm sure you've made the right decision not to go Ma'am," the Officer said and handed her times and arrangements for those who wanted to return to London. The majority of brides seemed to come from the capital and not from very savoury areas at that, so Hetty thought from the accents and attire.

"I won't be needing this," Hetty said to the young lieutenant, giving him back the piece of paper. "I've decided I AM going after all! My son needs his father."

Chapter 50

Just another Wooden House

March 1945.

After spending three nights at Tidworth worrying as to whether she had made the right decision, the buses arrived to take Hetty and the other GI Brides to Southampton docks. As Hetty walked up the gang plank to board the ship, which was also carrying wounded US Servicemen, she thought of the women who had so decisively made up their minds not to go; now at home with their parents, comfortable and secure. Descending one staircase after another, along narrow gangways and round tight corners, Hetty knew that in an emergency, she would never find her way out. The carry cot felt extra heavy after so little sleep, the air more stifling as she descended and the dim lighting cheerless. After the second flight of stairs, she lost sight of the last natural light and just knew that she would be sea sick, for even in the harbour, she could feel the small vessel shift slightly on its moorings.

Directed into a small cabin containing three sets of double bunk beds, Hetty would be spending the next fourteen days with five other women in this sickly yellow painted, unventilated room, where air moved only if a person did. Toileting and washing were difficult in the small space but having done so and eaten what little her appetite demanded, she lay on her bunk with Dalny asleep and considered that at least now, there was no turning back.

With early evening approaching, the vessel passed down The Solent into the English Channel and Hetty sensed a steady increase in the swell. She had never travelled by ship before and had no experience of sea sickness, but the feeling in her stomach told her this was the onset. By the time the convoy had assembled and was heading for the Atlantic, someone had to fetch a bucket for her. Already over-tired, beads of sweat lined her young forehead and vomit seemed to come with every roll of the tiny cabin. With eyes closed, she remained prostrate but there was no respite and no promise of one. The first few hours dragged by and then after heaving and retching until she thought that her insides would be lost, she knew that she could no longer look after her baby. Hetty had never travelled further from home than Ivy Bridge and what should have been the journey of a lifetime quickly became a dreadful ordeal. The other girls in the cabin, who were less affected by the continual swaying, tried to help Hetty, but after twenty-four hours she was extremely weak.

When the doctor was finally called, three aspects of the man were to stay with Hetty; his greying hair, his kind face and his choice of words, words he clearly felt appropriate for his twenty-two year old patient. "Which baby shall we tend to first then?" he asked.

The doctor insisted that Dalny be taken from Hetty to be looked after by the nurses and prescribed her drugs that would make her sleep. The drugs did their job and Hetty slept through much of the next two days. Although no longer vomiting, Hetty became weaker, for no food and very little water had passed her lips in seventy-two hours.

By the third night the convoy had sailed beyond the continental shelf where the depth of the ocean increased to 12,000 feet. Over two miles of cold, North Atlantic water now lay between them and the sea bed, water that was as dark as the night surrounding the ship. By two o'clock in the morning most of the wounded and GI Brides had settled, nurses caught up on some rest and Hetty succumbed to a further dose of the doctor's medication.

The sailors on night watch peered at their echo sounders wishing that they too might have some rest, until one picked up a blip; it was a sub, a German sub was stalking the convoy.

The wailing siren was loud enough to wake the dead, yet Hetty barely stirred. When the crew started telling the women to put on their life vests, Hetty's eyes opened momentarily and closed again, leaving her helpless, a bedraggled bundle within her bed. The sound of explosions sent a second, stronger shiver of fear through the girls. And as the explosions became more rapid and closer, they filtered into Hetty's dreams and seemed to be that of German bombs falling on the city. Rising anxiety forced her into semi- consciousness and gradually she was able to decipher the grey shadows in the dim light - hunched, frightened women sitting on the side of their bunks, clutching each other, silent, listening to events beyond their understanding and obediently wearing their life vests.

The sound of more explosions, closer now, thudding through the thin hull, shaking the flimsy bunks. The turmoil forced Hetty's mind to clear. She felt the ship stall, saw the lights flicker and go out to be replaced with nothing but blackness, blackness so deep she could not see the bunk above her. Women screamed, the crew shouted for calm and 'thank God' the reassuring dull light returned and the ship's rhythm continued as before. Hetty fumbled with her night clothes, "Sit up, sit up," she told herself. "Find your life vest, find Dalny!" More explosions. "Depth charges," Hetty said to herself. "Oh God, I must find Dalny. Where's my baby?" Hetty called out, trying to stand but fell backward, dizzy, weak and disorientated. Again she stood, groped around for a life vest and with the help of one of the other girls managed to put it on. Her legs shook from the exertion and by the time she reached the cabin door, she felt exhausted. With her body wet with perspiration and her night clothes bedraggled, Hetty lay limply back onto her bed, a pile of naivety, her head thumping and ears ringing with the intrusive noise. And as the minutes passed so acceptance finally expelled the panic. Wherever Dalny was, she was not going to reach him. If the ship was sunk by a torpedo as every woman feared at that moment, Dalny would not be saved by his mother.

The night grew long and as dawn started to establish itself across the ocean, the explosions ceased. The pulse of the engines and swaying of the ship were again apparent to the delicate cargo and everyone gradually relaxed. Even Hetty found some comfort in the monotonous movement as the ship continued its slow passage across the wide, deep ocean.

At St. John's, Newfoundland the women were allowed off the boat for a few hours and as Hetty stepped onto stable, unmoving land, the ground came up to hit her in the face. Determined to stay ashore, Hetty picked herself up and walked to some shops where she browsed along the windows. Of all the things she saw, her eye caught one in particular, Cadbury's chocolate. She had to buy it, to taste a bit of home. Peeling off the familiar wrapping, she snapped off a piece, but was disappointed, for it just didn't taste the same.

The break was short lived; the ship was on the move within hours and Hetty was bound for New York. When the Red Cross ship finally docked, Hetty had been fourteen days at sea.

The search for her luggage became a scramble as service personnel were shouting instructions to the women. Women were rushing off this way and that, luggage to be checked, papers scrutinized and buses to catch. Hetty found one of her trunks but not the one with all the expensive items in it, her keepsakes and the pretty green suit.

"I can't find my other trunk," Hetty said anxiously to one of the few remaining sailors, "it had my job references in and other papers," she added, omitting to mention all the lovely things. But no one seemed interested. With most luggage claimed the hall became quieter, women and sailors dispersed and in the empty, calm that followed, Hetty knew that all that she had so lovingly stowed away was gone forever.

'You're a lucky girl to have so much', the officer checking luggage at Tidworth had said to Hetty when he had sifted through several layers of her special trunk and it was only now that his words returned to her.

With her one remaining trunk loaded and the carry cot across her lap, Hetty was carried by bus from New York Docks to the Greyhound Bus station. There she managed to locate the Washington bound bus. A group of travelers were bunched around the front of it, mainly men and just a few women travelling with male partners. The men all seemed to be wearing wide brimmed hats, the sort Hetty had only previously seen on American movies - worn, she had assumed, only by gangsters and police detectives. They can't all be gangsters she thought. Struggling on board with Dalny she was told by the driver, "Sorry Ma'am, you can't take up two seats if you've only paid for one, the cot will have to go with the luggage." And as Hetty stood half way on and half way off the bus looking down into the cot he added, "You'll have to hold the little one on your lap."

"How long will it take to get to Fredericksburg?" Hetty asked, looking at the driver sitting on the wrong side of the vehicle.

"You won't go all the way to Fredericksburg on this bus, Ma'am," the driver said grinning and finally chuckling, joined by the passengers waiting to get on behind her. The English accent and the obvious lack of knowledge touched his male sense of humor. He'd been in the job a long time and was becoming hardened to the plight of ignorant travelers. Why the hell didn't they plan ahead, look at a map, ask someone else?

"First stop Philadelphia, that's about three hours. Now let's see," he said, grinning again, "It's usually another three to Baltimore, then an hour or more to Washington and another three to Fredericksburg. I know Ma'am I've driven them all many times, too many times, retiring this summer, thank the Lord. So to answer your question Ma'am, it's at least ten hours travelling time to Fredericksburg from here."

"Oh a long way then," Hetty responded and wondered just how much longer it would take to get to Church View.

People were passing Hetty and the bus was filling up, but the driver hadn't finished, "Then you have to add on bus changes, fuel stops and meal stops. Might be fifteen or more hours till you get to Fredericksburg," he said. And Hetty felt suddenly very tired and deflated and she could feel tears welling up. The long voyage, the sea sickness and her fretting at Tidworth in the noisy dormitory were all taking their toll. How could she cope so long on a silly bus, holding her baby? She daren't fall asleep. She would have to buy more food, change Dalny somewhere.

As she started to organize Dalny and take him from his soft bed, worried now that there would not even be a seat left for her, a man tapped her on the shoulder.

"Here sit with me, you can put the cot across both our laps," he said, and the tears of exhaustion nearly changed to sobs of gratitude, but Hetty had already embarrassed herself enough in front of 'the horrible driver'.

At a maximum speed of 35 miles per hour the Silverside bus headed south, crossed a river wider than Hetty had ever seen in her life and passed on into the evening hours. Evening hours that dragged by to bring darkness, a darkness which encircled her, sitting now beside a sleeping man, her spirit dwindling, an air of doom and a questioning of her actions deriding her soul. No blackout here she thought as lights of houses, businesses and advertisements slipped past the high bus window. Then leaving the conurbations behind, the bus entered real America.

Stopping at café's and hotels for the bathroom and meals, changing buses at the big cities, Hetty arrived in Washington in the morning hours of a gray, March day. The Post House Café in the Greyhound terminal was a welcome sight and after finding food for her and Dalny, made sure she sat in the correct waiting room for the bus to Fredericksburg, that wouldn't be leaving for two hours.

The older bus took three hours to reach Fredericksburg and there Hetty changed again for Newport News. Heading out along Route 17, the bus passed Fort A.P. Hill where Dalton had once trained and then on into the countryside. She had been in America for almost a day and still she was travelling, now in the depths of Virginia, along a quiet country road with hardly a property in sight. Around a curve beside a cultivated field, a man stood by an old truck parked up on the verge and on seeing the bus started to wave it down. He looked very at home, chewing, grinning as if he knew the driver and wore clothes befitting a farmer. The driver brought his vehicle slowly up alongside the man before opening the door to allow him to step onto the platform. "Do you have an English girl on board with a baby?" the man asked.

The voice and accent was so much like Dalton's that she knew it must be one of his brothers.

Edward Slaughter had come out to meet her and Hetty was so thankful of the gesture after two weeks of travelling. But as the bus left her standing with Edward and his farm truck on the otherwise deserted country road, the interviewing officer's words at Tidworth came back to her.

Despite all that Dalton had described, Hetty was taken aback by the extent to which the land was covered by trees. Her hop picking holidays in Kent made her no stranger to the countryside but this was different. There seemed to be woodland after woodland interspersed only by the very occasional farmhouse, with its barns and surrounding fields. She travelled with Edward for what seemed a long time before they came across anything resembling a village. Her journeys through Kent had been made interesting with the changing scenery, hills and farms, villages and towns. Passing through them on the hop picking truck she could look at the residents, the shops and peer through living room windows that in some cases you could almost touch, they were so close to the road. But here with still more pine trees slipping past, everything seemed to repeat itself: trees and more trees, a homestead, fields then more trees and then some more. It was so flat and the houses so far off the road that you couldn't even tell if anyone lived there, let alone see the color of their curtains.

"Do you live in an area like this?" she asked Edward.

"Pretty much," he replied with a smile. "You?" he asked.

"No not like this," Hetty said politely.

"How close are your neighbours?" Hetty enquired.

"Pretty close," Edward judged. But Hetty didn't believe they were 'pretty close' at all. Perhaps Edward caught her look of doubt, "The Greenwoods are right next door, then the Stovers and then the Thrifts and the Marshalls are right across the road," he added. Hetty just nodded.

Don't suppose you can nip next door to borrow some sugar and have a quick chat she thought to herself.

After some heavy rain in early March the dirt roads had been churned up and then had hardened as they dried to give an uncomfortable ride. It wasn't easy to talk above the engine noise and the vibration but what little conversation they had, served only to make Hetty more apprehensive.

"I hope your mummy is doing the right thing," she said under her breath as she moved Dalny to a more comfortable position on her shoulder, his dribble wetting her clothing for the innumerable time.

"Pretty close now," Edward said as he turned right to pass Hermitage Church and the Dragon Run Storehouse.

It was late afternoon when he stopped the truck outside the Slaughter home place and Hetty's journey with her seven month old baby finally came to an end.

Edward left the truck running and got out to pull on the rope which opened the large wooden farm gate. Hetty surveyed the house which she was destined to live in, at least for the foreseeable future. It was built not of brick with a Welsh slate roof but entirely of wood and to her the barns looked even less safe as structures. There were fences, animal pens and shed- like things everywhere and by a smaller isolated barn there stood a still smaller wooden building which resembled a squashed beach hut, but which was undoubtedly the toilet. Why was the toilet so far from the house she wondered? To the side and slightly to the front of the house was a well with a bucket and winch mechanism. There were no paths between the house and the other buildings or the well, just bare earth.

Edward helped Hetty down and led her into the house via the kitchen door. "I'll get all your things in a minute," he said with a sweet smile which reminded her so much of Dalton. Beyond the kitchen was a roughly partitioned dining area with a long wooden table with two benches either side, perhaps capable of seating eight to ten adults. In the kitchen there was a wood burning stove and a bucket containing water. Sitting in the bucket was what looked to Hetty like half a coconut shell with a long handle attached.

The first thing Edward did was to scoop water with it and take a long drink.

"Wanna drink?" he asked, waving the ladle at Hetty.

"Not at the moment thank you," she replied.

Edward dropped the ladle back into the bucket.

"I'll show you where you'll be sleeping and then fetch your things," he said as he led her upstairs to where there were two bedrooms, partitioned from the one large bedroom which once filled the loft space. The room was basic with bare wooden walls, no ceiling, a bed with a mattress and pillows but no sheets or pillow cases. There was nowhere to unpack her things, no wardrobe or chest of drawers, nothing but a few open shelves.

Edward got her things from the truck, hauled water from the well and provided Hetty with a basin so she could have a quick wash and clean up her baby.

"Need anything just holler," he said, "I'll be gettin supper on the table."

Sometime near dusk and too soon for Hetty, she could hear Edward talking to another man in the kitchen; a man with a voice coarsened by passing years and edged with authority, the Virginian accent beyond that even of Edward's. It had to be Mr. Slaughter, Hetty thought, yet hoped it wasn't. Not yet, not until she had got herself together. She still felt so grubby, her hair was all over the place and a bad impression now would be the finish of it, of that she was sure. Dalton had talked about his father less than his momma but Hetty had read between the lines. She combed her hair quickly, ran her hands down the fresh but creased skirt she had rescued from her trunk and tried to portray a smile, a pleased-to-see-you sort of smile, rather than one of trepidation tinged with exhaustion. Hetty descended the old wooden stair case into the darkness of the hallway; it seemed a dreary windowless house as if the outside brought unwanted sights. She held the smile despite the gloom and tried to put a spring back into her step as she walked the few yards into the kitchen, a spring which might portray a journey of little significance, as if from down the road.

Hetty pushed the dividing door open to reveal a tall, proud looking man standing with Edward. Not unlike her own father she thought but older, by twenty years she judged. The expression on his face bore a hint of youthfulness, dare-devilment even, the latter she had so often seen in Dalton. Mr. Slaughter's dark moustache contrasted with his otherwise gray hair, just as his smart attire contrasted with all that she had seen so far of the home place.

Kelly Granville Slaughter turned to look at his new daughter-in-law; his one good eye penetrating and searching. She felt as though he was mapping her frame, quickly reading her thoughts.

"Well I'll be darned!" Kelly exclaimed, "Dalton said you were pretty, might be my prettiest daughter-in-law yet," he said with a grin, holding out his hand. "Come a long ways, by looks of yer," he added still grinning. Hetty maintained the smile and reached out to shake Mr. Slaughter's hand. "DALTON JUNIOR!" Kelly bellowed, before Hetty could speak, as if announcing his grandson's arrival to the neighbors. "Just like Dalton when he was a youngen," he said watching for Hetty's reaction.

"How are you Mr. Slaughter?" Hetty asked politely, "I've heard a lot about you."

"How's my boy, is more the question?" Kelly replied, turning to place his chewing tobacco on the kitchen table. "Ain't heard from him in weeks! Only knew you were comin a few days ago."

Edward was smiling at Hetty, trying to communicate something with his facial expression but she was fixed only on Mr. Slaughter. "Hope it's not inconvenient for you ... me staying here Mr. Slaughter?" Hetty said almost too quietly for Kelly to hear.

Kelly took a drink from the bucket. "Thirsty?" he asked, waving the ladle at her and ignoring the question.

"No, thank you," Hetty replied still holding Dalny, her arms longing to put him down but the floor was too dirty.

"Well I'm hungry and dinner's a waitin," Kelly said pointing to the food and dropping the ladle back into the bucket.

Hetty watched Mr. Slaughter and Edward take what must have been their seats for an eternity at the far end of the long table. Edward smiled reassuringly at her whilst Mr. Slaughter merely watched as she chose a place on the benches, not too close to the men she decided and likely too far away as Mr. Slaughter would judge. She didn't clasp her hands together either when Mr. Slaughter gave 'thanks for the food' and nor did she relish what was on offer. For in the middle of the table sat a bowl of fatty bacon and cabbage. Seeing her reticence, the men tucked in and there would have been complete silence had it not been for the sound of chewing. Was this the atmosphere every meal time, Hetty wondered, or just because she was there and if she could have gone home at that very minute she would have done so.

"Daddy lost his eye when a piece of steel flew in it," Edward explained, noticing Hetty's uneasy fixation with it. To Hetty the glass replacement gave Mr. Slaughter an aura of even greater menace.

"Happened when he was working at a ship building yard on the Rappahannock River," Edward added as if trying to relax the atmosphere.

"Fifteen days is a hell of a journey, must sure love my boy to travel that far," Mr. Slaughter interjected loudly.

Hetty looked back at Mr. Slaughter's grinning and gave a weak smile.

"Never thought he'd end up marrying an English girl," he continued glancing across at Edward, but Edward just looked down at his bacon and cabbage.

"Has a parcel arrived for me?" Hetty asked trying to change the subject.

Mr. Slaughter shrugged his shoulders as though he didn't know.

"Baby food, Cow and Gate baby food," Hetty explained. "I posted it about three weeks before I left England."

"No can't say it has, aint seen nothin," Mr. Slaughter replied. "Is it important?" he asked.

After dinner and having fed Dalny with some of the food she had brought with her from the ship, Hetty prepared for her first night at the Slaughter home place. Taking the lantern given to her by Edward, she pushed her way out of the screen door and trod carefully down the wooden steps into the yard. She had no intention of using the slop pot as Mr. Slaughter had referred to the chamber pot in her bedroom. But it was so dark and so quiet outside that she was beginning to consider it.

No street lights, no traffic noise and no glow from the windows of neighbours' houses; my God it's like the end of the world she thought as she glanced back at the house to see an oil lamp flickering weakly, its light barely capable of demarking her return route. She walked cautiously towards the 'squashed beach hut', it seemed more inviting if she called it that and reached for the rusty handle to pull open the door. Hunting dogs barked in the distance and then went quiet and scuffling in the animal pens competed with the squeaky hinges. Need some oil on those, Hetty thought. Her father always had a small can at the ready for such needs and no way would there be all this unpainted wood she thought. Fancy leaving it unprotected ... her father always said that you can judge a man by what he surrounds himself with.

It was even darker in the confined space of the toilet away from the dimly lit night sky and she held the lamp up to each and every corner with her head barely inside the door frame. Hetty knew that there were poisonous spiders and snakes in Virginia and she didn't ever want to meet up with one, least of all on her own in the dark. Having lived all her life where the sting of a nettle offered the worst fate, Hetty felt sure that the shabby, smelly wooden contraption must act as a magnet for everything undesirable in the surrounding fields and woodland.

In every corner were webs and one or two horrible black legs still in view, belonging to spiders that had scurried away when she'd first opened the door.

The platform of wood with its hole looked ominous in the shadow of the lantern and from its depths came the sound of animals scurrying. Shortly after bravely 'hovering' herself above it, she heard more movement on the floor. It came from near her feet. Something touched her leg, she screamed. Surely a large animal, it was so noisy. She screamed again, grabbed the lantern and scanned the floor, what was it? What thing was sharing the toilet with her? She spotted it, screamed a longer more piercing scream, it was huge, monstrous and about to attack her of that she was sure. But then to Hetty in the pitch dark of a moonless Virginian night, the lizard looked as big as an alligator. The screaming failed to hurry it; it swaggered out under the door, its tail as if waving a nonchalant goodbye to the young city girl. The screaming also failed to alert anyone except for perhaps all the hunting dogs in Middlesex County and the city girl was now determined that this would be the first and last time she would go to the toilet in Church View.

Hetty hurried back to the house and lay down on the mattress without changing into her night clothes. She couldn't sleep despite her tiredness and the silver fish on the bare wood walls of the bedroom kept her company. Playing in the dimming light of the oil lamp that shook in her delicate hand, the insects moved this way and that, making Hetty forever fearful that they or some other 'creepy crawly' might end up on her baby and her night vigil seemed endless. Way into the ordeal, the snoring of the tired men culminated in a crescendo during the drowsiest hours, passing up through the floor boards and penetrating the thin partitioning as ease would have it.

Hetty felt a bad mother, a fool for agreeing to come over and angry at Dalton for encouraging her. Everything about the Slaughter home place was awful; it was dirty, uncomfortable, the slop pot even looked as if it still had slop around it, and that Mr. Slaughter, well, he had no manners. He's snoring away quite happily now despite all he said, Hetty thought and looked at her watch to see that another dreadful hour had finally crawled by. "AND there is no food for my baby and NOBODY CARES," she said into the night. She needed sleep, proper sleep, restful sleep, she was desperate for sleep ... "If only someone could look after Dalny for me ... JUST FOR FIVE MINUTES," she said almost too loudly and nearly woke Dalny. She didn't like the food, didn't like Mr. Slaughter, hated the toilet and in fact lying there feeling lonely and vulnerable, Hetty decided that she hated everything about Virginia, even all those silly trees.

It was well into the night before she finally fell asleep still clutching the envelope her mother had given her - an envelope not so different in thickness to the one Lucy Chapman, her grandmother used to receive.

It was to the sound of the roosters that Hetty woke just a few hours later, hogs snorted also, cows mooed and a guard dog un-relentlessly barked in the distance. The day before, the Virginian dusk had settled upon an English girl but the dawn had awoken an English woman. Her resolve to leave was unflappable, whatever Mr. Slaughter might or might not say, however he might look, grin or smirk. She had her responsibilities and he had his. The house needed a female touch to sort it out and so did the men and Hetty had no intention of being the one to do it. She had come over to be with her husband, not to take on his grumpy father and sort out a dilapidated old farm house. Like the new day, an image of her potential life at Church View had dawned on her. Preparing decent food, getting the house clean and organized, insisting they drink out of separate cups and curtailing some of the other bad habits they had undoubtedly developed in the ten months since the death of Dalton's mother.

Perhaps if Fleda was still around things would be different Hetty thought. But she wasn't and Dalton shouldn't have encouraged her to come over. His image of home was languishing in the past. Fleda was there no more, and when life had flowed from her, the Slaughter home had become just another wooden house. Hetty's few hours sleep had served only to consolidate her resolve to leave and without breakfast she did exactly that.

Edward stopped by the bus station and waited with the truck whilst Hetty found a pay phone. She needed to call the hospital and speak with Dalton. When eventually she had mastered the system and Dalton had finally reached the phone, she was well prepared for what she had to say.

Chapter 51

The Father of Her Child

Hetty looked out as the Virginian countryside again slipped past her - the trees, fields and occasional farmhouse, some of which seemed even less inviting than the Slaughter home and that, Hetty felt, was saying something. To her, the GIs swaggering around London had appeared to be so much better off than the British lads, yet many of their backgrounds were poor and their homes so uninviting.

Physically and mentally exhausted, Hetty could barely hold Dalny when he needed entertaining, her arms like lead, despair driving her deeper into tiredness; so little sleep and so much worry. How much longer could she cope with changing nappies on the move, feeding her baby and snatching what little food she could for herself? Going to the toilet was an expedition of placing bags out of the way, trusting that no one would steal anything and squeezing into a cubicle with Dalny finely balanced on one knee, for she dare not leave him unattended. A train journey this time, a long one so it felt to Hetty; boarding at Fredericksburg for Washington, instead of continuing all the way on the bus. At least there was more room to move around and an aisle down which she could walk to settle her baby to sleep, rocking him, talking gently to him in her quiet English accent.

When finally Dalny became content and she could leave him to lie in his cot so she fell into a fitful drowsiness, her night without rest at Church View having drawn her nearer to breaking point. The sun's rays warmed her through the glass window, glass which temporarily separated her from the crisp, lingering winter air outside. In her semi-sleep she dwelt on home and berated herself for being so stupid; stupid for having set out on such a journey, unprepared and with such naivety.

The train carried her out of Virginia into Washington D.C. and there Hetty came as close to Roosevelt as she had once been to Churchill. Union Station swung into view, its marble and white granite classical architecture presenting vaulted spaces to welcome the visitor. The domed Capitol building overlooked her arrival and presented a picture of civilization against which Middlesex County could not compete. Why did Dalton not live here, she wondered as taxi cabs and cars moved about proper roads and people filled the streets.

The platforms at Union Station were busy with men in different service uniforms, but not of different nations. No bomb damage here, she reflected as the coaches labored to a grinding halt. Hetty needed the Baltimore Ohio line and her nervousness intensified as she tried to get all her things together, worried that she might leave one of her belongings behind, or the train pull off before she had gathered everything. How stupid she felt dropping things but they just seemed to slip out of her hands. She felt clumsy when straps caught on handles and useless when two or three travelers offered their assistance almost in unison. Did she really look so pathetic? An airman helped her down the steps onto the platform, Dalny clutched in her arms. The conductor carried the cot and another older gentleman found the used nappies that she had stored in a bag beneath the seat; nappies which must soon be washed. Then finally standing amidst her belongings with a posture befitting a child abandoned, she waited anxiously for her trunk to appear from the luggage car and didn't notice the airman who hadn't moved far away.

"Need help Ma'am?" he asked, with his train about to leave but something had made him stay.

"I need to get to Martinsburg," Hetty said on the verge of tears and stood as if fixed to the spot, frightened to move in case the direction she took was the wrong one.

"Here, let me," the airman said and helped Hetty to the ticket office.

The attendant might have wondered at the young woman's health as shaking hands pulled out dollar notes from a thing she called a purse but looked more like a wallet. He wrote down the price of the ticket, for she didn't seem to understand English. Poor thing he thought, must be one of those foreign GI brides tracking down a wayward serviceman.

"Good luck Ma'am," he called as a porter and the airman helped her to the B & O line.

Powerfully built to haul freight, the 2-8-2 Macarthur steam loco easily drew the long Ohio bound passenger train from the platform - its whistle deeper than the chirpy whistle of the British trains, which only served to remind her that this was not familiar ground. The marble fell behind, then the suburbs - dowdy grim houses which looked older than the London tenements but which surely could not have been. Even newer territory now, western Maryland, strange sounding town names arrived and left the vista of her window, Rockville and Gaithersburg. The scenery becoming more diverse, a huge river to her left, a canal separating the tracks from the shallow rapidly flowing stream. Before Brunswick, the airman's address was discarded and numerous sidings branched off the main line to provide places for freight trains, long trains of up to 100 cars, many containing Kentucky coal; soft bituminous coal for the coastal cities and foreign parts. The freight cars were like British goods trucks except longer and deeper, but then everything seemed bigger here, the cars, the houses, the distance between stations, everything. Why did it have to be so big, Hetty wondered as her senses became saturated and her tiredness shaped all that was different into a threat.

Skirting the Potomac River with the Chesapeake Ohio canal entrenched between, the line entered the hillier terrain of the Appalachian Mountains; land over which the Civil War had washed time and again with battles at Antietam, Falling Waters and Harpers Ferry. A struggle which some might consider still needed to be brought to a conclusion.

The train passed through the gray slate cuttings carved into the lower levels of the mountains as snow on the higher reaches clung to trees and postponed their budding. Hetty pulled Dalny closer as if protecting him from the harshness and watched the seemingly desolate country slip past, it too waiting for the warmth of better days. After a blast on the whistle, Hetty would spot the dirt road which crossed the track and for which the warning was given, but rarely did she see a person or vehicle waiting. A short tunnel through the Maryland Heights made the steam linger above the cars and as the train emerged to cross a wide low bridge above the Potomac, the steam cleared to reveal the wide river. Ice held its grip at the edges, rapids upstream foretold a slow melt and trees dislodged by ice tumbled down to meet the Shenandoah River, merging with the Potomac just below the train bridge.

Leaving Maryland, the train reached the far bank and thus entered West Virginia at Harpers Ferry. The locomotive drew the carriages to a halt between the Potomac and the canopied station to pick up people travelling out west; Harpers Ferry no more than a few houses, of stone and wood, fixed to the side of Bolivar Heights. Within a few yards of the station lay the old arsenal, stormed by John Brown when he triggered the Civil War; history lost on most, not least Hetty.

With the distance between Hetty and Church View increasing so she came closer to Dalton, for having heard his voice on the phone it had seemed impossible to leave the love which she sought and now so desperately needed. Dalton asked her, even pleaded with her to go to Martinsburg and not leave America; to see him and 'try and work something out'. When she put the phone down, another long journey had seemed bearable, but her resolve was again running thin. There was little food left for Dalny, no prospect of a place to stay and Dalton was likely to have to remain in hospital for weeks, perhaps months. She felt very small in a big world, thoughts of her parents commanded her emotions and the comfort of home beckoned almost irresistibly.

Having left Church View in the early morning, it was approaching late afternoon before the train edged round a long right hand curve bordered by trees and Martinsburg came into view: Adam Stephens House, the B&O freight building and then the small station with hardly a platform to speak of. With a repeat of all her anxieties as she hastened to disembark, Hetty clambered down the two steps cut into the side of the carriage; the final step onto West Virginian soil taken via the box, placed there by the conductor to bridge the final step onto the blacktop. No raised platforms here, she was level with the tracks and marooned between the west and east bound lines to eventually be helped across the rails to the concrete slab in front of the balconied station building.

Dusk was already settling as was a light snow which swirled around the six steps up from the concrete slab to the adjoining road. Someone said that the wind was blowing down from Canada and might bring their last snow, 82 inches having already fallen that winter. Good that she had wrapped Dalny in an extra blanket she thought as the cold air whisked around her slim legs, her thin stockings inadequate for the dropping temperature. The town, situated on a plateau several hundred feet above sea level, looked out onto mountains in all but a few directions.

Hetty found herself on the edge of a cobbled street with buses soon due, so it was promised. A couple of service boys joined her, wounded but capable of getting to Newton D Baker Hospital under their own steam and there they waited in the wind. As the small group huddled together, the large workshops on the other side of the tracks issued forth their employees. The two round houses with their railway turntables and work pits and the switch and frog factory adding to the employment opportunities, in what was a small town. The employees poured across the lines and swept past the strangers, the helpful ones pointing the GIs to the bus into town. Hetty had assumed that the hospital would be near the town center and was disheartened to learn that it lay seven miles east and would need to take a connecting bus out along Route 9. She could have sat down and cried.

The buses were privately run with local drivers and with the help of the wounded, who wanted to prove they were not incapable, Hetty changed buses at the bus station on West

Kings Street. The one to the military hospital was a regular service, the war in Germany reaching its long awaited crescendo and large numbers of wounded were still arriving. Those who could, made their own way, whilst others were brought by troop train via a spur off the Baltimore Ohio railroad right into the center of the vast hospital complex.

Newton D. Baker Army Hospital was capable of treating several hundred patients; it had its own power plant, water treatment works, a gym, bowling alley, swimming pool, POW camp and church reflective of a small town and its demand for supplies was such that it had its own branch line.

The bus carried Hetty and Dalny from Martinsburg bus station back out into the cold, tree clad countryside, past dairy farms and finally to a hospital entrance lit by street lamps and manned by guards. Passing through the outlying gardens the driver pulled up right outside the administration building, the curved gravel road sweeping in between the tended verges.

Hetty had been expecting a city hospital like Paddington General with its multi-storey compact building occupying a premium of space, squeezed in by the diverse demands of city dwelling. But Newton D. Baker had been built army fashion in a country unrestricted by acreage, spreading out in mainly single storey units to reduce the impact of bombing.

Inside the Administration building there were still many people coming and going despite the evening hour, most in uniform. It felt to Hetty as if everyone was in the military except her; she as a civilian intrusion to the regime. The staff crisp and clean whilst she was all dishevelled and what's more, in foreign attire. As Hetty waited in line for the clerk's attention, holding her baby with her worldly goods surrounding her, she actually looked more like a refugee seeking sanctuary and that perhaps is what the clerk thought when he set eyes upon her.

"Come a long way Ma'am?" he said as she reached his desk.

"Yes from England," Hetty answered which resulted in eyebrows being raised in reply.

"Address?" the clerk asked in order to sign her in. But she didn't have one, not in the US at least.

"I'm not stopping in America," she said adamantly. It caused more raising of eyebrows and when she offered her British address it seemed to complicate matters for it didn't have a state name to put in the state box. Hetty felt as if she was making it up, like a spy trying to falsify her character. But then perhaps her imagination was running away with the weariness. The clerk misread tiredness for nonchalance.

"You see Ma'am, you need a pass to enter the building," he said in his West Virginian drawl, "we take security very seriously here," he added, perhaps to reassure her but in Hetty's growing weariness it seemed more like a threat. Dalny was becoming unbearably heavy in her arms, this final encounter sapping her last reserves. In more comfortable surroundings she might have said something to him, for obtaining a pass to go into a hospital seemed plain silly. The Germans were struggling to strike Britain now, let alone this far ... and anyway, had anyone ever hit America, she wondered.

"Guess you do things a little differently over there huh?" the clerk said taking Hetty from her private thoughts and handing her the pass, then proceeded to give directions on how to reach ward 210B. But he spoke too quickly and seemed to be pointing her towards a blank wall, directions which were further complicated by expressions such as 'takealeft' and 'likea'.

Hetty walked across the hall to find a wide central corridor behind the Admin block which ran down the middle of the hospital. She judged that this must lead to almost everywhere for it seemed endless and so took the chance. With the wooden floor and block walls a barrier from the cold outside, she passed X Ray and physical therapy to her right, lab and ear, nose and throat to her left, then long, long corridors branching off left and right for the ramp one wards. They seemed a mile in length, the people down the far end appearing as a child's miniature figure in a cardboard tube. She moved Dalny from one arm to the other to relieve her aching muscles and hoped her belongings would be well looked after as the clerk said they would.

Down the main corridor she came upon what looked like a two storey area, 'likea big hall', the second tier merely windows that in day time would have lit the large space below. Off this lay a barbers shop, PX, post office, movie theatre and huge restaurant area - 'Times Square' so called. Turning left and following the signs she headed for ward 210B and as her arms and legs weakened by what seemed to be miles of walkway and weeks of travelling, Hetty stepped into a ward in the hope of finding Dalton. Her eyes moved from one bed to the next until they fell upon a face, a face portraying a lovely smile with eyes beaming back at her. It was the biggest smile the nurses had seen from Dalton in a long time. And as the soldier so popular amongst them, hugged and kissed the pale cheeked English girl, it seemed as if he was taking sustenance from her touch.

"Hello son," he said, finally turning his attention to the sweet, handsome bundle in the girl's arms, "come to see your daddy?" he asked with such pride. And the baby's momma and daddy cried, cried with a mixture of relief and happiness, for they were together at last, together in America, the worry and arduous journey finally at an end. Hetty had found what she had travelled so far to find; the arms to hold her and the father of her child.

Chapter 52

The Stove on the Landing

March to June 1945.

Hetty was relieved to learn that she could stay in the hospital that first night and not have to travel back to Martinsburg and find somewhere to sleep. The guest house was situated on the far edge of the complex between the Chapel and the Post Theater and to the right of Times Square. Family members could remain there for a maximum of three nights. For the men from distant states it enabled parents, wives and siblings to visit without the expense of renting hotel rooms; while for GI brides like Hetty it was a God send. She could buy food for herself and her baby and visit Dalton with ease, temporarily delaying the difficult decisions which lay ahead.

Dalton, still on crutches, walked with her for a while each day and they might browse the PX to look at the clothes, food and household goods, all so different to Hetty. It was as if they were out shopping together, a normal couple, whiling away a few hours before eating lunch at the visitor's canteen. But to Hetty, everywhere apart from the PX felt military; the doctors were officers, the nurses the equivalent of and enlisted men carried out the vast array of menial tasks like the maintenance, laundry and the serving of food. Hetty saw higher ranking administrators brandishing medals checking on their staff. There was a separate canteen for the patients who could move from their beds to eat and even that seemed regimented. Yet amongst it all she felt welcomed. Few had travelled as far and the staff went out of their way to talk to the 'cute English girl'.

"You're a lucky man," they kept telling Dalton, "such a doll," and "a handsome little boy, just like his daddy," they said.

The serviceman in the bed next to Dalton took pleasure in the events unfolding beside him. He had no children and might never have for his burns were so severe, even his face was bubbled. Yet he liked to talk to Hetty and always made a 'fuss' of Dalton Junior, though it made Hetty feel uncomfortable. The sight of 'the poor man' made her feel sick in the stomach; for his face and body were so badly burnt and his hands so scarred that the flesh seemed as though it might tear at the slightest touch. Thank God his wife thought so much of him, Hetty thought, for she always kissed him on the lips when she said goodbye, the one part of his face that had been spared; and to the soldier, his wife's love was like the fall of rain on a dry earth, the sun's warmth on a frozen landscape.

Dalton had been placed with the burns casualties for the nature of his problems was similar in that large areas of flesh remained unhealed. But there were many more upsetting sights as Hetty walked the corridors: the boys blinded and trying to find their way around using a cane, the amputees on crutches or in wheelchairs, the shell shocked wandering aimlessly, muttering and shouting before being guided back to the psychiatric unit, soldiers with respiratory problems and wards dedicated to those with TB. It all made for a frank, unedited picture of war and a burden these men would carry long after the dust settled from the last shell.

After her three nights in the guest house, Hetty had to find somewhere to live if she wanted to remain in Martinsburg. Help came by way of an older lady, Emily, who worked at the hospital and who had befriended Hetty the day she arrived. On hearing of her predicament, Emily introduced Hetty to a doctor friend who took an instant liking to her. The doctor and his wife, without hesitation, insisted she live with them, at least until she found somewhere suitable for herself. Hetty was unable to refuse such a 'kind and generous offer'. The security of substitute parents was just what she needed and she could have cried at the relief she felt.

The doctor's wife showed Hetty how to make up six bottles of baby food at one time to cover a twenty-four hour period. Evaporated milk, with syrup added, which were then placed in the fridge and heated through when needed. It was just a case of familiarity and confidence; familiarity with shopping, the money and the products and the confidence that she was doing the right thing.

Hetty visited Dalton as often and for as long as she could and they likely spent longer together than they had in their entire marriage. Reminiscing on how they had met, their times together in London, their wedding, Ivy Bridge and their forced separation. But of the beach landings and the advance through Normandy, little was said; it was too soon to recall the odors and sights of battle. "I just keep thinking of all the mommas who won't be getting their boys back," Dalton said softly with reddening eyes and Hetty looked into them and saw a different man to the one she had married.

After ten days at the doctor's home, Hetty started to feel she had outstayed her welcome. She hadn't and the doctor told her so but Hetty insisted she find somewhere. But there were precious few places available and most were wholly unsuitable for a young mother and her baby. Hetty accepted what there was, a room that was no more than a glorified corridor providing access to two further rooms. A partition wall had been built across a landing to give a modicum of privacy, except of course when the occupiers of the other rooms wanted to enter or leave. With the unpredictability of people passing through, frightened to get undressed, Dalny's sleep being disturbed and her baby disturbing others, Hetty soon regretted her decision. There were so many partitioned off units with just paper thin walls that even the quietest of sounds seemed to pass from one occupier to all the others.

Hetty only persevered with the situation by telling herself that 'it will not be for long', Dalton would surely be discharged and then they could find somewhere together, just the three of them, a proper family.

The only advantage of the place was that it was near to Martinsburg bus depot at the intersection of King and

Queen Streets in the center of town. The Greyhound Bus Company had its terminal there also and local buses ran out to the suburbs and to the army hospital. Hetty could walk there holding Dalny and with the April weather turning warm, it was as comfortable as a British summer's day. She was starting to get to like the town. In particular she liked the large, clapboarded, white painted detached houses with equally large porches facing the road, where the occupiers sat in the shade to watch the world go by; the porch barely feet from the sidewalk. By late April, spring was gaining the upper hand, the altitude and surrounding mountains delaying it no longer. Daffodils and crocuses appeared in the yards and blossom trees such as apple, peach and cherry decorated the facades. The aroma of the mimosa trees and the yellow forsythias foretelling that hotter days were on their way and hot they would become for the temperature might vary from -10 degrees Fahrenheit in winter to 105 in summer. Hetty had never known it so warm so early and took optimism from the feeling. She was even starting to get used to the funny accents, like crik for a creek. She passed the Opequon Crik every day to get to the hospital, the Tuscurora Mountains way off to the right, the Blue Ridge ahead, with the Shenandoah Valley between - fresh green countryside with a pleasant, bustling town in its midst; not a bad place to live Hetty felt.

During April, wounded men continued to arrive at Newton D. Baker hospital from the final battles in Germany. By the 25th April, Allied troops including the 116th Regiment had reached the River Elbe, remaining there until the Russians finished off their thrust from the east to take Berlin. On the morning of the 30th April when Hetty was walking in warm sunshine along South Queen Street, Hitler shot himself in his bunker beneath the Chancellery in Berlin. The perpetrator of the war, who had caused the deaths of 35 million people in Europe and the suffering of countless others, was dead.

On 13th May, Winston Churchill officially announced to the British nation that the six long years of war had finally brought victory in Europe. "Although Japan remains to be subdued," he said, the war in Europe would end at midnight. "Advance Britannia!" he proclaimed, "Long live the cause of freedom. God save the King!"

Whilst Hetty sat at Dalton's bedside, the pent up feelings of the British nation were unleashed, some by partying in the streets and for others by crying alone in their homes, for they had lost so much. A massive 'hokey-cokey' snaked around Queen Victoria's statue outside Buckingham Palace where crowds shouted for the King. Alcohol licensing laws were suspended for the night in central London and uniformed servicemen were carried on shoulders through the crowds in the street. When the news reached Hetty, she pictured her family and friends and how they might be celebrating. Looking at Dalny asleep in his cot that night, she hoped that the life which lay ahead of her son would be one of peace. Her father had fought in the First World War, her husband and brother in the Second and Hetty prayed that her son would not fight in another.

At the beginning of June, Hetty received a letter from her mother telling of how the family was so happy. It had been placed in the strange box by the sidewalk, crammed in with all the other mail. She had read it even before entering the house, sitting on the edge of the porch to shelter from the heat; heat and humidity that the locals were saying was just right and wished it would stay that way all summer, rather than getting still hotter. Ethel Eaglestone's writing flowed unsteadily across the page, though the message it portrayed was more consistent. Jimmy would be home soon from the war and Thomas was back already after four years as a POW. She was inviting everyone to their house for a party, family and friends; their friends, Hetty's friends, if only Hetty could come home and be there too, she whimpered, then it would be perfect. Hetty was missed by everyone, particularly by her father, Ethel missed her terrible, the house wasn't the same. She needed her daughter to be there.

The boarding house was stifling hot when Hetty entered it, the letter intensifying all that she disliked about her surroundings. The many occupants and the rising temperatures making it feel even more stuffy and smelly than usual. Why did men not wash their feet and under their arms she wondered as the smell intensified near the partitioned off bedrooms; her windowless, landing bedroom claustrophobic and cheerless.

Next morning she walked again to the bus station pushing Dalny in his pram; another warm start, the sky blue and the papers predicting high eighties or low nineties. She could walk this route blindfolded now; ACME Supermarket on Burke Street, JC Penny on South Queen and the grand Berkeley County courthouse building opposite the bus station. The bus journey to Newton Baker didn't seem so pleasant this morning. The cement works of Standard Lime, the source of the fine white dust in town, seemed to obscure the view and the limestone quarries either side of the road scarred the landscape. The brick kilns of Continental Clay which had once appeared to her as smooth, perfectly rounded, red brick buildings now merely issued dirty smoke against a graying sky. After three months of living without privacy, Paddington and Thorngate Road filled her vision, the comfort and security of home was beckoning.

Hetty and Dalton with Dalton Junior had lunch in the visitors' canteen, strolled a while in the well maintained gardens and watched as staff with a few patients exercised in the pool. The freedom of outdoor living had begun in earnest, but Hetty could feel only the unbearable heat of the sun burning her sensitive white skin. The benches on the verge formed a good place to rest for Dalton and there Hetty showed him the letter from home. Dalton read what Ethel Eaglestone had to say and afterward, merely raised his eyes at Hetty, for he had long feared that which was now stirring in her heart. Frustrated by his predicament, Dalton felt the kiss which Hetty pressed on his lips to say goodbye and held it for as long as he could after she passed out of sight. His treatment seemed endless, ten months after his wounding he was still using crutches. What could he do? She had travelled so far to be with him and now he felt he was losing her.

Hetty passed the clothing shops and cafes which lined North Queen Street beyond the bus station, walking Dalny slowly, delaying the moment when she would occupy her room for the night. Perhaps if she hurried the stove on the landing might be available, but she didn't feel in the mood to make the effort. So often had she waited hours to use it that another night didn't matter. Odd that it was situated just outside her door, on what remained of the landing, yet others seemed to know before her when it was free. A café was advertising hamburgers at five cents. Hetty hadn't yet tried one and wondered if this evening she might. Another café was advertising meals from twenty-five cents, 'very reasonable' and there were already plenty of Martinsburg folk making the most of the offer. Might she buy something this night, for the money in her mother's envelope had been barely touched? It was her emergency fund and she always carried it with her. No she had best save it, she thought and go back and wait for the stove on the landing.

With fifteen people using the bathroom, Hetty didn't get in until very late and washed herself and Dalny as quickly as she could. Then retreating to her room, alone again for the night, she rocked Dalny in her lap, humming to him until he fell asleep. It was gone ten o'clock before she was cleaning the stove after the last user and started cooking for herself. And she made up her mind, there and then, that the number of days she remained in Martinsburg would be governed by the next available sailing on the Cunard White Star.

Dalton

Newton D. Baker Hospital,
Martinsburg, West Virginia.

Pictured with Harry Sanders, (sister
Myrtle's son) and
Dalton Junior far left.
1946

Chapter 53

The Kiosk

Paddington, London, Autumn 1949.

The evening light was fading and the crisp, late September morning had developed into an unsettled grey day, the weather as if disgruntled with the onset of autumn. With his white shirt sleeves rolled up to display his strong forearms, Jimmy Eaglestone appeared out of place, more as if about to play cricket, disharmonious with the change of season. His jaw set, his game plan rehearsed he walked down the Shirland Road, half of him focused on his destination, the other bored with the familiar surroundings. He cursed life itself for bringing him back to this; the bomb sites, barren except for the memories of better days, women haggling over food shortages and ex-servicemen still out of work.

Jimmy was out of a job and out of cricket but had a 'few irons in the fire' he had told his mother as she slipped him a few bob before he went out that morning; he'd been unemployed for over a year.

"Shame," Ethel told her husband when Jimmy left, "shame the boy can't find work."

James had only just got back from his night shift, boiled his egg just right, cut his Hovis into neat strips to dip into the yoke and there was Ethel going on about Jimmy.

"Got malaria fighting in the Far East, risked life and limb every time he went into the air and no one can offer him a job." James knew what was coming next. "And you go suggesting he applies to be a milkman," Ethel reminded her husband, though he didn't need reminding. "Not a job for someone who's done so well and been a famous sportsman," she added on cue. The yoke was perfect and James looked at his one minute saucepan and back at the yellow liquid running gently down the brown soldier and thanked God for small mercies.

Jimmy idled on down Shirland and passed Essendine Road with its school and entrance to the recreation ground. The kiosk wasn't far now, Hetty would be there, beavering away as usual, boundless energy, an irritation overcoming him as he compared her income to his. Unfair advantage with Dalton's money, he felt. Essendine Road brought back too many memories; the promise of a future as a great sportsman, watching the games of cricket in the recreation ground from the flat window at Kilburn Park Road and his father's amateurish assessment of the tactics.

Jimmy had finally signed for Middlesex County Cricket Club in 1947, a year after leaving the RAF, about the time Sir Pelham Warner passed the club presidency onto Frank Mann. Jimmy made a hit with the selectors after scoring 77 and putting on 128 with Denis Compton against Surrey in early May. It was a golden year for Middlesex and a golden year for Compton and Bill Edrich who each scored over three thousand runs to become national legends. Shortly after batting with Compton, Jimmy hit 55 runs in a century stand with Edrich who went on to score 225. Jimmy's flamboyant batting and sharp fielding in the covers provided good entertainment for the thousands of spectators. 1947 was the first big year of national competition following the war and with entertainment being a rarity, people flocked to the games. Yet the acclaim which Jimmy received seemed to dilute his commitment as the year progressed. Middlesex won the championship but to the surprise of the pundits Jimmy only played seven of the matches. The coach 'got touchy' about him not turning up for all the practices, having a little drink before games, 'stupid little things' so he told his mother.

For the '48 season Jimmy was persuaded to head west and join Glamorgan, 'a wise career move' he told everyone. Arnold Dyson was going to be coaching at Oundle Private School for much of the summer and Glamorgan needed a worthy replacement. It all started well, Jimmy became a regular player, scored 65 against Hampshire and knocked up 72 in 50 minutes against Sussex; whirlwind, attacking batting much liked by the crowds and Captain Wilf Wooller considered the runs Jimmy saved in the field to be as important as those he scored. 1948 was Glamorgan's year. They pushed Middlesex off their pedestal and took the Championship title away from them, giving Jimmy the unique distinction of winning the Championship in consecutive seasons with two different counties.

Yet despite such an achievement, during the winter break his old habits returned. He spent his money faster than he earned it, whilst his mother again worked to keep him in the lifestyle to which he aspired. In the '49 season Jimmy's innings were still attractive, but often too brief.

'Touchy lot the cricket coaches,' Jimmy told his mother when he came back from Glamorgan with his tail between his legs. A night out with the girls was human after all, and the girls liked a successful sportsman, he told himself. He would have been an idiot not to have taken advantage.

'Best you find a more rewarding endeavour,' the coach had said. 'Yea, something where your bosses aren't watching you all the bloody time,' Jimmy had responded.

Natural to want a drink he thought, his mother liked hers, calms the nerves. He was getting more of them lately, shaking hands, sometimes couldn't control them, not feeling so good, bit low, needed to get some money, maybe get even with that stupid Yank at the same time. Now that would help a lot he decided, make him feel much better. The thought gave him a new purpose and he picked up his stride, squared his shoulders and walked more confidently in the direction of the Chippenham; now intent on catching his gullible sister without any family being around.

Jimmy couldn't understand why she'd gone to America in the first place, just upset his mum. No one seemed to consider her feelings, not even Edith. She soon moved out when Tom came back from being POW. He just turned up 'out of the blue'. Edith opened the door and there he was, home after almost five years. The first time Georgina had seen her father.

Mum had offered to house Hetty and Dalton as well as Edith and Tom, but everyone had turned their back on her. Tom said that Ethel visited them 'fifty times a bleeding day'. Rude bastard, Jimmy thought, arrogant lot, policemen. Tom put it round the Met that he needed somewhere else to live and quick. They pulled 'out the stops' and despite the shortage of housing, a maisonette was found within weeks. At least Edith felt 'guilty and a bit sad really' she told her brother, because her parents 'had looked after me and Gina during the war years'.

"Hello luv," Jimmy said to Hetty as he approached the counter of the kiosk. It was gone half past six and he knew he had to be quick before the 'old man' arrived.

"Couldn't lend me a few bob could you? Had a marvellous offer from Glamorgan. Want me to come back. Just need the train fare and enough to stop over for two nights at the local B&B. Need to discuss plans, could be playing county cricket again by next summer," he said convincingly.

Hetty started to refuse, he had lied to her before, but she stopped herself. This could be the break he needed. Mum was so worried about him, what with getting depressed and all. Hetty opened the till and pulled two crisp green pound notes from the back section, equivalent to a week's wages for many.

"Here," she said handing over the notes, "I really hope it goes well for you this time."

"It will," Jimmy replied, walking off with a grin.

James Eaglestone watched his son as he strode off from the kiosk, shoving the pound notes into his trouser pocket and making his way across to the Chippenham Pub. When James looked back at Hetty she was fastidiously serving her next batch of customers, arrivals from the number 36 bus, heading home after work and buying a bit of tobacco to help pass away an otherwise uneventful evening.

His daughter was a real worker, of that he was proud. Surprisingly determined when she wanted to be, rebellious almost, then easily manipulated at other times, not that he ever tried to manipulate her. Just told her straight, she could take it or leave it.

An older man was chatting Hetty up now, happened all the time; some came just to see a pretty face, still no harm in that and good for business James considered. James always came to the kiosk around 7p.m. to put up the shutters and walk his daughter home with the takings. But he had decided to drop by early for there were one or two questions he needed to ask, to sort out things that were on his mind.

"How's it going sweetheart?" James asked Hetty as he walked over to her, a respite from customers giving him an opportunity to talk.

"Really well Dad, rushed off my feet as usual," Hetty replied.

"Still making good money then," James said as yet another customer approached.

Terrible shame she was thinking of going to America again he thought. What with all the time and money she'd put into the business; worked 7a.m. to 7p.m. seven days a week. Tidy bank balance now by what he had heard from Ethel, though he wouldn't have asked, wasn't his business.

"Have all your regulars called by today?" he asked her out of something to say to fill the gaps between what he really wanted to ask.

"All but one, but he'll call in the morning now," she said knowingly.

How many more times would his daughter try and settle in America he wondered? Even he was getting confused as to when she had gone over. The first time was when the war was still on, came back too late to vote; Churchill's Tory Party lost to Clement Atlee's Labour, fickle nation James thought.

James watched Hetty restock the shelves in preparation for the next bus to arrive. She had enough money now to keep stock for her regulars rather than having to sell everything in order to buy more. Had widened her range of tobacco products and was even selling sweets and ice creams.

The second time she went to America was, now he had to think ... around January '46, yes that's right, shortly after the New Year he recalled. Herded through Tidworth

Barracks again with all the other GI Brides, a veteran of the process, James thought. He'd taken her down himself. At least he would have been there if she'd decided not to go. But no, off she went.

James watched his little girl as she smiled and chatted and plied her trade, still only twenty-seven years old, the world still her oyster. When he had left Hetty amongst all the other women at Tidworth she was as worried about going as she had been the first time; another 4,000 mile journey ahead of her with an eighteen month old and yet her determination won through. A devoted, hard working woman, Dalton couldn't have asked for more, James felt. 15,000 GI brides were processed through Tidworth and James reckoned that his daughter was likely the only one devoted enough to put herself through it twice.

Hetty was home within a few months but at least Dalton had followed her back over that time. He was finally released from hospital around February '46, after being hospitalised for twenty months. He had to wear a brace on his left lower leg which was attached to an adapted shoe; two thin metal arms came up either side of his leg with a leather strap to tie around just above the calf muscle. This helped him raise the front of his foot so that he didn't stumble whilst walking; his ligaments having been severed by the shrapnel. He walked with a limp which became a characteristic of his person and couldn't run to save his life. Well Dalton was still with her after almost three years, James reflected, but not for much longer apparently, for he was going home. They'd had an argument, a big one according to Ethel. Hetty was travelling on afterwards as soon as everything was sorted with the kiosk business, but James didn't like the sound of it.

"You sure you want to risk all your hard work by going to America again?" James asked Hetty. He hadn't intended to quite say it that way, sounded like his wife, but it just slipped out, couldn't help it, it was such a bad idea he thought.

"Dalton wants us to try one last time Dad. Buy a farm. We've got money in the bank now and there's something called the GI Bill of Rights which he thinks will help us. Cheap loans and grants for machinery, things like that."

"He's already spent a lot in setting this up," James said nodding towards the stock behind the counter.

Hetty was surprised at the comment, generous of her father, she thought. No one was ever generous towards Dalton, gave him no credit, didn't ask him about anything, not his family, Virginia, nothing.

Her dad did have a point about the business though, they would soon be able to afford a house in Paddington if things carried on the way they were. The kiosk was well sited by all the bus stops; the 28, 31 and 36 all passed the Chippenham. People could buy what they liked without the trouble of going in anywhere, have a quick chat and still keep an eye out for their bus. 'A little gold mine' her brother said.

The kiosk sat where the Chippenham, Walterton, Shirland and Cambridge Roads all met, though it was slightly into Walterton Road, where it was chained to the railings just below the road sign. Walterton and Chippenham formed a V and as the buildings between the two roads reached the end of the V, so the last shop, the corn chandlers, had a rounded frontage. They owned the frontage and Dalton and Hetty paid them a small rent to locate the kiosk there.

Her dad had built the kiosk in five sections in the garden of the prefab and he and Dalton had carried them down the Kilburn Park Road and assembled them in situ. They'd given him the money for the wood of course.

"Who's going to look after everything whilst you're gone sweetheart?" James said, finally asking the question he had mainly come to ask.

"It's all been sorted Dad, I thought you knew. Mum said she'd talked with you about it and you'd thought it a good idea."

James just looked at his daughter and tried not to give his thoughts away.

"Dalton and I made Mum a joint partner with executive rights in our absence."

"Over everything?" James asked as if merely clarifying, but Hetty knew him too well.

"Yes Dad, it seemed the only thing we could do."

James wanted to ask why it was necessary to make Ethel a partner but held his tongue. Perhaps the bank manager had suggested it but he wasn't comfortable with the idea. Wasn't sure about his wife managing all that money, then chastised himself for the disloyalty. But it had been difficult enough for Hetty to obtain a tobacco licence in the first place and then even more so to persuade the tobacco companies to give her a quota; Players, H.O. Wills, St. Julian and Ogden's all sent out a representative to discuss things and somehow Hetty won them over. On top of that and to give him his due, Dalton called in at different wholesalers after work to try and get extra stock. Wasn't easy for Dalton either, working sixty hours a week at Selfridges and James was surprised that he was being so benevolent towards the foreigner, but credit where it's due, yep, credit where it's due, he said to himself.

Yet Dalton had then been stupid enough to agree to the stock being delivered to Thorngate, James reminded himself. Why not their own home at the prefab? 'Safer' at Thorngate, Ethel had said. But James knew Ethel was helping herself. She smoked over forty a day and he couldn't remember the last time she'd bought a packet. AND Jimmy was stealing Ogden's pipe tobacco from them like it was going out of fashion. Surely Hetty knew. Maybe even Dalton knew? No it isn't a good idea her going to America, wasn't before and definitely isn't now, he concluded.

"You alright Dad?" Hetty asked her father as he stood deep in thought.

"Yes sweetheart, just thinking I might er, er renew that felt on the roof, two years old now. We need to make sure it keeps water tight, don't we luv."

"Looks fine to me Dad ... just gone seven o'clock, time to close up and for my security guard to walk me home," she said smiling as the last customer of the day left the counter.

The kiosk had never suffered a break in but she didn't want to leave cash there just in case.

"Here you are Dad," Hetty said, after James put the shutters up, and placed an ounce of Golden Virginia into his hand. She tried to give him an ounce a week, he didn't expect it, it just made her feel better. He could have a smoke working the night shift, stoking at the local police station.

"I'll call by Sunday," James said as he left her at the prefab after walking her home, "seeing Dalton's leaving Monday," he added. And the gesture wasn't lost with the noise of the passing buses.

Chapter 54

The Leaving Party

As it turned out, there was a little gathering on the Sunday; Mr. and Mrs. Bush dropped in with their 'crippled' daughter, and Hetty's Uncle Len who happened to be visiting at Thorngate, came round with James 'for the walk'. There were three prefabs on the larger bomb site of Kilburn Park Road, where odd numbered houses from 169 to 175 once stood. Two prefabs at the front by the pavement, Dalton and Hetty's on the left and the Bush's on the right and one at the back. The prefab at the back was reached by a path, fenced off with wire and which ran between the two prefabs at the front. With over half a million homes destroyed across the country, the prefabricated units were seen as a quick answer to the housing problem, delivered by lorry and erected on site.

With Dalny riding his three wheeled bike around the small garden and calling for his daddy to come out and play, Hetty served her visitors with 'a nice cup of tea'. The cakes she had baked the night before were going down a treat. She was pleased her uncle Len had come, he kept the conversation going. Talking about the old days when he and James had worked the building sites at Wembley, Sudbury and other places; and of course about his contribution towards D-Day.

"The invasion couldn't have happened without me," he told Mr. Bush. "I built the Mulberry harbour," he said as if single handed. "British idea and British built," he said proudly with a wink to Dalton. "How could we have invaded Europe without a port, so we built two and floated them over the channel in sections, brilliant idea, pure brilliance. Bloody great things the size of ships, made of concrete and we floated them over to form a harbour wall." There was always banter when Len was around, never very complimentary about the Yanks of course, but Dalton liked Len, 'always laughing and joking, no malice'.

Mr. Bush said that there were more British and Commonwealth troops involved than Americans on D-Day, but out of the 2,500 Allied troops killed, over 1,000 of them were Americans on Omaha. Hetty stopped and looked aghast, "One thousand!" she repeated. It was the first time anyone had spoken of the casualties and it seemed incredulous to her that Dalton had been involved in it all.

"You should try and visit the cemetery there one day," Mr. Bush told Dalton, "Our boys go back to the British cemeteries. Pay your respects to one or two of your old army chums," he added. And Hetty decided she liked Mr. Bush very much. She was going to miss him as a neighbour; she was going to miss a lot of things.

Hetty got up and went out to make some more tea and listened to the banter from the other side of the double glass doors which separated the kitchen from the lounge. Visitors sitting on their cosy furniture, she thought; hadn't happened very often, they always seemed to be visiting at Thorngate. Hetty and Dalton had purchased most of the furniture from the Grange on Kilburn High Road, all on hire purchase. The two seater sofa and matching arm chairs, the bed with its headboard and footboard matching the bird's eye maple wood wardrobe had all been bought brand new. The prefab was so modern and lovely that they had wanted the best and felt they could afford it, 'didn't think' they might not stay. Now they would have to maintain the payments. Wasn't going to be easy, Hetty thought, what with keeping the prefab on as well, just in case.

With the cakes devoured, Hetty put some custard cream biscuits onto a plate to take in with the tea and was reminded of their first day in their new home. She had gone over the road with Dalny to buy Peek Freans custard creams at Frenche's, just like she used to when she was a child. Dalton had liked them too and strange how his liking of them had made everything seem right. He was much stronger by then, even carried her over the threshold. 'Put me down, what will the neighbours think?' she had screamed amongst the laughter, which encouraged him even more. They had been so happy then, their first home, with everything new and modern. There were three doors off the entrance hall, one to the lounge, one to the bathroom and one to the toilet; a toilet actually in the house. There was even a gas heater on the bathroom wall which supplied hot water to the bath - a built in bath, very posh!

It was the miscarriage which had changed things, of that she was convinced, for she was six months pregnant at the time. Ethel had 'called by' and saw that she wasn't well. She was bleeding badly and Ethel told her that she had had a miscarriage and 'cleared everything up'. But a few days later Hetty came over very ill in the street. With Dalton at work, Ethel called in the doctor, who told her that the baby was still there. Mortification was setting in and she had to go into hospital for a few days and be 'washed out.' 'No good you rushing round to the hospital,' Ethel had told Dalton when he came back from work to find the prefab empty, 'visiting hours are finished and you can't do anything anyway.' Then unable to refrain Ethel added, 'You tried for a baby too early!'

Dalton wasn't coping well with her family either, Hetty reflected. He didn't like Jimmy working at the kiosk when her mum couldn't work a shift and thought that Ethel purposely chose not to work so Jimmy could do it. AND he didn't like them dipping into the profits. Dalton thought that all the kiosk work, house work and standing on her feet as well as the family shenanigans had lost them the baby. He never did like the idea of her crawling in and out under the low counter, not with her history of problems. 'And you do all that and let others take a slice of the profit,' he had said angrily. It had all come to a head, a blazing row and that's when he told her he wanted to go home.

Hetty placed the tea and biscuits on the lounge coffee table and sat back down on her nice furniture. Detached from the conversation, she looked out of the L shaped window onto the Kilburn Park Road where buses, cyclists and pedestrians passed beyond the wire fence, twelve feet away from her. The road separated Paddington from Middlesex

County. How strange, she thought, that soon they would be living in Middlesex County, Virginia. Not quite as interesting, she predicted. Probably the odd leaf fluttering past from all those trees she thought and the nearest neighbour ten miles away. 'Pretty close' to his brother Wilson, Dalton had said, but she knew what pretty close meant in Virginia. 'Beautiful spot', he'd told her, 'big yard!'

Church View hadn't been connected to electricity yet and she had sensed that even Dalton was going to miss the luxury of their prefab. Dalton liked having a separate bedroom for themselves and she loved her kitchen. Apart from the accumulating electrical goods, sink and running hot and cold water, it even had an ironing board which folded out as did the table and both could be folded back to make more preparation space. Hetty kept meaning to ask if the storehouse had running water. Surely it must she thought, after all it was nearly the start of a new decade, the 1950's were just months away.

Mr. and Mrs. Bush and her dad were saying they must leave when Vera Rantell popped in to say a 'quick hello and goodbye'. The new arrival, as so often happens in such situations, pushed the intent to leave into action.

"Well, we'll say goodbye Dalton," Mr. Bush said standing up and reaching out his hand, "we wish you all the best, come back and see us sometime." He didn't expect Dalton to of course, not with the distance and cost involved, but it was the right thing to say. Mrs. Bush gave Dalton an unexpected kiss on the cheek. It surprised everyone, not least her husband, for she was normally a very reserved lady. With a quick brush away of a tear, she turned and taking her daughter by the hand said, "See you tomorrow Hetty."

James Eaglestone reached out to shake Dalton's hand, but Mrs. Bush's gesture had taken his words away. "Don't worry, he'll be back, he'll miss us all too much," Len said jokingly and the humour eased the moment and James bid Dalton a safe voyage home.

Vera Rantell lived at number 167, the house next to Hetty and Dalton's prefab. Hetty knew her from before they moved in; she had been dating Jack Young of Middlesex County Cricket Club who had played with Jimmy in the '47 season. Vera didn't stay more than two minutes, just came to say a quick goodbye and to ask Hetty if there was anything she needed from Sainsbury's. She was going up the Kilburn High Road in the morning 'to do a bit' for her mum.

"I'll have a think and call round," Hetty said as Vera closed the gate to the garden and headed back next door.

Whilst Dalton finished his packing in the main bedroom off the lounge, Hetty retreated to the kitchen to wash up the few things. She seemed to find as much to do in the kitchen as he did in the garden, yet both were immaculately tidy. Hetty had started to pack some of Dalny's things ready for when they too left for America. He'd been a lucky little boy to have his own bedroom she thought. It lay off the kitchen and she could see the grey short trousers, blazer and red cap of his school uniform hanging there ready for the morning. Dragging Dalny away from school and all his friends wasn't fair on him she felt. He had only just started at Essendine Infants and he looked so grown up in his uniform. The thought upset her, time passed too quickly she reflected and that, she knew, was partly the problem for Dalton; he felt that his dreams were slipping away from him. Hetty closed Dalny's bedroom door to concentrate on the food she must prepare, Dalton had a long journey and she didn't want him to go hungry.

Hetty was still at the kitchen sink when he came out of the bedroom. He stood behind her as he so often did and placed his arms around her waist to hold her close.

"How can I do anything with you in my way?" Hetty said as always and as always, Dalton ignored the comment and Hetty was glad he did.

Neither spoke for a while; it was if they knew what the other was thinking. They had worked so hard, built up so much and it all seemed to be worth nothing now.

"Going to miss you," Dalton said.

"Don't be soppy, it won't be long before I come over," Hetty replied. But her words didn't seem to cheer him.

"You will come?" he asked.

"How many times have I told you? Of course I will," Hetty said smiling at his child like stance and the insecurity written across his face. She could read Dalton like a book, 'wore his heart on his sleeve'.

"I know," Dalton said kissing her neck, with tears starting to flow.

"You big softy," Hetty told him as she turned to look at him.

"You'll always be my girl," Dalton said, getting more upset.

"Come on," Hetty said squeezing his hand, "why don't you go and check the garden? You're leaving early and I know what you're like, you'll want to leave it just so."

And strange that he did, for he had no intention of ever coming back. It was perfect anyway, not a weed in sight and passers-by always commented on how pretty it was. Brightened up the street they said. It was only small but Dalton spent most of his free time there. After digging out all the old bricks and rubble from the demolished houses, he had worked the soil until it was as productive as any garden in the borough. The summer of 1948 had been the first to see flowers again and he had given Hetty the first rose of the season, a red one as it happened. 'You shouldn't have, it will only die now', she had told him, but then carefully placed it in water and kept it in pride of place.

Hetty finally finished in the kitchen and waited for Dalton to come in from the gathering dusk. She could never understand how he managed to see anything when it got so dark? Loved gardening she reflected, came back from Selfridges and out he would go until she called him in for dinner. Always on his feet doing something. In truth, she was worried how he was going to manage a farm with the ulcer which had recently broken out on his left ankle. The doctor had said that it was because he worked too hard. The blood vessels which had been damaged prevented the normal blood flow and he needed 'to rest more and raise his leg to help reduce the swelling', but he rarely followed the doctor's advice. Every night he now had to clean and redress it and she wondered how he was going to cope with the hygiene as well as with the physical demands of farming. But her dad had told her 'that's the least of your worries!'

After sitting alone for some time, Hetty stepped out of the front door, "Dalton.. Daltonn... Daltonnn...." she called into the darkness, "time to come in... Daltonnn...... it's getting late........ big day tomorrow!'

Chapter 55

The Old Storehouse

Autumn 1949 to Spring 1950.

This would make three westward crossings of the Atlantic in five years, Hetty told herself with a sigh as she boarded the Queen Mary in late September. At least this time her son would be easier to manage and likely good company. He had already forgotten the upset of leaving his nanny and grandad and was excitedly chatting away to her about 'the big ship' and going to America to see his 'daddy'. As she looked down at her growing son she wondered how many journeys the other GI brides had made to maintain their marriages. They had all spent their English money at Tidworth as if they would never need it again; buying cigarettes and posting them back to families, magazines half read and generous tips for the newsagent girl who posted the parcels.

The preparation for this trip had seemed much less fraught than the first two. This time she was travelling as a fee paying passenger and her mother was surprisingly neutral about her leaving. Not the 'You'll put yourself through all that travellin' again and for what?' and 'How's it going to be any different, you'll just be seasick and come back poorer?' No, this time her mother seemed merely intent on understanding the kiosk business as if resigned to losing her.

Having unpacked in her cabin, Hetty roamed the vast ship with Dalny, fascinated by the multiple passenger decks, overawed by the many shops and restaurants and the sheer size of the vessel. The Queen Mary was very different now to when the 29th Division had sailed on her, having been refitted to cater for the travellers for which she was originally intended. By the time Hetty had explored the open deck with the English Channel breeze buffeting her, the Mary was already approaching the Scilly Isles. You weren't supposed to be sea sick on the Queen Mary but as soon as the open ocean loomed, Hetty knew she was going to be. And for the duration of the voyage Dalny came back after each meal to tell his mummy in great detail what he had just eaten.

Hadn't been an easy first five years of marriage Hetty reflected as the huge liner pushed into the Atlantic, barely swaying for most but swaying too much for her. At least this time there was a good chance of them settling down, she thought. That second trip over in '46 had been a big mistake, but when she had left him in Martinsburg in August '45 she had felt so guilty about it. For the entire journey home she had worried about her decision, condemning her actions, scolding herself for having given up on her husband when he needed her most. Then, when she had got home, found it difficult to face up to people. So, back to America she had to go.

Hetty had stayed with Dalton's sister Myrtle that second trip and not surprisingly, she was a lot happier than living in the rented room with the stove on the landing. She often babysat Myrtle's son Harry whilst Myrt worked nights at the Black and Decker factory and once a week went to the pictures with Fleda, Myrt's daughter. But when Dalton was discharged from the army in February '46 there seemed to be little prospect for them. With no jobs, no home and with Dalton still convalescing, they relied on family hospitality, moving from one home to the next. They had both been foolish, Hetty reflected, Dalton for encouraging it and her for agreeing to try again so soon.

At least Dalton was strong now, Hetty reminded herself, trying to be positive as the expanse of water between the liner and the British coast widened with every passing moment. They had money in the bank and more importantly, they would have their own home, even before buying the farm. This trip would be different she hoped, hope that for the moment was outweighing the doubt.

Dalton was going to meet Hetty at Boston when the Mary docked there but decided against the long journey in his 'beat up old car' and left money in order for her to travel down to Washington by train. When she arrived there, Hetty thought Dalton looked like a kid who'd just won a year's supply of sweets. He was so busy making a fuss of her and Dalton Junior that he almost forgot the suit cases, which he had trouble fitting into the boot, or trunk as Hetty learnt to call it, so dented from the poplar tree falling across it.

The journey from Washington to Church View was likely the most pleasant she had made in America, and Dalton felt as if he was flying along at over 50mph yet was doing not much more than half that. The early October sunshine felt warmer to Hetty than a British summer's day and even the trees seemed to be creating happy thoughts as they reflected warmth toward her. As they drove through the countryside, Hetty's pale, city girl face contrasted with Dalton's already hardy outdoor appearance. With her hair blowing around from the open window and her eyes darting this way and that, almost nervously to absorb the scene and later to catch the first glimpse of their new home, Dalton thought her the most attractive woman in the world.

When they arrived outside the old storehouse Hetty had to agree that it was a beautiful spot. Situated within open ground a few feet off the dirt road, it was surrounded by trees which autumn was changing to a colorful array of summer's memories; the rose dogwood leaves almost ruby red, the crepe myrtle orange and the maple with seemingly every shade on the same tree. There was just one other home in sight, Wilson and Ada's, 100 yards up a track on the opposite side of the dirt road. Hetty didn't know it yet, but that was where she would have to get every bit of water from, Wilson's well, just beside his house.

Dalton, with the help of Junior, parked the car on the grass by the storehouse and before Hetty knew what was happening, her two 'boys' jumped out and raced each other to the front door. With Dalton Junior beating his daddy by a good margin, much to the youngster's delight, Dalton grabbed his son to stop him entering. "Wait, wait!" he said to Junior and ran with his lolloping stride back to the car, swept Hetty off her feet and carried her over the threshold and into their new home.

"Oh it's not too bad," Hetty said with a hint of relief as she was placed down onto the freshly brushed floor boards.

One large open space stretched out before her, rising to a high ceiling and providing an open and airy feel. No separate rooms and not even a recognizable kitchen area except for the metal wood burning stove, but 'it was ... nice'. "Very modern," Hetty joked. "I like the kitchen fitments and the bathroom," she added with a straight face and then couldn't help but smile at Dalton's look of anxiety.

In response Dalton grabbed her around the waist and swung her so that her hair and skirt flared out into the wide expanse, then picking up his son, drew both in close saying "We're gonna be real happy here darrrlin."

"Funny, your daddy sounds like a Virginian again, just like when I first met him," Hetty said, which resulted in her being inundated with more wet kisses and Junior asking if he could be put down so that he could "Go outside and explore."

 "Damn it Slaughterrr, put that woman down and let me give her a hug," Robbie announced, walking into their home without a knock. Robbie had been the only family member to visit Hetty in England; Hetty liked him and could forgive him for just walking in. But suddenly she noticed a three legged hunting dog in her home and then the gruff voice of its master and knew immediately that Wilson had arrived. "Where's the whiskey little brother?" he joked as he walked over to Hetty. "MRS. SLAUGHTERRR, welcome to Middlesex Coun'y," he bellowed, whilst grinning from ear to ear. Soft city girl, he thought, soon be a runnin back to her momma. "Little late to plant your purple tops," he said with a hint of sarcasm, referring to the turnips that housewives normally planted in early September.

When Kelly arrived with Edward, he went straight to the fridge and asked where his son kept the whiskey and Hetty started to worry that she'd married into a drinking family. It took a while for her to get used to the humor and not least all the hugging and kissing that went on between family members. She had never before seen Dalton loved by anyone other than herself and sometimes he got so much fuss that they seemed to forget she was there.

In their first few days in Virginia, Hetty and Dalton went shopping for all the things they needed. It was fun and Dalton loved showing Hetty around. They bought a white, wood burning stove, bedroom furniture and kitchen table and chairs. The front door to the storehouse opened onto the dirt road and looking inward from the door they made their kitchen/living area to the right and the bedroom area to the left. After a few weeks Hetty was becoming a little more relaxed about cooking on the wood stove, "So different to my gas cooker," she told Ada, who couldn't understand why she was making so much fuss about it. But then Hetty fussed about everything, so Wilson said; the walk to the well, the outside toilet which Dalton had to clear of 'creepy crawlies' every morning and the 'smelly, dangerous oil lanterns'.

Hetty tried to relax about her son playing out but couldn't help but worry about the swamps, poisonous insects, animal traps, the hunters and about him getting lost in the woods. Dalton's indifference to it annoyed her, but she couldn't remain angry with him for too long - just long enough.

Dalton had 'gotten involved' with the family planting of wheat, barley, oats and clover through the fall. He kept about thirty chickens down by the side of the storehouse in a wired off area and Hetty exchanged eggs for goods at the Dragon Run Store. To the right of the house Dalton built a pig pen and Junior adopted one of the 'little white, baby pigs' perfectly at home in his country playground. Evelyn with her four children often called by, like the rest always unannounced and entered as if into their own home, which Dalton was always at ease with. Hetty and Dalton became real friendly with Dalton's brother Amos, wife Callie and their children; going to the pictures once a week at Tappahannock and buying ice cream cake and eating it back at Amos's house. They once waved Dalton and Hetty down at the local gas station and said 'we'll come with you', shopping as it happened, and just left their car at the station.

When it rained Dalton loved the sound of the rain drops on the cypress shingle roof and when the snows came, the wood stove created an oasis of warmth for family life. The smell of cooking and the sound of family banter interweaved with the crackling of the wood as it gave up its energy, accumulated over many Virginian summers. Hunting for the Christmas tree was so exciting for Junior and Dalton was in his element. The sunlight sparkled off the new snow, crunchy, clean snow which fluttered down off branches pushed aside in their quest; searching for that special tree, pointing to one and then changing their minds again and again, until the perfectly shaped one was found. Lopping it, Hetty's two men dragged the quarry back through the woods, to be decorated with American trinkets of the season, some purchased and some picked, like holly from the plants around them.

Hetty wrote to her mother asking her to post blankets to help see them through the winter, then wished she hadn't, for when the blankets came they were accompanied by words which expressed how much Hetty was missed; the first letter with such sentiment.

Hetty told Dalton that their fridge was even more prehistoric than the oil lanterns, though she had to reluctantly agree that the lanterns gave out a cosy glow. Dalton's brother Preston was still delivering ice for a living and every week or so brought them a large block; carrying it into the house on his back and sliding it into the ice box compartment situated at the top, to then keep the food cold in the lower compartment. Preston even arrived in a motorized truck Hetty remarked, but then her humour was reciprocally lost on the locals.

Being 'a little short of kitchen cupboards' Hetty kept pies and cakes on the stairs within the storehouse, stairs which led nowhere for the loft had been boarded up. And the run of delights reminded Dalton of his momma and the way she had kept her cooking and jarred fruit on one side of their stairs.

When Dalton started farming in the spring of 1950, Hetty got up early, stoked the stove and baked biscuits and fried eggs for his breakfast and lunch. Leaving with a kiss and a hug, Dalton was content in the knowledge that they were now looking for their own farm and might soon buy one. They had looked at the Thrift Farm and as soon as Dalton heard back from the Department of Veterans Affairs, they were going to make an offer.

Dalton's leg ulcer was more of a nuisance than a hindrance; it swelled up and pained him real bad after a long day on it, but it was nothing he couldn't deal with he said. Sometimes taking pain killers, he would lay on the wood floor with his leg up the stairs to drain the blood away. He dressed it daily, being careful not to get it infected, kept it away from bath tub water and out of rivers. So as the warm spring weather arrived he could only tell his family how he used to play in the Dragon Run, but his animations were more than an adequate portrayal. Standing on Wares Bridge, he pointed to spots, uncertain to Hetty and Dalton Junior where he used to swim, cut Mr. Lumpkin's cypress trees, had shot a wild turkey or swung on the birches. He told Hetty that with the Piankatank, the Dragon Swamp marked the southern boundary of Middlesex County all the way to the Chesapeake Bay. "How many other county names have you copied from us?" she asked.

Dalton had no idea, "Well Essex, Gloucester and Lancaster border Middlesex," he told her.

"Essex! Can't you Yanks think of your own names?" she said and Dalton grabbed her and held her over the river. Hetty screamed, Junior got upset and tried to help his mummy but then he too got dangled over, almost by his ankles.

When Dalton showed them the northern boundary of Middlesex, at Whiting's Landing, Hetty thought the Rappahannock River 'one hundred times wider than the Thames'. Dalton led Hetty and Junior down a long grass slope to the water's edge, a sandy beach attracting both father and son. The blue sky and early afternoon sun would have felt hot had there not been a breeze coming from across the water. Summer had seemingly arrived as if winter had slipped quietly away with no intervening spring; the temperature on some days had exceptionally been well into the eighties.

"Feels like the British seaside," Hetty said, remembering her visits from childhood before the war, the sea breeze a persistent irritation, "except hotter here," she recalled.

"A few more weeks and you can take Junior swimming. There's a roped off area near the harbor at Urbanna," he told her and Hetty quite liked the idea of a warm beach so close to home.

"That's where Daddy went fishing for oysters," Dalton told her, pointing across the river to a long sweeping section on the far bank where the Corrotoman River entered the Rappahannock.

"How far across?" Hetty asked as Junior started to paddle his now bare feet in the shallow water.

"About four miles to the Corrotoman," Dalton answered.

"Robbie, Edward, Daddy and I worked together from a thirty foot boat which every evening we had to haul back out of the water onto Daddy's trailer. Sure took a while to get home when the horses were doing the pulling," Dalton said starting to reminisce. "One evening the wheel of the trailer hit a stone and twisted across my foot tearing my big toe nail right off," he told her, still grimacing with the memory. "Daddy gave me a rag and told me to wrap it up and shut up."

A hard man, so Hetty felt and decided she liked him even less this trip. Why did he have to say 'now who's my prettiest daughter-in-law' whenever the family were together, or keep reminding her of when the 'enormous turkey' trapped her against the barn wall at the home place. He still found it funny, silly man, she thought and reminded herself to answer him back more, just like she did about going to church. Kelly was always asking her to attend Wares. Just before Easter he'd paid a special visit to them at the old storehouse to ask her if she'd attend, 'just this once, for me', he'd said 'seein it's Easter Sunday'. Despite her misgivings, Hetty had reluctantly agreed, 'but just this once' she had told him, 'because you only go to catch up on the gossip'. And that had taken the wind out of his sails; either because of there being some truth in her words, or Hetty's growing confidence. It wasn't the last time Hetty would attend Wares, but proved to be the last but one.

A bald eagle swept out over the water then back across open ground to weigh its chances of picking up a small dog which had strayed from its owner. Dalton pointed out the national symbol to Hetty and Junior who followed its every move. "Will it attack us?" Hetty asked.

Dalton chuckled and held Hetty around the waist from behind and kissed her neck. "The only thing that might attack you here is ... me," Dalton whispered into her ear. The eagle decided against the dog, circled and glided effortlessly over the crab and oyster fishing boats to cross Whiting Creek and reach the island where perhaps the tall sea oats harbored easier quarry.

Dalton skimmed some stones with his son who splashed more than skimmed and threw grass into the river to prove to his mummy as his daddy said he should, that he would not be swept away by the current, for there wasn't one this close to the bank.

With their hearts light, Hetty and Dalton walked with Junior, still with wet feet, back up the grassy slope to the car. Her hand in his, Hetty looked to Dalton like best white china, the sun just adding a hint of rose on her cheek, his 'English Rose' he said of her and couldn't wait to get her home, well, get her home and Junior asleep.

The conversation in the car again turned to the Thrift Farm; Hetty of the farm house, furnishings and of Junior's schooling, Dalton of the crops, animals and machinery. Occasionally the conversation crossed to common territory as men and women by chance sometimes manage. Hetty was still anxious about buying the farm, it all seemed so permanent. They would have to settle up completely in England for it would be pointless to keep the prefab and the business. And anyway, they needed the money. She wanted to delay the decision until the summer, but summer wasn't a good time to buy or sell a farm she was told. And anyway Dalton was happier than she had seen him for a long time and that was saying something, for he was such a contented man, not restless like me, she reflected. Uncomplicated, that was Dalton; stoic, the doctor at Martinsburg had called him. Irrespective of how hard things became he just shrugged his shoulders and got on with it. 'No matter' he so often said, which sometimes annoyed her. Perhaps he was too easy going as her sister said he was. 'Dalton lets people walk over him', she'd said more than once. At Ethel's insistence Dalton even used to go up to Grandma Lucy's each evening after working so late, took coal in and stoked up her fire. Lucy only lived a few doors away on the Kilburn Park Road and the penny hadn't dropped right away when Ethel had said just how convenient the prefab would be. Dalton didn't get any thanks for it but he didn't seem to mind ... if it hadn't been for that miscarriage, Hetty thought, they might still be in Paddington.

On the way home Dalton couldn't help but go by the Thrift farm, as if it was a magnet, compelling him to drive straight on at Hermitage Church instead of turning left for Wilson's and their storehouse. The Thrift farm was no more than a couple of hundred yards along the Wares Bridge Road from the Slaughter home place. Its land curved round the back of the Stovers and Greenwoods and met up with the Slaughter land to then be bounded at the rear by the Briery Swamp.

Dalton pulled onto the Thrift farm track and approached the house which sat on a slight knoll some 400 yards from the road. With fields either side of the track and woods bordering them, the warmth of the day still lingered. Trees were in bud, the lighter green of the tall poplars contrasting with the darker loblollie pine, beech and maple which bordered the 50 or so acres of cultivated land. The green shoots of barley created a patchwork effect with the bare soil and an array of stalks from the previous harvest of corn stood as if guarding the way for the new crop. They stood two feet or more in height and although solid, looked hollow, like bamboo.

Dalton parked the old Ford over by the barns which stood to the left of the farm house; the smoke house, corn crib, fences and animal pens fulfilling Dalton's needs, so he felt, to make a good living from the place. Sixty-five acres for $6,500, a good price he considered. He was entitled to a Government loan arrangement at reduced interest and owing to his disability might get a grant for a tractor to work the farm. What's more, Kelly and Maggie Thrift wanted to move quickly and because they knew Dalton, might reduce the price further. Their son Albert had also married an English girl, Florence, whilst in the services and had moved to Water View. Kelly and Maggie wanted to move there with them, sell up and use the money to enjoy their retirement.

As Dalton and his family got out of the car the guinea hens squawked louder than the warning welcome of watch dogs and one flew off as if to remind the strangers that he had other talents. "Noisy critters," Dalton remarked, "but good at keeping the ticks and bugs at bay. Come on," he said and led Hetty and Junior behind the barns away from the gathering noise. The hens seemed to be getting into a frenzy and the dairy cows and hogs had responded as if the guinea fowl had set up a chain reaction. The cultivated land sloped gently away toward the left and rear of the gray wooden structures - lean-to sides, hay lofts and feeding stalls in plenty. Out into the open field, he led them toward the woods, a cooling breeze sweeping over them. "Deer tracks," Dalton said, pointing down to the triangular indents in the bare patches between the young shoots. "Looks like he hung around here wondering which way to go," he said, as the tracks pointed this way and that, some clearer in the damper ground. Hetty looked back toward the road, it seemed a long way off; a farm truck passed along it but its engine could not be heard. Dalton bent down, pushed his fingers into the soil and took hold of a clump of brown, red tinted earth and rubbed the fine grains between his fingers, the grains falling back to do their work. He was positioned just as she had so often seen him in the garden at the prefab, a posture developed over years, during childhood and adolescence.

"You know when my fingers are working the soil, I feel as if I'm doing the work God put me on this earth to do," he said looking back up at her.

Junior crouched down by his daddy and rubbed the soil as if to acquire the same feeling, whilst Dalton's words settled on Hetty's heart to make her feel uneasy. She drew in a deep breath, in part to calm her nerves, but with Junior loving the fun and freedom of the countryside, her anxiety of living permanently in Virginia was starting to fade. There was something about the fresh air that she too was getting to like. London air wasn't like it used to be - more and more vehicles and more coal fires with people affording greater luxury. She hadn't noticed it before but there was always change about her here in Middlesex, slow relaxed change, of color, sounds and odors; signs that farmers read without consciousness. Nature seemed to almost imperceptibly transform, doing so with such surety but without anxiety, and people by necessity flowed with it. Maybe she was relaxing, now that would be a miracle, she told herself.

"Come," Dalton said with a big grin and led Hetty and Junior into the adjoining woods. He stopped a few yards in, "listen," he prompted as the breeze pushed through the upper branches, creating a sound as of a stream tumbling off Dartmoor.

"Can you hear it?" Dalton asked her.

"The wind in the trees?" she replied.

"And something else," he said now grinning even more broadly. Hetty tried her hardest but couldn't hear anything else. Even the frogs had gone quiet as if to help her; strange how they all seemed to know at once when someone was snooping about. Dalton pulled branches out of the way to guide her onward down the slope onto wetter ground. "There," he said pointing to a pool beneath a bank where water issued from the fields above. The noise had for Hetty merged with that of the breeze. The spring water fell into a pool leaving a clear patch in the muddier surround and ran on down the stream bed.

"Perfect, a spring here in the shade and a well over by the house. Shade and protection, perhaps twenty acres of woodland, fuel and building materials all in one," he said with such glee that he couldn't help but flick water at Hetty and Junior in his excitement. Picking his son up to carry him on his shoulders Dalton strode back up the bank. Hetty followed, Dalton reached for her hand and they pushed out into the openness of the fields again and made for the farm house.

The conversation with the Thrifts was brief and promising. The house seemed quite large in Hetty's assessment, potential for a nice home she thought; surely they could get the water running to the house and to flow away like at Thorngate, she told herself. And electricity was promised in a year or two; perhaps she could survive till then and things would surely become easier. Anyway, it would take that long for Dalton to get his farm into full swing. The thought of owning their own place and yet still being so young started to excite her. The feeling was an unusual one, but then Dalton had always caused her to surprise herself; even back to when she first held his hand within seconds of meeting him, and she couldn't help but smile at the thought.

They turned onto the Wares Bridge Road in the old Ford and headed back toward the Dragon Run Storehouse to pass it as if travelling parallel to Route 17. The elementary school, where the Slaughter children had attended, lay just on from the store and the arrival of the summer weather was causing marooned forsythia in its muddy grounds to flower; its yellow contrasting with the purple red bud in the farmyard beyond. With the car at full throttle Junior slipped over onto his daddy's lap and pretended to drive. "I'll let you have a go at driving soon," Dalton promised, with Junior's hands beside Dalton's on the steering wheel.

"Dalton!" Hetty exclaimed on hearing her husband, and both father and son laughed, "Like two naughty boys," she told them.

Approaching the old storehouse, their temporary home as Hetty now regarded it, they saw Wilson standing as if waiting for them. Strange, he came across the road but rarely, his own home seemingly too much of a consuming endeavor. He held a letter in his hand and as soon as Hetty spotted the white flash in the evening sunlight, her heart sank and nervousness overcame her. It was a letter from home, of that she was convinced.

Dalton stopped the car and all got out to stand before Wilson as if for judgement.

"Robbie brought this for you from the post office," he said looking at Hetty and waving the letter as if she hadn't noticed it.

"Thanks," Hetty responded after a pause and reached out to reluctantly take possession of it. She recognized her father's hand writing immediately. It must contain bad news she thought, for her father had promised to let her know if there was anything to worry about. Well he had written and in many ways she had been expecting it.

Hetty and Dalton became so quiet that even Wilson got the hint that he should leave. And as Wilson walked back up his farm track, Hetty peeled open the envelope with the familiar British stamps. It began,

'Dear Hetty,

I am sorry to have to write to you but your mother and brother have got into serious difficulties'. James Eaglestone didn't mince his written word any more than his spoken.

He went on to explain that he had delayed writing for as long as possible, hoping that Ethel would sort things out. But the longer he left it, the more serious the problem became ...

Likely even when Hetty was still on her journey to America, Ethel took Jimmy to see the bank manager and made him an equal partner in the kiosk business with his own cheque book.

James wasn't aware of this at first but when in October Jimmy turned up at the house on a new motor bike and then a car in November, he should have realised that Jimmy wasn't just 'helping out' at the kiosk.

Only a handful of people owned cars in Thorngate and James realised that Jimmy must have access to a sizeable sum of money.

The letters from the bank became more frequent and then Ethel had been summoned in order for the manager to spell out the consequences of her four month denial. The account initially facilitated substantial funds, then a large loan because of its history, but the account was now in 'serious debt.'

James went on to explain that the situation was made worse by the fact that profit margins had dwindled since Hetty had left. Jimmy and Ethel were employing young lads who didn't care what they sold and they had stupidly taken out a lease on the Corn Chandlers shop to sell the very same products as in the kiosk.

The bank manager had told Ethel and Jimmy that they, as well as Hetty and Dalton, were equally responsible for the debt. Court action was being considered and property repossession was the likely outcome.

Several weeks after the meeting with the bank manager, when cheques were no longer being honoured, less savoury characters started to call at the house. It transpired that Ethel had also accumulated a large debt betting on the horses; perhaps in the hope of paying off the bank loan.

The final straw, James wrote, was when the police called at the house and accused Ethel and Jimmy of 'buying cigarettes off the black market'. Someone had reported them and provided evidence and that was when Jimmy lost control and had a nervous break down ... 'Jimmy's in hospital, with charges pending.'

Hetty skimmed the rest of the letter, her face wet with tears, hands trembling and falling limply with the letter barely held between her fingers. "What's wrong Mummy?" Junior asked anxiously clutching at her skirt.

Dalton slipped the letter from Hetty's hand and walked away over Wilson's freshly hoed earth. The breeze brought the sweet smell of spring from the woods beyond, but he didn't notice it. The mud stuck to his boots making them heavy and the sun dipped low as if deciding that evening had come. He stopped and leant against the barn wall, his frame heavy as he read the unwelcome news, whilst Hetty still stood on the dirt road as if fixed on the very same spot, not sure of which way to tread.

Chapter 56

For Love

When the ropes binding the Queen Mary to American soil were finally unleashed, the great ship slipped down the Hudson River and out into the wide Atlantic. Picking up speed with the vast wake stretching out behind her, it looked to Hetty as if the Mary was drawing a line across the ocean, retracing the path she knew so well. She stood now at the rail with Dalny and pointed to the sky scrapers of Manhattan as they gradually shrunk in size, until they were mere blips on the skyline and buildings only in the imagination. With her long hair blowing haphazardly in the breeze, her clothes rippling in its wake, Hetty somehow knew that she would never see this view again.

Dalton watched too, the unsettled weather just as it had been when he first set forth to war eight years earlier. So much had happened in the intervening years. The battles and the dread, the love and the passion and the dreams, some fulfilled and some perhaps never to be; falling from his grasp, like fine soil through his fingers.

He watched as his country became nothing more than a pencil line on the horizon, to then finally slide away and be gone. And though his heart was heavy, he found comfort in his belief that all things were meant to be. And after all, just how much more could a man ask for he thought; he had a beautiful wife and a lovely son and he knew without doubt that his place was with them. Thus with the gray sky for the moment arching over him, Dalton came up behind Hetty, placed his arms around her waist and told her just how much he loved her .... but then Hetty already knew.

Journey's End.   The Epilogue.

15th June 2008, Church View, Virginia.

It was Father's Day, a Sunday with a clear blue sky and the temperature in the comfortable eighties. William Sapp, Dalton's nephew, opened up his home, the old Slaughter home place to the friends and family who gathered there. The yard slowly filling with modern day cars to surround the flat bed horse drawn wagon that would lead them to Wares.

At around one in the afternoon, three grandsons and three great nephews carried the English coffin across the front yard and placed it gently on the wagon. The Stars and Stripes flag of the USA draped and sitting comfortably over the English oak. This would be Dalton's last journey to church, like his first, by horse power and the last of Kelly and Fleda's children to be laid to rest.

The cortege eased out onto the quiet country road, a police car leading and one following; and keeping to a respectful pace, the horse clip clopped its way down to the Dragon Swamp, crossed the bridge and entered King and Queen County. Dalton was carried past the farms he had known so well, the wheat and corn fields and the long sweeping curve of the narrow road that had changed little in the 60 years since he had last resided there. Some 800 yards from church, those who were able walked behind the wagon; his two sons, Dalton and Robbie, their families and many, many nephews and nieces, whilst Hetty followed in the first car. Hetty had borne another healthy son between several miscarriages, Robbie arrived in 1954, ten years after Dalton Junior; Hetty's last miscarriage being as late as 1962.

Where the Wares Bridge Road met the Timber Branch Road, the horse-drawn hearse was steered gently right to come into view of the church. Still white, though no longer painted and still surrounded by trees and farmland, the grave yard opposite similarly veiled. Even those in the cortege who had anticipated that many might attend were surprised when they turned the corner, for there were so many people waiting outside the church to welcome the country boy home.

After returning to England from America in 1950, Dalton and Hetty didn't stay long in their prefab on Kilburn Park Road. To cut costs and help pay off the debts, they moved into the middle flat at 43, Thorngate Road, a situation which Ethel had always wanted. By 1955 they had paid off all the debts accrued in their absence, including Ethel's betting debt, without recourse to those who had caused them. After initially buying 41, Thorngate in 1959, they finally increased the distance between themselves and the Eaglestones in 1961, moving five miles west of Paddington to 53, Monks Park, Wembley in the county of Middlesex, England. The following year they moved around the corner to 162, Vivian Avenue in order for Dalton to have a bigger garden.

For fifteen years Dalton's contact with home remained the simple letter and the occasional expensive telephone call. But in 1965 there came a turning point when a certain young, adventurous nephew arrived on Dalton's front door step in Wembley - Harry Sanders, Dalton's sister Myrtle's boy. Harry came back again in 1967 and it made Dalton realise that transatlantic travel wasn't as expensive or time consuming as it used to be. Instead of several days, it now took several hours to get to America; the era of cheap charter flights had arrived.

In the summer of 1968, Dalton went home for the first of many annual holidays, took his two sons with him and attended a huge family reunion at his brother Amos's place on Route 17 in Church View. Much came of the visit; a determination in Dalton to return as often as he could and an awakening in his sons that their father was a much loved and respected man.

For the next thirty-five years Dalton visited Virginia almost every year, sometimes on his own and sometimes with a son, grandson or both. Thus Dalton maintained his close relationship with home and enabled two further generations on either side of the Atlantic to become as one extended family.

The membership of Wares as well as Dalton's family and friends now watched as the horse pulled Dalton toward his church; long grasses on either side of the track causing the flag draped coffin to appear as if it was grazing across the tops of the stems. Then coming to a halt in the shade of the two huge gum trees in front of Wares, it was as if time itself had stopped and all waited for Dalton to be carried inside.

In the warm sun, mourners were silent with memories and tears of plenty and formed a corridor from the hearse to the steps of the church; ladies holding a red rose presented to them by the younger generation of Dalton's nieces. When Hetty received hers with the words, 'Please accept this as a token of Dalton's love,' she couldn't help but cry. For she had always received the first rose of the season, every season from 1948 to the year Dalton suffered a severe stroke in February 2000.

Wherever Hetty and Dalton lived, Dalton had always nurtured a garden equal to any 'English garden'. But when they moved from Vivian Avenue to 1, Joiners Close, Chalfont St. Peter, Buckinghamshire County in 1974, Dalton indulged himself in the largest garden he would ever have the pleasure to work. Resplendent with rose beds, productive with vegetable patches and a green house with tomatoes, squash and cucumbers, grown with seeds sent from America. Dalton spent every minute he could working the soil and after his retirement in 1985, threw himself into his hobby with a passion. He would be in the garden 'from dawn till dark, if I let him', Hetty recalled. 'Didn't even come in when it rained', just stood in his shed, listening and looking out onto the fruits of his labour.

Before his retirement, Dalton had worked for twenty-five years as a civilian employee with the US Military in the London area: on the bases around Ruislip and the premises serving the US Embassy. Working with US servicemen and women as well as other US citizens probably helped him feel closer to home.

Dalton's leg ulcer never did heal but he remained immensely fit and strong. It was likely his strength which ultimately proved his downfall. The stroke followed his carrying of a concrete garden ornament to the front of the house; an ornament too heavy for the workmen who had wheel-barrowed it to the back of the house when fixing his driveway.

The stroke left Dalton paralysed down the right side and unable to speak or see very well and Hetty cared for him for four years. But when her health deteriorated he was cared for at The Cherry Trees Nursing Home, near his son Robbie in Redditch, Worcestershire. It was a difficult eight years but nonetheless still a wonderful, loving period in his life, for Dalton never lost the ability to love. And reaping what he had so long sown, he received love from his wife, children and grandchildren to feel safe and secure; secure from the daily visits, of being tucked into bed at night and the covers pulled up to his chin. But likely more secure in the knowledge that all things were meant to be; a patient man to the end, comfortable in the knowledge that God would call him when he was ready.

The end came not without a fight. Two successive bouts of pneumonia and still Dalton held on to his precious life, but when a third grasped him, all knew that it was time to let go. Dalton died at 4.30a.m. on the 18th May 2008, aged 88 years.

After Dalton's coffin was raised from the wagon, the six pall-bearers carried him through the gathered mourners to the steps of the church, and it was as though he was finally coming home for good. Back into the heart of his family and back into the family of the church of which he had always remained a member.

With prayers, tributes, memories and the eulogy by those close and with David Medlen, the pastor, knowing him well, the service proved to be a wonderful celebration of Dalton's life, even for those who felt such terrible loss. The loss of a husband, a dad and best friend, a grandad to five grandchildren and a precious uncle to over seventy of those present.

When all had filed out into the sunshine, Dalton was taken the few yards across to the cemetery by the horse drawn wagon, the road separating the two, closed by police as a mark of respect to the old soldier. Dalton's coffin, still clad in the flag of his country, was placed on a plinth and beneath a canopy. The pastor and nephew Harry Sanders said a few fitting words, Harry that he was pleased the 'old warrior and patriot had come home' and then the soldiers in the burial detail performed the final honors – the Taps and Flag. If there had been a dry eye beforehand, there surely wasn't after the short military ceremony. For the bugler sounded the last post, spreading its message across the otherwise quiet countryside. The flag was folded and 'on behalf of a grateful nation' it was presented in crisp military fashion to Hetty by the Sergeant of the Honor Guard as he knelt before her.

Whilst mourners slowly left to return to the fellowship hall, Hetty remained at Dalton's side. A red rose had been brought over from his English garden and she placed it on his coffin to mark her last goodbye. Then the few who still stood there, watched as the Country boy was lowered - to lay by his momma and rest in peace for an eternity, close to the Virginian soil.

Dalton Roy Slaughter

30th June 1919 - 18th May 2008.

" ... to have and to hold,
from this day forward, for better,
for worse, for richer, for poorer,
in sickness and in health,
to love and to cherish,

till death do us part ..... "

Dalton's fresh grave,
Wares Church.

Timber Branch Road,
King and Queen County
Virginia.

June 2008

Hetty.

In the early hours of March 27th 2011, Hetty Elizabeth Slaughter nee Eaglestone, slipped away to rejoin Dalton. After a brave and absolutely determined fight against secondary breast cancer, she died aged 88 years in her own home; the home that had been Dalton and Hetty's since 1974, 1, Joiners Close, Chalfont St. Peter, Buckinghamshire. "Dalton will be tired of holding the gate open for me," she said, days before her death ... but he waits no longer.

Hetty had a memorial service at St. Peter's Church, Chalfont St. Peter and was cremated at the Amersham Crematorium, Buckinghamshire, 8th April 2011. Her ashes were placed in Dalton's grave at Wares Church, on 25th March 2012.

Hetty Elizabeth Slaughter

13th May 1922 – 27th March 2011.

Dalton and Hetty
celebrating their
62nd Wedding Anniversary.

4th September 2005

Thanks, Acknowledgements and Sources

My most prolific sources of information were of course my parents Dalton Roy and Hetty Elizabeth Slaughter nee Eaglestone.

Sincere thanks must be given to my three sons, my dear Mum Hetty and special friends who motivated me to persevere with this book. My Mum's endorsement was very important to me.
I thank in particular my wife Lorna, for her enduring encouragement and support. Lorna was the first to read it from cover to cover and her comments and suggestions were invaluable.

Dad died three years before I completed the book, but I am glad that I read some of the unfinished chapters to him. If the smiles and raised eyebrows were anything to go by, then I think he liked what he heard. Good that we travelled to Normandy and the USA together when we had the chance. Needless to say, Dad was my motivation throughout.

My heartfelt thanks and immense gratitude to the following veterans of B Company, for the letters, telephone conversations and in particular their enthusiasm and support:

John	**Andryka**	(Normandy)
Richmond	**Bell**	(Normandy)
Ted	**Broeckling**	(Normandy)
Darrell	**Broome**	(Normandy)
Charles	**Conner**	(Omaha Beach, Normandy)
Fred	**Danzig**	(Normandy)
Ted	**Daubresse**	(Normandy)
O'Dell (Toad)	**Padgett**	(Omaha Beach, Normandy)
Robert (Bob)	**Sales**	(Omaha Beach, Normandy)
Robert	**Torrence**	(Omaha Beach, Normandy)

and to

John Robert Slaughter D Co. (Omaha Beach, Normandy)

My special thanks to the following:

Evelyn Ashley nee Slaughter, Dalton's sister. For the cosy chats in her kitchen telling me about life at the Slaughter home place and of Dalton as a boy.

Ted Baker Local Historian, Ringwood nr St. Leonards. For helping me locate the American military hospital and for the information on Ringwood and local transportation during the war years.

Joseph Balkoski Director of the 29th Div. Archives, 5th Rgt Armory, Baltimore, MD. For his interest, help in locating relevant documents and enthusiastic support.

Noel Blackler of Plympton, Devon, the paper boy for the 1st Battalion at Ivy Bridge and very likely handed my father his newspapers. For showing me exactly where the B Company Nissen huts were situated in what is now a sports field. Explaining what life was like with the GIs in town and for walking me around the fitness training circuit on the edge of Dartmoor and the regimental training manoeuvre areas up on the moor.

Elizabeth Brooks Dalton's childhood school friend and lifetime member of Wares Church. For the many detailed letters of life in King and Queen County and Middlesex County during the twenties and thirties.

Lucy Carlton For the many telephone conversations telling me about the early days; of meeting Dalton in church and of their dating.

John Clatworthy Curator Lapworth Museum of Geology, Birmingham University. For the maps, profiles and his interpretation of the geology of Normandy and the Omaha Beach cliffs.

Shannon Clever Librarian at the VA Hospital Library, Martinsburg. For the e mails, photos and contacts.

Ethel Duckett nee Eaglestone, Edith in the book, Hetty's sister. For the information she gave me and her perspective on the past.

James Eaglestone my grandad. For all those 'little chats' we had, long before I ever considered writing a book.

David C. Evans City of London Guide. For his knowledge of London during the war years and help at Westminster Archives.

Terry and Jackie Evans of Ivy Bridge, Devon. Who welcomed me into their home and provided photos, old newspaper cuttings and invaluable contacts like Noel Blackler.

Jimmy Green British Royal Navy Volunteer Reserve, Sub Lieutenant, Commander of the first wave on Dog Green, Omaha. For the many long telephone conversations, correspondence, his support and depth of firsthand knowledge.

Jean Louis Hennequin of La Luzerne, France. For showing me where the water pump was in the field near the hamlet of Bretel. Ivy clad and looking as a tree stump I would never have found it without his help. Clearly, there is at least one young Norman farmer who is aware of the blood that was spilt on his land and appreciates the fear and suffering experienced behind his now quiet hedgerows.

Karen Gilgar of Cardiff, Wales. For her proof reading, invaluable advice and support.

Dennis Howell my father-in-law, who was a wonderful source of information; facts, figures and detailed memories of life in London before and during WW2. Always happy to answer my questions.

Joanne Huntsberry of the Berkeley County Historical Society in Martinsburg, WV. For the e mails, photos and contacts regarding the town and hospital.

Richard King of Poole, Dorset. For being so helpful in giving me a tour of the derelict buildings that once constituted St. Leonards American Military Hospital.

Virginia Mae Knapp nee Emme, daughter of Bertha Lee Slaughter. For recounting her memories of living at the Slaughter home place and of Dalton as a young man.

Netty Longest of King and Queen County Va, lifetime member of Wares Church, who knew the Slaughters and of course Dalton when he was young and not so young. For the telephone conversations and information about Wares Church and life during the 1940s.

Vera Luckham of Ivy Bridge, Devon. Who was the landlady of the Sportsmans Inn, Ivy Bridge during the war and may have even served my father a drink. For the long chat in her lounge about her life as landlady and the GIs as customers and temporary residents of Ivy Bridge.

Clarence Elmore Marshall of Church View, Virginia. For the information on the Thrift farm and Thrift family, the Slaughters and Church View.

Valerie McTurk of Heslington, York. For her proof reading and providing encouragement during the final push to complete.

Lucille Miller nee Slaughter daughter of Preston Slaughter. For the many telephone chats, meetings in Virginia, recounting her memories of living at the Slaughter home place and of Dalton when he was young.

Paul Mummert of Martinsburg, WV. X Ray Chief Technician of Radiology at the Newton D. Baker Army Hospital. For the long telephone chats, his description of the hospital and local history, the e mails and photos of the town and hospital as it was in the 1940's. Not least for looking after me for a weekend in Martinsburg providing me with an invaluable view of the hospital and town as it was in 1945.

Edward Parsons of Dewlish, Dorset. A lad of fifteen years when the 116th was marshalled at Dewlish ready for the invasion. For his tour of Dewlish and the grounds of Dewlish House. For the long chat at his home explaining how the GIs transformed life in the village, and for the telephone calls, correspondence, references and photos.

John Pennells Member of St. Peter's Church, Elgin Avenue, Paddington, where Hetty and Dalton married. A member there from 1932 to 1960 and Church Warden 1950-1955. For the telephone calls, correspondence and photos of St. Peter's.

Kevin Richards of Ludgershall, Wiltshire. For his local knowledge and tour of Tidworth, Tedworth House and Tidworth Camp where I was able to walk along the same verandas and touch the same Dodsdown bricks my father did 64 years earlier. For his interest, time and support.

David and Susan Reynolds of Redditch, Worcestershire. For their help in digitising my hand drawn maps and improving my IT skills. By generously giving me a few hours of their time, they saved me many.

Jean Sawyer, nee Carter of Carter's Cottage, Tidworth. Who lived in Carter's Cottage during the war, worked with her mother in the CWL canteen on Tidworth camp and attended camp dances. Later, Councillor of Tidworth Parish Council. For the long chat in her garden one summer's day in 2006, her family's hospitality, the photos, her guided tour of Tidworth and the telephone chats.

John and Valerie Slater of Rushden, Northamptonshire. For their proof reading, advice and resolute support. Their help in preparing the book cover notes and to Valerie for her invaluable research into family connections, Americus Slaughter and other aspects which assisted the fine tuning.

Allan Soper of East Allington, Devon. For the long chat we had in the unusually warm March sunshine of 2007. Standing by the dry stone walling of the typical Devon village he told me about his experience of the evacuation of

South Hams which together with Slapton Sands became the American military training area in preparation for D-Day.

Roger Surville, Monsieur and Madame of Bretel, Normandy. For their unquestioning hospitality and information regarding the Bretel area during the war. In particular, a big thank you to Madame Surville for walking me along the sunken track to the field with the water pump. My story clearly touched her heart and her empathy touched mine.

Carol Tuckwiller Director of Research and Archives, National D-Day Memorial Foundation, Bedford, Virginia. For the 116th Infantry Regiment 'After Action Reports', the contacts, and informing me of the existence of morning reports. The telephone conversations and correspondence.

Anne Wheeldon of Hammersmith and Fulham Archives & Local History Centre. For being so helpful in hunting out information on the Hammersmith Palais and providing useful references.

Thanks must also go to;

Michael Ashley and Tommy Ashley of King and Queen County VA. For taking me to the Thrift farm and their perspective on farming and the surrounding countryside.

Eric Bacon of Isleworth, Middlesex and previously of Holton Saint Peter. For his childhood memories of the USAF in East Anglia.

Paul Baillie researcher at the National Archives in Kew. For his help in directing me around the maze of information.

June Bayliss of Dewlish, Dorset.

Roger Bettle of Ringwood, Hampshire.

Robert Bond of Bromsgrove, Worcs. For his cricketing knowledge.

Steve Cable of the National Archives, Kew. For going out of his way to help me through the 'maze' of infomation.

Bill Carlton of West Point, Virginia. For his contacts and support.

Leonard Alfred Chapman Hetty's uncle Len. For the information about life on the building sites with James Eaglestone between the wars and about the fairground days.

Leonard Peter Chapman Hetty's cousin Lenny. For the information on family life during the Blitz and of Samuel Hitchcock.

Roberta Chilcoat of Urbanna, VA.

Verna Cook of Dewlish, Dorset.

Dr Kevin Elsby of Stratford Upon Avon. For information on the Omaha Beach landings, Dog Green sector.

Dan Gill of Remlik and the 'Something Different Country Store' Pine Tree, VA. For the information on the Pine Tree Store House, store houses in general and Urbanna.

Isabella Hall of Worcester. For the information on dance bands in the 1940's.

Sandra Hawkins of Tidworth Library.

Bill Hibbert, the landlord of the Sportsmans Inn, Ivy Bridge.

David Howell of Christchurch, Dorset. Collector of WW2 artefacts, for finding me an original US WW2 helmet which I subsequently used for one of the cover images - taken on Omaha Beach.

Jean Jeffreys of Virginia Beach, VA. For several of the photos used in this book and the information relayed to me during our many telephone conversations.

Richard Marshall of Marshalls Drug Store, Urbanna, VA. For the information on how the store was organised in the forties.

Marian McCormack of Martinsburg, WV. Nurse at the Newton D. Baker.

Nicholas McNeal for being as he was, a kind hearted man.

Bill Meade of Earls Barton, Northamptonshire. Bowman, B Company LCA.

Lori Miller, Researcher, of St. Louis, Missouri, USA.

Gene Nicolelli, Director, Greyhound Bus Museum, Minnesota.

Phil Landlord of The Windsor Castle, Lanark Place, Paddington.

Hannah Rider, my daughter-in-law, and **Padraic O'Hara** for helping me to get started on the book cover design.

Martin Rider of Redditch, Worcestershire. For the UK weather records.

Harry Sanders of Kingsville, MD for his company and support on the Harpers Ferry and Martinsburg, WV trip.

David Snelling regular at the Kings Arms, Ivy Bridge.

Marilyn South and **Richard Shores** of Middlesex County, VA, Historical Society and **Babara Payne** of Urbanna, regarding photos of Middlesex County in the 1940's.

David Willey Curator of Bovington Tank Museum.

The staff of Alcester and Studley Libraries in Warwickshire, for being so professional, helpful and very patient in dealing with my regular requests for books, internet and support information.

The staff of the City of Westminster Archives Centre. For their untiring help and looking after me so well.

The staff of National Personnel Records Center, St. Louis, Missouri. For providing extra B Company morning reports.

Book sources.

John S. Allsup   ISBN 2 902 17116 1
Hedgerow Hell.

R. Bailey & Imperial War Museum   ISBN 0 091 93011 0
Forgotten Voices of D-Day.

Joseph Balkoski   ISBN 0 811 70079 8
Omaha Beach. D-Day.

Joseph Balkoski   ISBN 0 8117 3237 6
Beyond The Beachhead.

Anthony Beevor   ISBN 0 6709 1809 6
D-Day.

Steven Brindle   ISBN 1 873 59295 7
Paddington Station Its History and Architecture.

David J. Croman   ISBN 0 850 33812 3
A History of Tidworth and Tedworth House.

Joseph H. Ewing   ISBN 0 898 39018 4
29 Let's Go! A History of the 29th Infantry Division in World
War II.

Terry Gander and Peter Chamberlain ISBN 0 354 01108 1
Small Arms, Artillery and Special Weapons of the Third
Reich.

Juliet Gardiner   ISBN 1 855 85019 2
Over Here. The GIs In Wartime Britain.

Juliet Gardiner   ISBN 0 755 31028 4
Wartime Britain 1939-1945.

Louise Eubank Gray and Ella Garrett Ammons
A History of Lower King and Queen Baptist Church 1772 –
1980. Donated to Dalton Slaughter April 20th 2003 on his
visit home for the family reunion.

Maureen Hill   ISBN 1 405 43734 0
Britain at War.

Ian V. Hogg and John Weeks.   ISBN 1 854 09034 B
Military Small Arms of the 20th Century. A Comprehensive
Illustrated Encylopedia of the Worlds Small Calibre
Firearms. 6th Edition.

Edwin P. Hoyt   ISBN 0 709 03266 8
The Invasion Before Normandy.   The Secret Battle of
Slapton Sands.

Bernard Ireland   ISBN 1 844 15001 1
Battle of the Atlantic.
N. D. G. James   ISBN 0 946 41803 9
Plain Soldiering.
A History of the Armed Forces on Salisbury Plain.
Alex Kershaw   ISBN 0 7434 7791 X
The Bedford Boys.
Rodney Legg   ISBN 0 948 69979 5
Dorset's War Diary, Battle of Britain to D-Day.
Colin G. Maggs   ISBN 0 750 90076 8
Branch Lines of Wiltshire.
Laurent Mari & Jean Jaques Gaffie   ISBN 2 950 84251 8
GO. Omaha Beach. 6 Juin 1944.
Richard Natkiel   ISBN 0 861 24208 4
Atlas of World War II.
William A. Powell   ISBN 0 750 92138 2
Middlesex County Cricket Club.
Robin Rose-Price and Jean Parnell   ISBN 1 898 96461 0
The Land We Left Behind.
A pictorial history & memories of the war years in South Hams.
John W. Schildt   ISBN 0 936 77209
The Long Line of Splendor. 1742-1992.
John. R. Slaughter   ISBN 0 760 33141 5
Omaha Beach and Beyond.
Ken Small   ISBN 0 747 50433 4
The Forgotten Dead.
David A.Thomas & Patrick Holmes   ISBN 0 850 52548 9
Queen Mary and the Cruiser. The Curacoa Disaster.
David Westwood   ISBN 1 844 86001 9
The U Boat War. The German Submarine Service and the Battle of the Atlantic.
Pamela Winfield   ISBN 0 094 65440 9
Sentimental Journey, The Story of the GI Brides.
Jane's Fighting Aircraft of WW II.   ISBN 1 851 70199 0
A Comprehensive Encyclopedia.
Jane's World War II Tanks and Fighting Vehicles.
The Complete Guide.Leland Ness. Harper Collins.

The **Dewlish Millennium Committee** and supporting contributions.
Dewlish 2000.
Supplied by Verna Cook of the Cottage, Dewlish. Dorset.

Maps.

Dartmoor. Ordnance Survey. Outdoor Leisure Map 28.
ISBN 0-319-26028-3
Omaha Beach West. Top Secret Map.
Prepared by Commander Task Force 122, April 21,1944.
Pointe Du Hoc. Omaha Beach.
Carte De Randonnee 14120 T.   Institut Geographique
National.
ISBN 000014120T
Ste Mere Eglise. Utah Beach.
Carte De Randonnee 1311 E.   Institut Geographique
National.
ISBN 00001311 E.
Torigni Sur Vire.
Carte De Randonnee 14130 O.   Institut Geographique
National.
ISBN 000014130 O
Salisbury and The Plain. Ordnance Survey. Landranger
Map 184.
ISBN 0 319 22862 2

Other sources.

City of Westminster Archives Centre, 10, St. Ann's Street, London.
References;
CD131.3, C11.6,
CD142 Bomb Damage Map of Westminster
Westminster Bomb Damage Incident Reports; 753 and pictures, 1329 and pictures, 1287 and 1321
Paddington Borough Engineers War Damage Index.
The London County Council, Bomb Damage Maps 1939 - 1945,
London Topographical Society 2003   ISBN 0 09 208 7517
Hammersmith and Fulham Archives & Local History Centre, 191, Talgarth Rd, W6 8BJ.
The National Archives, Kew, London.
Medal Cards WO 372/6
Medal Roll, London Regiment, WO 329/1927
Personal Service Records WO 364
WW1 Soldier Service Records, WO 363 micro film E5
Regimental War Diaries 1/15 London Regiment WO95/2732
The Twenty Niner
March 2005 Vol 49. No.1. Military Service of Dale Monroe Brown
July   2005 Vol. 49. No. 2
November 2005 Vol. 49. No. 3
November   2006 Vol. 50. No. 3 Wartime Letters of Gordon Golding.
Wisden Obituary, Wisden Cricketers' Almanack 2003.

Appendix A

Events of 3rd Platoon, B Company and the 116th Regiment immediately after Dalton was seriously wounded.

3rd Platoon.

The probing action in front of the Martinville Ridge had confirmed what the infantrymen knew already, that the enemy were there in force and prepared to fight at all costs to hold their line.

On 2nd July, the day Dalton was seriously wounded, 3rd Platoon lost several men including older hands in the field with the water pump. Some were lightly wounded and returned to fight, but they likely thought themselves in the wrong outfit, for there were so many new faces.

The B Company morning report for the 2nd July, together with attached sheets, listed the following casualties.

Seriously wounded in action.

Baldwin Frank T.	Pvt
Bowers Charles W.	Pvt
Boyd Richard H.	Pfc
Hoffman Leonard R.	Pfc
Lahan Joseph P.	Pvt
Petredis George C.	Pfc
Slaughter Dalton R.	**Sgt**

Lightly wounded in action.

Bowers Edward F.	Pvt
Brennen James A	S/Sgt
Clawson John J.	Pfc

Fezza Michael	Pvt	
Flynn George T Jr	Pvt	(Morning report 5th July)
Jones Lewis R	2nd Lt	(Morning report 3rd July)
Kennedy Luthor	Pvt	
McBee William	Pfc	
Mikesh Joseph	Pfc	
Mlinario Elmor F.	Pfc	
Mosher Richard L.	Pfc	

Killed in action.

For the morning report of 2nd July, either no record was made for KIA, or the record was not copied to the archive. From later morning reports and other research, I have found three men who were killed in action on the 2nd July.

Barile Pasquale A.	Pvt	(Morning report 11th July)
Butler Bobbie O.	Pvt	(Morning report 11th July)
Davolt George E.	1st Lt	(Mrep5thJulyandGravePic)
Bowers Charles W	Pvt	(Reported SWA I understand later died of wounds.)

A total of 22 casualties.

Sam Baker replaced Dalton as squad leader.
Richmond Bell, the anti tank grenadier lasted exceptionally well and wasn't seriously wounded until November 14th 1944. When Sam Baker was wounded, Fred Danzig took over as squad leader. Fred joined B Company on July 11th and lasted until August 26th. He was replaced by yet another new squad leader but there the trail goes cold. Sam Baker recovered from his wounds and returned to B Company only to be killed

somewhere in Germany. Dalton's assistant squad leader, Sergeant Sorrow, was killed in action.

B Company.

On the 6th June Dalton had landed with 193 B Company men and officers. By the time he exited the war twenty-six days later the company had received over 220 replacement men, making a total exceeding 410 men with whom Dalton had served. It would be fair to say that his turn was long overdue and inevitable. However, Bob Sales made it all the way to Germany before being severely wounded guiding a tank to a machine gun emplacement. I understand that Robert Austen returned to the company some time after being lightly wounded on D-Day; so too did 1st Lieutenant William Williams. On the 31st July, Williams became B Company's Commander on the rank of Captain

Only one B Company man is believed to have lasted right through from stepping off his LCA on Omaha Beach to the end of the war - Robert M. Campbell; still serving when General Montgomery accepted Germany's unconditional surrender on 4th May 1945. Campbell had been a sergeant on D-Day, was promoted to Staff Sergeant and then officially to Technical Sergeant on 9th July. In the morning report of the 9th July, Sergeants Britt and Davison together with Privates Braun and Charles Campbell were officially made Staff Sergeants, but not Sergeant Slaughter; Dalton's only mention being that he had been moved to hospital in England, effective 5th July.

Apart from Robert Campbell, the rest of the original B Company D-Day Veterans were either killed or wounded. Many spent over a year and in some cases two years in hospital being operated on and recovering from their wounds.

The 116th Regiment.

In early July most men on the ground doubted St. Lo would ever be taken. The Germans had certainly used the hedgerow country to their advantage, countering their initial slow response to the invasion. But having squandered the opportunity of driving the Allies back into the sea, they were never going to win.

The Martinville Ridge was finally taken during the second week of July, but it cost the families back home a further 1,000 of their boys, killed and wounded. The gully leading to the higher summit behind St. André de- l'Epine claimed so many casualties that it gained the name of "Purple Heart Draw". The taking of the higher eastern section enabled the 29th Division to press on down the ridge towards the village of Martinville and then the smaller summit coded as Hill 122 just north of St. Lo. The leading regiment for the 29th Division's attack was once again the 116th Infantry. In the two further days of fighting, the 116th alone suffered some 400 casualties. The hill was eventually taken by the 35th Division on 15th July and the 116th Regiment then pressed on to the Madeleine Crossroads the next day. It took another full day's fighting before Brigadier General Norman Cota, Assistant Division Commander of the 29th Division, finally entered St. Lo on 18th July, over a month later than planned. The way out of the Normandy hedgerows was open; the 116th broke through into Brittany, whilst British and Canadian forces drove south and east. By 20th August Allied forces were at the Seine River and by 25th August, they had liberated Paris.

Having lost seventeen hundred men in June, the 116th Regiment lost a further seventeen hundred men in July and another thirteen hundred in August, bringing the 116th Regiment's total losses in three months to 4,700, almost equivalent to every soldier being replaced twice.

29th Infantry Division Casualties.

The 29th Division suffered over 16,000 casualties for the three months, June to August 1944.

Appendix B

Of the 413* men who served with Dalton in B Company between

6th June and 2nd July 1944,

176

Were killed in action**

This appendix is dedicated to them

To my knowledge this is the most comprehensive listing of 116th Regiment, B Company men KIA during WW2. However it only includes soldiers who served with Dalton and may represent no more than two thirds of the total B Company boys KIA during WW2. It was compiled from B Company morning reports and cross referenced with names originally supplied to me by Robert Sales of B Company and the 'Roster of the Battle Dead', J. Ewing, 29 Let's Go.

* Approximate. I regret that there may be others who I have been unable to locate or verify.
** KIA between 6th June and the end of the war.

Surname	Forename	Middle Initial	Rank
Abernethy	Julius	F	Sgt
Anderson	James	F	Pvt
Anderson	Lloyd	J	Pfc
Appleby	Leonard	V	Pvt
Avery	Blane		Pfc
Baker	Samuel	J	S/Sgt
Banton	Cyrus	E	T/4
Barile	Pasquale	A	Pvt
Barnes	John	G	S/Sgt
Barnett	William	D	Pvt
Benton	Clarence	J	Pvt
Bercholz	Joseph	M	Pfc
Black	Reese	P	Pfc
Bleecker	Robert		Sgt
Bowers	Charles	W	Pvt
Bowling	Aaron	J	Sgt
Brannen	Miles	E	Pvt
Bratten	Thomas	E	Sgt
Bray	Claude	V	Pvt
Brinton	Walter	S	Pfc
Brooks	James	L	Pfc
Brown	Staunton	M	Sgt
Brownell	Claude	H	Pfc
Brulotte	Roger	G	Pvt
Buckner	Clyde		Pvt
Burk	William	L	Pvt

Butler	Bobbie	O	Pvt
Byrnes	Charles	T	Pvt
Cantara	Rudolph	A	Pvt
Carnrike	Frank	E	Sgt
Charter	Clifford	H	Pvt
Cheek	Frank	J	Pfc
Chesney	Benjamin		Pfc
Chipps	William	R	Pfc
Churchill	Joseph	B	Sgt
Clarke	Robert	L	Pvt
Clawson	John	J	Pfc
Clinton	Boyce	T	Pvt
Conatser	Edgar	M	Pfc
Cooper	William	V	Pfc
Cunningham	Patrick	M	Pvt
Dearing	Leonard	F	Pvt
DeWitt	Harry	J	Pfc
Dickey	Leonard		Pfc
Dirtoma	Frank	J	Pvt
Dittmar	Robert	L	Pvt
Donaldson	Harold	C	1st Lt
Driskill	Robert	R	S/Sgt
Drumheller	William	A	Pfc
Eckardt	George	F	Pfc
England	George	R	T/ Sgt
Evans	Everette	E	Pfc
Felix	Joseph	A	Sgt
Ferrell	William	E	S/Sgt
French	Julius	E	Pfc

Fridley	Thomas	H	Pvt
Garbett	Robert	L	Pfc
Gentry	Robert	B	Pvt
Godwin	James	D	Pvt
Hartigan	Charles	W	Pfc
Hawn	George	A	Pfc
Hawthorne	Lester		Pfc
Heese	Walter	B	Pfc
Hoag	Earl	A	Pvt
Hoffman	Eugene	L	Pvt
Holmes	John		S/Sgt
Holt	Adrian	M	Pfc
Huggins	Julius	E	Pvt
Iannarilli	Mario	P	Pfc
Jennings	Ralph	E	T/Sgt
Johnson	Hogan	M	S/Sgt
Johnson	George	E	Pfc
Kafkalas	Nicholas	S	Pvt
Kane	Thomas	M	Pfc
Kaufman	Herbert		Pfc
Keller	Charles	W	Pvt
Kennedy	Paul	M	Sgt
Kernoll	Russell	T	Pvt
Kincer	John	T	T5 Sgt
Knight	Alva	J	Pfc
Knupp	Robert	G	Pvt
Koshinski	Francis	E	Pfc
Kovach	Chester	J	Pfc
Kozak	John	E	Pfc

Kucera	William		Sgt
Kufta	Conrad	V	Pfc
Laffin	William	C	S/Sgt
Leach	Eugene Jr		Pvt
Lee	Basil		Pfc
Lifsitz	Mortimer	N	Pvt
Lurie	Harry		Pfc
Macaluso	Eugene		Pfc
Maffe	William	J	Pfc
Malmberg	Mayo	T	Sgt
Mandino	Vincent	J	Pfc
Manos	Aristeded	P	Pfc
Marks	Thomas	J	Pfc
McCarthy	William	J	Pvt
McLouth	Richard	E	Cpl
Mehring	David	C	Pfc
Messer	John	L	Pvt
Miller	Ralph	J	Pvt
Miller	Axel	J	Pvt
Miller	John	O	Pfc
Monroe	Russell	G	Pfc
Morse	Robert	W	Pvt
Murphy	Francis	J	Pvt
Newman	Lyman		Pfc
Nickol	Dallas	A	Pvt
Nuzzo	Frank		Pfc
Odee	Charles	W	Pfc
Osier	Albert	A	Pvt
Ott	Maurice	J	Pfc

Overman	Clifford	C	Pvt
Palmer	Robert	E	Pvt
Patton	Harry	G	Pfc
Payne	Ardell	W	Pfc
Peacock	Edward	E	Sgt
Pelc	Joseph	A	Pfc
Pellegrini	Joseph	L	Pfc
Perrone	Peter	W	Pfc
Pillen	Vernon	W	Pfc
Pisar	George		Pvt
Planster	Joseph	J	Pvt
Pluta	Metro		Pvt
Pohlmann	William	C	Pvt
Polk	Olan	D	Pvt
Post	Reuben	C	Pfc
Powell	Bruce	M	Pvt
Prescott	Charles	W	Pvt
Pruett	John	W	Pfc
Ratliff	Frenchman		Pfc
Reyes	Robert	B	Pfc
Riggs	Clairus	L	Pfc
Riley	Leonard	J	Sgt
Rinker	Garnet	L	Pfc
Roach	Walter	W	Pfc
Roach	Larry	J	Pfc
Roberson	Clarence	E	S/Sgt
Robertson	Herman	S	Pvt
Robey	Kermit	J	Pvt
Roddy	Travis	A	Pvt

Rodriguez	John	B	Pvt
Rose	Albert	C	Pvt
Rowe	Guy	H	Pfc
Sadusky	Frank		Pfc
Sawicki	Joseph	H	Pvt
Schauer	Albert	W	Pfc
Scherz	Edwin	C	Pvt
Schlamowitz	Milton		Pvt
Schools	William	E	Pfc
Settles	Durwood	C	Lt
Severino	Frank	J	Pfc
Shope	Forrest	C	Pfc
Smalley	George	T	Pvt
Smith	Paul	W	Pvt
Sorrow	William	O	Sgt
Stanton	Byron	L	Pfc
Stedman	William	A	Pfc
Stone	Harry	N	T/5
Stover	Robert	W	Pvt
Tatterson	Carl	E	Pfc
Thomas	Herbert	A	Pfc
Wade	Audy	F	Pfc
Waite	Richard	A	Pvt
Ware	Robert	B	Capt
Weaver	Louis	W	Pvt
Wesolowski	Stanley	C	Pfc
Wilson	Jerome	E	Pfc
Winkler	Emil		1st Lt
Womack	Daniel	P	S/Sgt

Wright	James	A	S/Sgt
Wright	Samuel	L	Pvt
Young	Willie	E	Pvt
Zappacosta	Ettore	V	Capt

Appendix C
Dalton Roy Slaughter
US Army Record.

Inducted.   8th May   1941 at Fort Meade Maryland to
                                B Co. 116th Regiment, 29th Infantry Division.

Separated. 14th February 1946 at Newton D. Baker Gen. Hospital,
                                Martinsburg, West Virginia.

Served country for 4y 9m; incl, 2y 4m abroad and 20m in hospital.

Active Service record.
Private. Infantry, basic	3 months.
Private first class. Automatic rifleman	34 months.
Sergeant and Squad Leader	1 month.

Responsibilities as Squad Leader,
1. Directed the activities of an infantry squad of 12 men in action against the enemy.
2. Led his men during combat and directed their dispersal and advance for their protection and to destroy enemy personnel.
3. Responsible for the feeding and equipping of his men and that they were continuously supplied with ammunition and weapons during an engagement.

Medals and Awards.
The Purple Heart.
The Bronze Star - awarded for 'acts of gallantry or meritorious service' and thus recognising 'performance of duty beyond the ordinary'.
Good Conduct Medal and the Combat Infantryman Badge.
The American Defense Service and Campaign Medals, The European Campaign Medal, , World War II Victory Medal, Army of Occupation Medal, Honorable Service Lapel Button.

Appendix D

A letter from Dalton to his sister Evelyn

Somewhere in England.
Jan. 24,1943

Dear Darling Baby Sister
Well Sugar this letter leaves me well as usual and getting along fine.
Hope this letter will find you all the same.
Sugar, I guess the little boys are getting along in school very fine. Hope they are anyway. Bet Tommy is a little bird at school. Ha. Tell them, that Dal says he loves them all ... they are three cute boys.
Sugar I am sorry to tell you, that I never got your package. But please Sugar don't worry about that. See everything can't reach us safe. We have to leave some things anyway. So please Sugar don't worry about the package.
I appreciate it just as much as if I had got it, because it showed that you sure thinking about me.
Tell Steve that D says Hello. Is he still working at the mill?
Sugar we are making out pretty good over here. Really we are. We are sitting around waiting for our Sunday night supper. Wish I could be home eating supper tonight.
Oh Boy how would I feel, just to sit down at Mother's table again.

Will say, Bye Bye
Your Loving Brother Dalton.

Hello little Sonny, kisses for you from Dal.

Answer soon

Appendix E

Paul Kennedy.

Killed by a sniper's bullet on the cliffs of Omaha, 6th June 1944, Paul Kennedy was often mentioned by my parents. Reminiscing as they so frequently did about their early days, they told of events which remained both bitter and sweet in their memories. In particular Paul's words to Dad just before embarkation; 'Tell Hetty, if anything happens to you, I'll look after her'.

It was a conversation with Bob Sales that brought home to me that like so many young men on D-Day and later, Paul lost not just the life as he had known it or of the terrible burden of life at his moment of death, but all the splendours that life had to offer; of a love, children, grandchildren, 50 Christmases, 50 thanksgivings, countless family occasions and loving moments. All those things we, who have not known war, too often take for granted.

Paul's body was retrieved along with perhaps 1,400 other American soldiers who died on Omaha that day. After a temporary burial behind the sea wall, midway between Vierville and St. Laurent, he was eventually laid to rest in the Omaha Beach, United States Cemetery.

Dalton didn't know whether Paul's parents had ever been able to visit their son's grave; to stand and think of how he was when he was little, to lay flowers and mourn his loss. But 46 years after Paul's death, again, there on the cliff edge in the June of 1990, Dalton at least did go back and pay his respects to his best buddy.

Appendix F

The Children of Kelly Granville and Fleda Mae Slaughter with Dates of Death

KELLY GRANVILLE SLAUGHTER
14th Sept. 1877 Church View
21st July 1954 Wares
Fleda Mae (Fletcher)
16th October 1885 Gloucester Co.
27th May 1944 Wares

GRANVILLE PRESTON
4th Sept.1906 Ch. View
16th Mar. 1975 Wares
EDWARD KELLY
20th Jan. 1908 Ch. View
24th June 1963 Wares
MYRTLE MAE
21st Dec.1909 Ch. View
12th Jul'89 Kingsville MD
BERTHA LEE
2nd June1911 Ch. View
15th April 1992
AMOS BENNETT
10th Nov.1912 Ch. View
21st Nov. 1968 Hermitage

WOODROW WILSON
28th Aug. 1914 Ch. View
12th Mar. 2002
EVELYN SALOME
3rd Mar. 1916 Ch. View
23rd Oct. 1999 Wares
ANNIE RUTH
Feb 1918 Church View
July 1918 Wares
DALTON ROY
30th June 1919 Ch. View
18th May 2008 Wares
WILLIAM ROBBIE
31st July 1920 Ch. View
15th Sept. 1973 Wares

Appendix G

Finding the field with the water pump.

Dad and I first searched for the field with the water pump during our visits to Normandy in the mid 90's. We were not successful, but two years after Dad died, in June 2010, armed with recently acquired military documents and Institut Geographique National Maps where 1cm represents 250m, I made another attempt.

I had gone to France for the 66th Anniversary of D-Day with the aim of finishing my research there. At day break on the 6th June I was of course on Omaha Beach. Later I scaled the same cliff as Dad had done and explored the old German emplacements of WN 73 and others. After some more exploration on the 7th, I decided on the 8th that it was time to take another look for the field with the water pump.
It was a cloudy, damp day as I headed for the hamlet of Bretel, deep in hedgerow country. The warm, wet spring had produced the characteristic lush green ambiance of Normandy; the woodland and hawthorn hedgerows coming to life as summer beckoned. After trawling around Bretel Woods for some time, I headed a little further south to Bretel and its two remaining residences. I found a sunken track, walked along it for several hundred yards to again find nothing and reminded myself not to be too disappointed if this proved to be another fruitless search. Sixty-six years had passed, the water pump was surely long gone, the fields enlarged and hedgerows removed, time and farming practices having progressed with the years.
I consoled myself with the fact that I must at least be close to the spot, perhaps within a hundred yards of where Dad was wounded and made my way back to the car.
Low grey cloud was racing across an even darker sky above as I drove along the rough dirt road towards the main Couvains Road. The way was slow and as I passed the second of the two houses in Bretel I looked up towards

what was an old farm, with farm house, surrounding barns and outbuildings. Without a second thought I turned in and drove up to the house, parked and approached the front door.

'Well why not give it a try?' I thought as I knocked and prepared my explanation in French. Within seconds an elderly man, walking with the aid of a stick, came out of one of the barns and a woman sturdier by comparison, still wearing her kitchen apron, appeared before me at the now open farmhouse door.

The first thing that struck me in our initial, difficult conversation, difficult because of my poor command of French, was the immediate trust these folk showed in me, a mere stranger at their door in the midst of the countryside. I was quickly invited in and armed with my French dictionary, I eventually communicated why I was there, 'To search for a field with a water pump!' As soon as the words had left my mouth, I realised just how crazy they must have sounded, not just because of the intervening years but also that there may have been several water pumps, servicing many fields in the area, installed or replaced over the years to leave my search hopelessly flawed.

They looked at each other enquiringly for some time and then back at me. Were they about to laugh at l'homme Anglais, I wondered?

"Yes," the Madame said, they knew of one, "but the pump is no longer there."

Did they know of other fields with a water pump or only this one, I asked with difficulty, trying to get to grips with the turn of events.

"Only the one," they replied and they had "lived here since the war," they explained reassuringly.

Things were looking up, but started to look decidedly less good when they drew a map to help me find the field. I could make no sense of the symbols and even less of the words they used to describe them.

"Would you come with me and show me where the field is?" I asked as politely as possible, knowing I was now pushing their hospitality a little far.

"I can't," the man said pointing at his stick and shrugging, but as soon as his wife understood my request she put on her cardigan and changed her shoes.

So that was it, I was driving off with the wife of the farmer into the fields of Normandy! We parked at the end of the rough dirt road and she led me slowly down the same sunken track I had found earlier. "Les Allemands," were on the left she said pointing southward through the hedgerow and "les Americains," to the right, 'the front line' she said of the track on which we walked. She looked so serious, that I knew without question she understood the gravity of what went on here. A few hundred yards down, she stopped and looked towards the field on what was the American side, "The field with the water pump," she said. I stood by her side and just looked, looked through the thin broken hedgerow into the field. So this was it ... the place where my Dad was seriously wounded. Incredible, unbelievable I thought, but could this really be the field? "There are no other fields with a water pump near here?" I asked again ... just to make sure. My voice betrayed my emotion. Madame Surville turned and looked at me with such empathy that I could have hugged her, "No others," she said "no others ... I am sure."

After dropping Madame back at the farm, I left the car there and returned to the field on my own, armed with lunch, a camera and most importantly my raincoat. I passed the place where we had stood together, turned right and right again along tracks to bring me to the north side of the field. An oak tree in the hedgerow gave me shelter from the rain and I sat at its base alone with my thoughts. I tried to imagine events so long past, of the American line being stalled here, pounded day after day, the snipers and the patrols. Then amongst the patter of rain, the rustle of wind in the leaves and the company of greenery, I suddenly realised that a man was walking across the field straight towards me. The farmer for sure, I thought, coming to ask what I was doing there. And as it turned out, I was right.

"I am doing research for my book, a biography," I explained and told him something of the background. "My father was a soldat de le debarquement ... I think he was wounded in this field," I said. The farmer seemed moved; he nodded in approval of the exploits of such men. He was just a young man himself, a pleasant and warm hearted one as it turned out. "Madame Surville brought me to this place," I told him. "She was confident this field had a water pump during the war," I went on, "but the pump is gone."

He smiled and stared at me with bright excited eyes. "Follow me," he said and led me across the field. As we came up to the edge of the field beside the sunken track he pointed to what I had thought to be a broken tree stump, clad with ivy. "La pompe," he said with a bigger smile than ever.

I approached in disbelief to slowly move the ivy aside. Sure enough, there beneath the greenery was the rusted metal of the water pump, still intact as if waiting for this day. I was dumbfounded! It was exactly as Dad had described; situated in the right hand corner of the field, next to a sunken track, its red rust coloured long pumping handle now in my hand!

With my mind whirling from the discovery, I explained to Jean Louis the events of the 2nd July; that B Company were entrenched in his fields to the north and Dad's platoon had been caught here in the sunken track, close to the pump. I re-enacted Dad's wounding, even crawling to make up for my poor command of French. When I got up from the ground, it struck me that I had just acted out Dad's terrible ordeal on the very spot where it happened - the place Dad first described to me when I was just a boy!

The 8th June 2010 was truly an amazing day for me and the highlight of many, many discoveries and enjoyable times throughout the seven years of my research. I would love to tell of them all, but think it best to simply conclude that although I am very proud to have finished my book, I am also sad that the work has come to an end.

Looking eastward along the sunken track.

The ivy clad water pump can be seen rising
above the hedgerow to the left side of the track.

The field to the left, the north side of the track,
is where Dalton lay seriously wounded.

INDEX -

by section - including casualty lists, maps and photographs.

Epilogue

Thanks, Acknowledgements and Sources

Appendices

Photographs

To write a review or to purchase further copies please go to –

www.freewebstore.org/mybookstore

If you wish to communicate more directly with Robbie about his
book then you are welcome to do so via:

slaughterrjmybook@yahoo.com